PROBLEMS IN QUANTUM MECHANICS

V. I. KOGAN AND V. M. GALITSKIY

PROBLEMS IN QUANTUM MECHANICS

Translated from the Russian by
SCRIPTA TECHNICA, INC.

Edited by HAROLD GERSCH, Georgia Institute of Technology

PRENTICE-HALL, INC., ENGLEWOOD CLIFFS, N.J.

PRENTICE-HALL INTERNATIONAL, INC., *London*
PRENTICE-HALL OF AUSTRALIA, PTY., LTD., *Sydney*
PRENTICE-HALL OF CANADA, LTD., *Toronto*
PRENTICE-HALL FRANCE, S.A.R.L., *Paris*
PRENTICE-HALL OF JAPAN, INC., *Tokyo*
PRENTICE-HALL DE MEXICO, S.A., *Mexico City*

 Library of Congress Catalog Card Number: 63-14548. Printed in the United States of America. C

Foreword

The present book contains one hundred and sixty problems, most of them simple, in nonrelativistic quantum mechanics. Some of these problems were used previously by the authors in their courses at the Moscow Institute of Engineering and Physics. However, the majority were drawn up or selected in the course of work on the book.

This book is designed for physics students who are studying quantum mechanics approximately at the level of D. I. Blokhintsev's book or Part II of "Theoretical Physics" by A. S. Kompaneyts. A number of problems is intended primarily for students who are beginning to specialize in theoretical physics and who are partially familiar with the contents of "Quantum Mechanics" by L. D. Landau and Ye. M. Lifshits.

Some problems illustrate individual theoretical questions which have scarcely been considered in textbooks: sudden and adiabatic changes; Heisenberg representation of operators; probability relations in addition of momenta; isotopic spin; parity; and others. The authors have tried to use relatively elementary mathematical tools of quantum mechanics to facilitate use of the book by nontheoretical physicists.

With a few exceptions, the authors have not included in this book problems which are considered in sufficient detail in the basic textbooks mentioned above and in the problem book on quantum mechanics written by V. G. Levich. Therefore, this book should be regarded chiefly as an auxiliary textbook in the study of the above books.

NOTE

Russian notation has been followed throughout the text. Some differences that might not be immediately apparent include:

tg for *tan*
ctg for *cot*
ch for *cosh*
sh for *sinh*
th for *tanh*

Contents

PROBLEMS IN QUANTUM MECHANICS

PROBLEMS

CHAPTER I

Operators. Constants of Motion

1. Given three operators $\hat{A}$, $\hat{B}$, and $\hat{C}$, express the commutator of the product $\hat{A}\hat{B}$ and $\hat{C}$ in terms of the commutators $[\hat{A}, \hat{C}]$ and $[\hat{B}, \hat{C}]$.

2. Show that the distributive law holds in algebraic operations with commutators, i.e., that the commutator of a sum is equal to the sum of the commutators:

$$\left[\sum_i \hat{A}_i, \sum_k \hat{B}_k\right] = \sum_{i,k} [\hat{A}_i, \hat{B}_k].$$

3. Derive the rule for differentiation with respect to time — the product of two operators.

4. Show that the mean value of the square of a self-conjugate operator is positive.

5. Is the complex conjugate operator: 1) linear? 2) Hermitian? and 3) what is the operator which is the complex conjugate of a complex conjugate operator?

6. Assuming λ to be a small quantity, find the expansion of the operator $(\hat{A} - \lambda\hat{B})^{-1}$ in powers of λ.

7. Find the condition under which the Hamiltonian of a charged particle in a magnetic field

$$\hat{H} = \frac{1}{2\mu}\left(\hat{p} - \frac{e}{c}\hat{A}\right)^2$$

will have the form

$$\hat{H}' = \frac{1}{2\mu}\hat{p}^2 - \frac{e}{\mu c}\hat{p}\hat{A} + \frac{e^2}{2\mu c^2}\hat{A}^2.$$

8. Write the commutation relations for the velocity components (v_x, v_y and v_z) of a charged particle moving in a magnetic field.

9. In a state of a quantum-mechanical system described by a given wave function Ψ_A, the dynamical variable A has a definite value.

In this state, does the quantity B also have a definite value in the cases where: 1) the operators $\hat{A}$ and $\hat{B}$ commute, and 2) they do not commute?

10. Express the operator for rotation through a finite angle φ_0 about the $\boldsymbol{n}$-direction in terms of the angular-momentum operator (for a system of N particles).

11. Show that the equation $\overline{M^2} = \hbar^2 l\ (l+1)$ is obtained from the elementary equations of probability theory on the basis of the following facts: the possible components of the angular momentum along an arbitrary axis are equal to $m\hbar\,(m = -l, \ldots, 0, \ldots, l)$, all these projections have the same probability, and the axes are equivalent.

12. Interpret simply the commutativity property of the operators for the linear momentum components and the noncommutativity property of the operators for the angular-momentum components on the basis of the kinematic significance of these operators associated with infinitely small displacements and rotations.

13. Derive (in tensor form) the commutation relations between the angular-momentum components and the momentum components.

14. Show that the angular momentum of a system of two particles relative to their center of mass is "perpendicular" to the axis passing through the two particles.

15. Show that the transformation operator for the coordinates of a system commutes with the Hamiltonian if the transformation operator leaves the Hamiltonian unchanged.

16. Show which dynamical variables or combinations of variables (energy, the components and square of the angular momentum, momentum components, parity) are preserved when a system of N particles moves under the following fields:

1) free motion;
2) in the field of an infinite cylinder;
3) in the field of an infinite plane;
4) in the field of a sphere;
5) in the field of an infinite half-plane;
6) in the field of two points;
7) in an alternating field;
8) the field of a conductor with a variable charge;
9) the field of a tri-axial ellipsoid;
10) the field of an infinite cylindrical helix;
11) the field of an infinite prism;
12) the field of a cone;
13) the field of a circular torus.

Also, find whether the corresponding operators commute.

CHAPTER II

Stationary States. Penetration of Potential Barriers

1. Find the wave function of a particle moving in a one-dimensional potential of the form

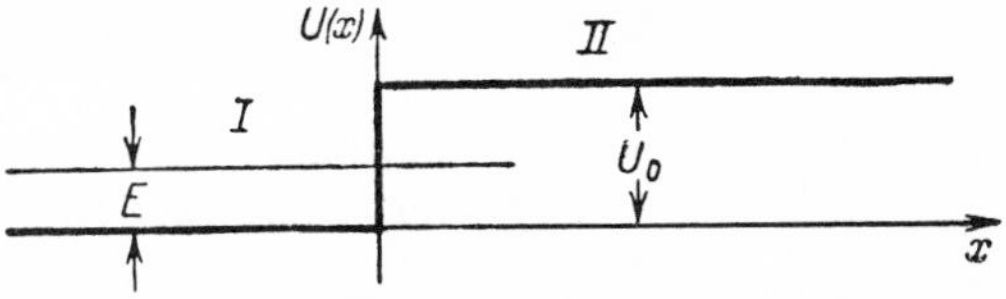

for the case where the energy of the particle E is smaller than the height of the potential wall U_0.

2. Find the wave function of stationary states and the energy level of a plane rotator with a moment of inertia I.*

3. Find the wave functions of the stationary states and the energy levels of a spatial rotator with a moment of inertia I.

4. Find the wave functions of the stationary states and the energy levels of a particle with mass m in a uniform gravitational field $\boldsymbol{g}$ for the case where the region of motion of the particle is limited on the bottom by a perfectly reflecting plane.** Carry out the limiting transition to classical mechanics.

5. Find the degree of degeneracy of the energy levels of an isotropic ($\omega_1 = \omega_2 = \omega_3 \equiv \omega$) oscillator in space.

6. Find the wave functions of the stationary states and the energy levels of a particle in a two-dimensional potential well of the form (ρ being the polar radius)

---

*A rotator is a system of two rigidly connected particles which rotates in a plane or in space; see below, Problem No. 3. The moment of inertia of a rotator is equal to $I = \mu a^2$, where μ is the reduced mass of the particles, and a is the distance between them.

**A classical analogue of this system is provided by a heavy solid ball bouncing on a slab of metal. We note that all the computations and results of this problem are correct for the case of motion of a charged particle in a uniform electric field $\mathcal{E}$ (in the presence of a reflecting plane), if g is replaced by $\frac{e}{m}\mathcal{E}$ in all the equations.

$$U(\rho)=\begin{cases} 0 & \text{for } \rho \leqslant a, \\ \infty & \text{for } \rho \geqslant a. \end{cases}$$

7. Find the wave functions of the stationary states and the energy levels of a particle in a spherical, infinitely deep potential well of radius a.

8. Find the wave functions of stationary states with zero angular momentum and the corresponding energy levels of a particle in a three-dimensional potential well of the type

$$U=-U_0 e^{-\frac{r}{a}}.$$

9. For a one-dimensional potential well with one energy level, find the condition which must be satisfied for the energy level to remain unchanged as the width of the well approaches zero and its height approaches infinity.

Find the boundary conditions for functions outside the well in this limiting case.

10. Find the ψ-functions of the bound state and of the continuous spectrum for a particle in an infinitely narrow potential well (see the previous problem).

11. For a three-dimensional isotropic harmonic oscillator, find the wave functions and the energy levels of the stationary states, in which, in addition to the energy, the square of the angular momentum and the component of the angular momentum along an axis have well-defined values.

12. Find the wave functions of stationary states and the energy levels of linear harmonic oscillator in a uniform electric field.

13. Study the motion of a negatively charged μ-meson in the field of a nucleus with charge Ze (which is regarded as a sphere of radius R throughout the volume of which the charge is evenly distributed) under the assumption that the forces of interaction of the meson with the nucleus are purely electrostatic in nature.

Find the wave functions of the stationary states and the energy levels of a meson in the limiting cases of small Z and extremely large Z.

14. From the expression for the energy levels of a particle in a one-dimensional rectangular potential well of infinite depth, obtain expressions of the correct order of magnitude for the energy levels of the following systems:

1) a linear harmonic oscillator;
2) a charged particle in a uniform electric field when its motion is limited by a perfectly reflecting plane;
3) a hydrogenlike atom.

15. Show in general form that, for a barrier of arbitrary shape, the equation

$$R+D=1,$$

where R is the reflection coefficient and D is the transmission coefficient, is automatically satisfied.

16. Compute the transmission and reflection coefficients of a

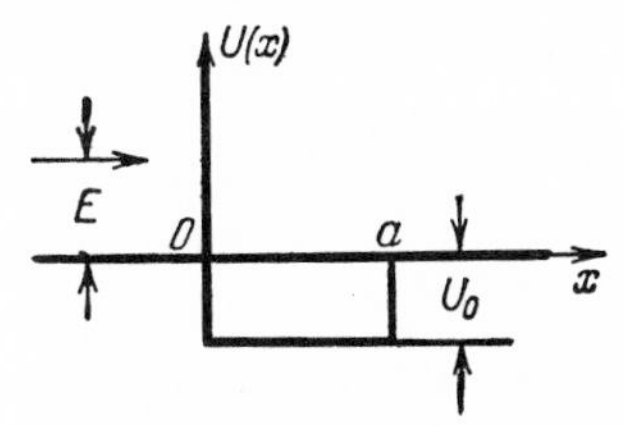

particle incident on a one-dimensional potential well of the type

$$U(x) = \begin{cases} 0 & \text{for } x \leqslant 0, \quad x \geqslant a, \\ -U_0 & \text{for } 0 \leqslant x \leqslant a. \end{cases}$$

17. Find the transmission coefficient of a particle for a triangular barrier of the form

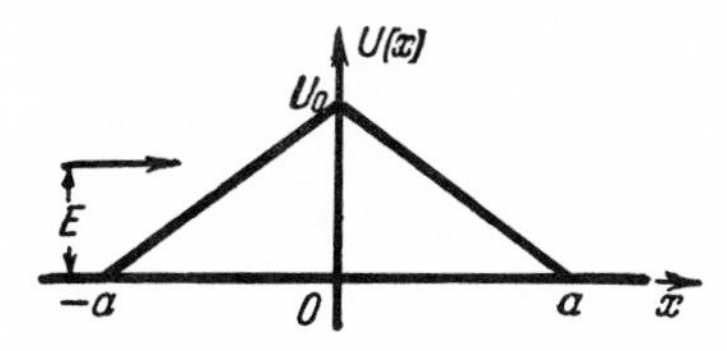

Consider the limiting cases of large and small probabilities of penetration.

CHAPTER III

Computation of Probabilities and Average Values. Transformation to Other State Spaces

1. Compute the probability current density for freely moving particles.

2. Given the wave function of a particle $\Psi(x, y, z)$, compute the probability of finding the particle within the range of values of z from z_1 to z_2 and within the range of values of p_y from p_1 to p_2.

3. Find the possible values of the angular momentum, their probability, and the expected value of the angular momentum for a plane rotator in a state described by the wave function

$$\Psi = A\cos^2\varphi.$$

4. A three-dimensional rotator is in a state having an angular momentum $l = 1$ and a z-component of the angular momentum $m = 1$.

Find the possible values of the component of the angular momentum along the z'-axis, which is inclined at an angle α to the z-axis, their probability, and the expected value of $M_{z'}$.

5. Find the energy level and the probability distribution function of the position and the momentum of a particle in a one-dimensional rectangular potential well of small depth.

6. Consider a particle in a one-dimensional symmetric potential well, in which, as we know, there is always at least one energy level.

If the width a of a well of given depth U_0 is reduced to a quantity satisfying the inequality

$$a^2 \ll \frac{\hbar^2}{mU_0}$$

(see the solution of Problem 5), it would seem at first sight that "the spatial localization of a particle confined within the well will become more accurate ($\Delta x \sim a$), while the spread in momentum Δp will be bound in any event from above by a quantity of the order of $\sqrt{mU_0}$. Consequently, the inequality

$$\Delta p\,\Delta x \lesssim \sqrt{mU_0}\cdot a \ll \hbar$$

will hold, contradicting the uncertainty principle."

Show the error in this argument and compute the uncertainty in the position and momentum of the particle.

7. Compute the average value of the n-th power of the radius r and also the standard deviation of the radius in the ground state of the hydrogen atom.

8. How does the probability that a negative meson will be captured from the K-orbit of a mesic atom depend on the charge of the nucleus Z?

9. Find the probability distribution function of different values of the electron momentum in the ground state of the hydrogen atom.

10. Find the effective (average) potential φ acting on a charged meson flying through an unexcited hydrogen atom (neglecting the polarization of the latter). Obtain the limiting expressions for φ, at large and small distances between the meson and the nucleus.

11. A particle is contained in a one-dimensional rectangular potential well with infinitely high walls. Compute the average force with which the particle acts on a wall of the well.

12. A state of a particle in an infinitely deep rectangular potential well is described by the wave function

$$\psi(x) = Ax(a - x),$$

where a is the width of the well and A is a constant.

Find the probability distribution function of the different values of the energy of the particle, and the mean value and the standard deviation of the energy.

13. A particle is located in a state described by a plane wave $\psi = Ae^{ikr}$. Determine the probability of finding it at a distance r from the origin of coordinates with a total angular momentum l relative to this origin.

14. Find the wave function in the momentum space for a particle in a centrally symmetric field, if the particle is in a stationary state with definite values of the square of the angular momentum and of one component of the angular momentum (the wave function in the position space is assumed to be known).

15. Find the probability distribution function of the different values of the momentum for a particle in a spherical potential well with infinitely high walls, if the particle is located in a stationary state with definite values of the square of the angular momentum and of one of its components.

16. A system of two particles connected by an elastic force moves freely in space with a velocity $\boldsymbol{V}_0$ relative to some local laboratory system of coordinates.

Find the distribution of the probability of different values of the momenta of the two particles in the (local) laboratory system of coordinates for the case where the system is in the ground state (from the relative motion).

17. A three-dimensional isotropic harmonic oscillator is located in a state with definite values of the energy of its motion along

the x, y and z axes, the corresponding quantum numbers being

$$n_1 = 2, \quad n_2 = 1, \quad n_3 = 1.$$

Find the probability distribution function of the different values of the total angular momentum (l) and its z component (m) in this state.

18. A stationary state of an electron in a hydrogen atom is characterized by the "parabolic quantum numbers" $n_1 = 1$, $n_2 = 0$ and by the magnetic quantum number $m = 0$.

Find the probabilitity functions of the position z and the total angular momentum l of the electron in this state (z being the axis of parabolic quantization).

19. Let the commutator of the operators $\hat{L}$ and $\hat{M}$ for two physical quantities be $i\hat{K}$ ($\hat{K}$ being a Hermitian operator):

$$[\hat{L}, \hat{M}] = i\hat{K}.$$

Show the correctness of the uncertainty relation

$$\Delta L \cdot \Delta M \geqslant \frac{1}{2} |\overline{K}|,$$

where ΔL and ΔM represent the standard deviation of the quantities L and M:

$$\Delta L = \sqrt{\overline{(\hat{L} - \overline{L})^2}},$$

$$\Delta M = \sqrt{\overline{(\hat{M} - \overline{M})^2}},$$

and $|\overline{K}|$ is the absolute value of the average of K.

20. Show that in a transformation from the position space to the momentum space, the parity of the wave function relative to the corresponding variable remains invariant.

21. Write the wave functions in the $\boldsymbol{r}$- and $\boldsymbol{p}$-spaces: 1) for a particle at rest; 2) for a particle localized at the point $\boldsymbol{r}_0$.

22. Write the simultaneous eigenfunctions of the operators for the square of the angular momentum and the component of the angular momentum of a particle in the (M^2, M_z)-space (the eigenvalues of these operators are assumed to be known).

23. Assuming the energy spectrum of a system to be known, write the wave functions of its stationary states in the energy representation.

24. Given two Hermitian operators $\hat{A}$ and $\hat{B}$, show the relation between the eigenfunctions of operator $\hat{A}$ in the B-space and the eigenfunctions of operator $\hat{B}$ in the A-space.

25. Illustrate the relation established in the preceding problem and its probability significance on the basis of the following sets of quantities:

1) the momentum and the position;

2) the momentum and the set consisting of the square of the angular momentum, the component of angular momentum, and the energy — for free motion;

3) the energy of motion along the axis of a Cartesian coordinate system and the set consisting of the square of the angular momentum, the component of angular momentum, and the total energy — for a spherical isotropic oscillator;

4) the parabolic and "spherical" quantum numbers — for a hydrogen atom.

26. Write in the $\boldsymbol{p}$- and $\boldsymbol{r}$-spaces the expressions for the operators for a finite displacement in momentum space.

27. Express the operator $\frac{1}{r}$ in the $\boldsymbol{p}$-space and the operator $\frac{1}{p}$ in the $\boldsymbol{r}$-space.

28. Express the operator $\frac{\hat{1}}{p_x}$ in the x-space and the operator $\frac{\hat{1}}{x}$ in the p_x-space.

CHAPTER IV

Matrices. Addition of Angular Momenta

1. Find the matrices of position and momentum in the energy space for a particle in a one-dimensional rectangular potential well of infinite depth.

2. Show that the average value of the time derivative of a dynamical variable, which does not depend on time explicitly, is equal to zero in a stationary state in a discrete spectrum.

3. Prove the virial theorem in quantum mechanics.

4. For a particle in a spherically symmetric field, determine the selection rules for transitions between stationary states under the effect of a perturbation whose operator is proportional to the gradient (∇).

5. Show that the average value of the dipole moment of a system of charged particles in a state characterized by a definite parity, is equal to zero.

6. For a system of N charged particles moving in a finite region in space, show that the following equation is true (a so-called "sum rule"):

$$\frac{2\mu}{\hbar^2 e^2} \sum_n (E_n - E_m) | d_{mn} |^2 = N,$$

where d_{mn} is a matrix element of the component of the dipole moment of the system along an arbitrary axis and the summation is taken over all the states of the system, and μ and e are the mass and charge of each particle.

7. Show that, in the case of second-order matrices, the matrices $\hat{a}\hat{b}$ and $\hat{b}\hat{a}$ have the same eigenvalues.

8. Can a unitary matrix also be Hermitian?

9. If Ψ_{LM} is simultaneously an eigenfunction of the operators $\hat{L}^2$ and $\hat{L}_z$, having the eigenvalues $L(L+1)$ and M respectively, what does the application of the operators $\hat{L}_x$, $\hat{L}_y$, $(\hat{L}_x + i\hat{L}_y)$, and $(\hat{L}_x - i\hat{L}_y)$ to it reduce to, and what are the average values of these four quantities in the state described by this wave function?

10. As is known [1, Section 30], in the addition of the angular momenta $\boldsymbol{L}_1$ and $\boldsymbol{L}_2$ of two weakly interacting subsystems $(\boldsymbol{L}_1 + \boldsymbol{L}_2 = \boldsymbol{L})$

there is a transformation from the complete set of quantities L_1^2, L_{1z}, L_2^2, L_{2z} to the set of quantities L_1^2, L_2^2, L^2, L_z.*
Show that this new set is also complete.

11. A system consisting of two weakly interacting subsystems 1 and 2 with angular momenta $j_1 = 1$ and $j_2 = \frac{1}{2}$ is in a state with a total angular momentum $j = \frac{1}{2}$ and a component of angular momentum along a given axis (z) $m = \frac{1}{2}$.

Determine the probabilities of the possible values of m_1 and m_2 — the components of the angular momenta of the subsystem along this axis — and also their average values.

12. There are two weakly interacting subsystems 1 and 2 whose states are characterized by the quantum numbers of the total angular momentum and of its z component (L_1, M_1) and (L_2, M_2), respectively.

Indicate the possible values of the total angular momentum L of the aggregate system $(1 + 2)$, and compute the average value of L^2 in the given state.

13. Given the conditions of the preceding problem, compute the probabilities of the different possible values of L for the special case where $L_2 = \frac{1}{2}$.

14. Illustrate the relation established in Problem No. 24, Chapter III, and its probability significance on the basis of the addition of the angular momenta of two weakly interacting subsystems.

---

*In addition, each of these two sets includes identical quantities (in particular, the energy) which do not play a rôle in the addition of angular momenta and which, for brevity, we shall not write.

CHAPTER V

Variation of States in Time. Operators in the Heisenberg Space

1. How does the state of a plane rotator change with time, if it is described by the wave function $\Psi = A \sin^2 \varphi$ at the initial time $(t = 0)$?

2. At the time $(t = 0)$, a particle of mass m is in a state described by the wave function

$$\Psi(x, 0) = \text{const}\, e^{-\frac{x^2}{2a^2} + i\frac{mv_0 x}{\hbar}}$$

(a Gaussian "wave packet" of width a, moving with a velocity v_0).

Determine the change of the state of the particle with time, assuming that there are no external forces for $t \geq 0$.

3. How will the state of a linear harmonic oscillator change with time, if it is described at the initial time by the wave function

$$\Psi(x, 0) = \text{const} \cdot e^{-\frac{1}{2}\alpha^2 (x-b)^2},$$

where $\alpha = \sqrt{\frac{\mu\omega}{\hbar}}$? Investigate the limiting cases of small and large b and trace out the transition to classical mechanics.

4. A particle is contained in a rectangular, infinitely deep potential well of width a. At the time $t = 0$, one of the walls of the well begins to move according to a given arbitrary time dependent function.

Reduce the problem to a wave equation with a Hamiltonian depending explicitly on time, and indicate the particular case of motion of the wall for which the variables of this equation are separable.

5. Prove the invariance of the nonrelativistic Schrödinger equation with respect to Galileo's transformation.

6. Ordinarily, in the Heisenberg space (i.e., a space in which the time dependence is transferred from the ψ-function to the operators) [11], the operators for physical quantities have a form in which the energy is taken to be the independent variable (the Heisenberg energy space). In this case, the matrix elements of the operator $\hat{L}$ have the form

$$L_{nm}(t) = e^{-\frac{i}{\hbar}(E_m - E_n)t} \int \psi_n^* \hat{L} \psi_m \, d\tau.$$

Show that, if the quantity A is taken to be the independent variable, the operator $\hat{L}$ in the Heisenberg space (the Heisenberg A-space) will have the form

$$\hat{L}_A(t) = e^{\frac{i}{\hbar}\hat{H}_A \cdot t} \hat{L}_A e^{-\frac{i}{\hbar}\hat{H}_A \cdot t},$$

where $\hat{L}_A$, $\hat{H}_A$ are the operators $\hat{L}$ and $\hat{H}$ in the A-space and $\hat{H}$ is the Hamiltonian of the system.

7. Find the position operator in the Heisenberg space for a freely moving particle.

8. Find the position and momentum operators for a linear harmonic oscillator in the Heisenberg space by solving the equations of motion for these operators.

9. Show that the function Ψ, which describes a state with a definite value of the physical quantity A at $t = 0$, will be an eigenfunction of the operator $\hat{A}(-t)$ for $t > 0$ corresponding to the same eigenvalue. Here $\hat{A}(\tau)$ is the operator for the quantity A in the Heisenberg space at the time τ.

10. Using the results of Problems No. 7 and No. 9, find Green's function for free motion of a particle, i.e., the function $G(\boldsymbol{r}, t; \boldsymbol{r}_0)$ satisfying the corresponding Schrödinger equation and the initial condition $G(\boldsymbol{r}, 0; \boldsymbol{r}_0) = \delta(\boldsymbol{r} - \boldsymbol{r}_0)$.

11. Using the results of Problems No. 8 and No. 9, find Green's function for a linear harmonic oscillator, i.e., the function $G(x, t; x_0)$, satisfying the corresponding Schrödinger equation and the initial condition $G(x, 0; x_0) = \delta(x - x_0)$.

12. The equilibrium point x_0 of an oscillator in the ground state begins to move at the time $t = 0$. The equation of motion of the equilibrium point is given: $x_0 = x_0(t)$. At $t = T$, the equilibrium point stops moving.

Using the methods of solution of the preceding problems, find the Ψ-function of the system at an arbitrary moment of time $t > 0$, as well as the probability of excitation to the n-th level as a result of the given process.

Examine the limiting cases of rapid and slow processes ($\omega T \ll 1$ and $\omega T \gg 1$, where ω is the frequency of the oscillator).

CHAPTER VI

Perturbation Theory. Sudden and Adiabatic Changes

1. Compute in the first approximation of perturbation theory the shift in the energy level of the ground state of a hydrogenlike atom or ion resulting from the fact that the nucleus is not a point charge.

Regard the nucleus as a sphere of radius R, throughout the volume of which the charge Ze is evenly distributed.

2. A plane rotator with a moment of inertia I and an electric dipole moment $\boldsymbol{d}$ is placed in a uniform electric field $\mathcal{E}$ lying in the plane of rotation. Regarding $\mathcal{E}$ as a perturbation, compute the first nonvanishing corrections to the energy levels of the rotator.

3. A rotator in space with a moment of inertia I and an electric dipole moment $\boldsymbol{d}$ parallel to the axis of the rotator is placed in a uniform electric field $\mathcal{E}$, which is regarded as a perturbation. Compute the first nondisappearing correction to the ground-state energy level of the rotator.

4. Compute in the first approximation of perturbation theory the energy of the ground state of a two-electron atom or ion having a nuclear charge Z, taking the interaction between the electrons to be the perturbation.

Compute also the first ionization potential for a single electron of the above atom (ion).

5. A linear harmonic oscillator is subject to the action of a uniform electric field, which is regarded as a perturbation* and which changes in time according to equation

$$\mathcal{E}(t) = A \frac{1}{\sqrt{\pi}\,\tau} e^{-\left(\frac{t}{\tau}\right)^2}$$

where A is a constant.

---

*Since the action of a uniform field is equivalent to a shift of the equilibrium point (see Problem No. 12, Chapter II), this problem can be solved not only on the basis of perturbation theory, but also, accurately, on the basis of Problem No. 12, Chapter V.

Considering that the oscillator was in the ground state until the field was switched on (at $t = -\infty$), compute in the first approximation the probability of its excitation as a result of the action of the above perturbation (as $t \to \infty$).

6. Solve the preceding problem for a field changing according to the equation

$$\mathcal{E}(t) \sim \frac{1}{t^2 + \tau^2},$$

for a given, clasically imparted momentum P.

7. At $t = 0$, a hydrogen atom in the normal state is acted on by a uniform electric field periodically alternating in time.

Determine the minimum frequency of the field necessary to ionize the atom and, using perturbation theory, compute the ionization probability per unit time. For simplicity, the electron in the final state should be regarded as free.

8. Find the probability that a K-electron will be ejected from an atom as a result of direct electrostatic interaction of the electron with the protons of the nucleus (internal conversion neglecting the lag, see [17], pp. 143-144).

For the initial wave function, use the ψ-function of the K-electron of a hydrogenlike atom. Consider the velocity of the electron in the final state to be much larger than that of the atom.

9. At a certain moment in time, a uniform electric field (which remains constant in time from then on) is applied to a linear harmonic oscillator.

Find the probability that the oscillator will be excited to the n-th level as a result of this sudden application of the field.

10. The nucleus of an atom which is in a stationary state ψ_0 is acted on by a sudden impulse of duration τ, as a result of which it acquires a velocity $\boldsymbol{v}$.

Assuming that $\tau \ll T$ and $\tau \ll \frac{a}{v}$, where T and a are the orders of magnitude of the electron periods and of the electron shell sizes respectively, express in a general form the probability that the atom will make a transition to the state ψ_n as a result of this "jarring" [18].

11. Using the results of the preceding problem, compute the total probability of excitation and ionization of a hydrogen atom (which is initially in the ground state) as a result of a sudden "jolt" in which a momentum $\boldsymbol{p}$ is imparted to the proton.

Show the conditions for applicability of the result.

12. The Hamiltonian $\hat{H}$ of a system in finite, one-dimensional motion depends explicitly on time. For each moment of time t the spectrum of eigenvalues $E_n(t)$ of the "instantaneous" Hamiltonian

and the complete system of orthonormal functions $\psi_n(t)$ corresponding to these eigenvalues are assumed to be known.*

Write the wave equation of the system in the representation whose base is the system of functions $\psi_n(t)$.

13. The Hamiltonian of the system described in the preceding problem is a slowly changing function of the time t. Assuming the system to be in the m-th quantum state at the time $t = 0$, find its wave function for $t > 0$ in the first approximation of the adiabatic perturbation theory and give the range of validity of the result.

14. At the time $t = 0$, the equilibrium point of a linear oscillator in the ground state starts in a slow, uniform motion, and at the time $t = T$, it stops. Find the probability that the oscillator will be excited by the adiabatic approximation** and determine the range of validity of this approximation.

15. A rectangular, infinitely deep potential well of width a contains a particle in the n-th stationary state. At the time $t = 0$, one of the walls of the well begins to move slowly according to a given time-dependent function. By the adiabatic approximation find the probability that the particle will be in the m-th state ($m \neq n$) for $t > 0$.

---

*Here, the term "instantaneous" is used in the sense of "at a given moment of time" as distinguished from the solutions of Problems No. 5 and 6, where it is synonymous with "sudden." For brevity, from now on we shall omit everywhere the dependence of the ψ-function on the position (q).

**Cf. Problem No. 12, Chapter V.

CHAPTER VII

The Quasi-Classical Approximation

1. Obtain the quasi-classical expression for the energy levels of a linear harmonic oscillator.

2. Obtain the quasi-classical expression for the energy levels of a particle in a uniform gravitational field in the case where its motion is limited from below by a perfectly reflecting plane.

3. Compute in the quasi-classical approximation the coefficient of transmittance of a parabolic barrier of the form

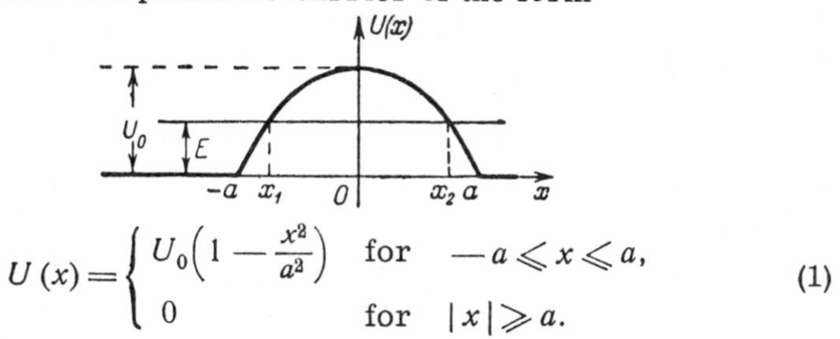

$$U(x)=\begin{cases} U_0\left(1-\dfrac{x^2}{a^2}\right) & \text{for} \quad -a\leqslant x\leqslant a, \\ 0 & \text{for} \quad |x|\geqslant a. \end{cases} \tag{1}$$

Indicate the criteria for the result to be valid.

4. The field $U(x)$ appears as two symmetric potential wells (I and II) separated by a barrier. If the barrier were impenetrable for a particle, there would exist energy levels corresponding to the motion of the particle only in one well or the other and they would be identical for the two wells. The possibility of passage through the barrier causes splitting of each of the levels into two nearby levels corresponding to states in which the particle moves simultaneously in both wells.

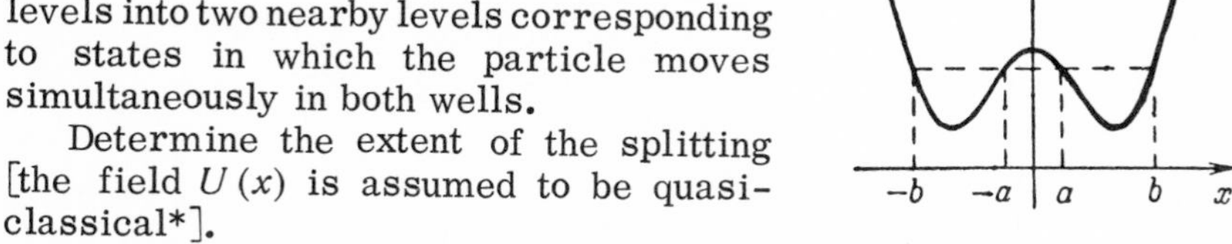

Determine the extent of the splitting [the field $U(x)$ is assumed to be quasi-classical*].

5. A particle moves in a periodic field $U(x)$:

$$U(x+a)=U(x).$$

---

*This problem is solved somewhat differently in [1].

Considering the quasi-classical approximation to be applicable, obtain a transcendental equation for the permitted energy zones.

6. The usual rule for quantization in the quasi-classical approximation holds for the case where the region of motion of a particle is limited by two points of return, close to which the conditions for the validity of the quasi-classical approximation are violated. A different case is encountered in examining the motion of electrons in a Thomas-Fermi distribution* occupying the s-state. On the side of small values of r, the region of motion of these electrons is limited only by the point $r = 0$, which is not a point of return. On the other hand, it would be wrong to require that the quasi-classical functions be finite at the point $r = 0$, since the conditions for the validity of the quasi-classical conditions are violated near this point.

Obtain the quantization rule for electrons in a Thomas-Fermi distribution occupying the s-state.

7. Find the quasi-classical solution of Schrödinger's equation in the momentum space.

Show that this same quasi-classical function is obtained from the ordinary, quasi-classical position ψ-function by transforming from the x-space to the p-space.

---

*What we say here holds for the motion of electrons in any spherically symmetric field which becomes a Coulomb field at small distances from the center. We have selected the Thomas-Fermi model only to be specific.

CHAPTER VIII

Spin. Identical Particles

1. Write the operators for the electron-spin components $\hat{s}_x$, $\hat{s}_y$, $\hat{s}_z$ (the Pauli matrices) in the s_x-space.

2. Find the eigenvalues of the operators for the electron-spin components $\hat{s}_x$, $\hat{s}_y$, $\hat{s}_z$ and their eigenfunctions in the s_z-space.

3. Can the squares of the electron-spin components along the x-, y-, and z-axes have definite values simultaneously?

4. Compute the square of the scalar product of an ordinary (nonoperator) vector and of the spin vector $\frac{1}{2}$.

5. Compute the values of the scalar product of two spin vectors $\frac{1}{2}$ in the triplet and singlet states of a system with these two spins.

6. Write in the s_z-space the operator for the electron-spin component along the z'-axis inclined at an angle α to the z-axis.

7. Find the probabilities of the possible values of the electron-spin components along the z'-axis (inclined at an angle α to the z-axis) in a state with a definite value $s_z = +\frac{1}{2}$, and also compute the mean value of $\overline{s_{z'}}$ in this state.

8. Using the results of Problem No. 1, find the transformation matrix for changing the electron-spin operators from the s_z-space to the s_x-space.

9. Given a system of two weakly interacting spins $s_1 = s_2 = \frac{1}{2}$, find the eigenvalues and the corresponding eigenfunctions of the total spin $\boldsymbol{S} = \boldsymbol{s}_1 + \boldsymbol{s}_2$, and determine the nature of the symmetry of these spin functions.

10. For a particle with spin $s = 1$, write in the s_z-space the spin operators $\hat{s}_x$, $\hat{s}_y$, $\hat{s}_z$, $\hat{s}^2$ and the orthonormal spin wave functions for states with definite values of s^2 and s_z. Give also the transformation rules of these spin wave functions under the action of the spin operators, including the operators $\hat{s}_x \pm i\hat{s}_y$.

11. For a system of two weakly interacting spins $s_1 = s_2 = 1$, find the values and the corresponding eigenfunctions of the operators for the total spin $\hat{S}^2 = (\hat{\boldsymbol{s}}_1 + \hat{\boldsymbol{s}}_2)^2$ and $\hat{S}_z = \hat{s}_{1z} + \hat{s}_{2z}$. Determine the nature of the symmetry of these spin functions.

12. Show that, for a system of two identical particles with spin I, the ratio of the number of states which are symmetric under

spin interchange to the number of states which are anti-symmetric under spin interchange is equal to $\frac{I+1}{I}$.

13. Write the normalized wave function for a system of three identical, weakly interacting Bose particles which occupy given states.

CHAPTER IX

Atoms and Molecules

1. Find the possible atomic terms for a configuration of two equivalent d-electrons, and, using Hund's rule, give the normal term.

2. What are the rotational states of a deuterium molecule D_2 (in the ground electronic state) from the point of view of the parity of the orbital angular momentum in these states?

3. Show that the average velocity of atomic electrons in the Thomas-Fermi model is proportional to $Z^{2/3}$.

4. Determine how the number of electrons in a Thomas-Fermi distribution occupying s-states is related to Z.

5. Evaluate the order of magnitude of the polarizability of the Thomas-Fermi model of the atom, i.e., the ratio of the dipole moment d of a Thomas-Fermi electron distribution arising under the action of an external electric field to the magnitude of the intensity of the field $\mathcal{E}$.

6. For a diatomic molecule, evaluate the relative orders of magnitude of the following quantities: 1) the intervals between the vibrational and rotational levels of the electrons; 2) the internuclear distance and the amplitude of the zero-point oscillations of the nuclei; 3) the characteristic periods and velocities of the electronic and nuclear motions.

7. Study the effect of the finiteness of the mass M of a nucleus on the energy levels of an atom with n electrons (assuming the energy levels to be known for $M = \infty$) [14].

8. Compute the "exchange" correction (resulting from Pauli's exclusion principle) for the finiteness of the nuclear mass in the terms of a two-electron atom (or ion), neglecting the electrostatic interaction of the electrons and considering that one of them is in the $1s$-state.

CHAPTER X

Motion in a Magnetic Field

1. A charged particle (with zero spin) moves in a uniform constant magnetic field. Find the wave functions of the stationary states of the particle, if both energy and the component of angular momentum in the direction of the field have definite values.

2. For a charged particle in a uniform constant magnetic field, find the operators for the coordinates of the center of the orbit, for the square of the radius vector of this center, and for the square of the radius of the orbit.

Determine whether these quantities are constants of motion. Which of them have definite values in the states considered in the preceding problem and what are these values [28]?

3. On the basis of the results of Problems No. 1 and No. 2, describe the character of electron states for which $l = 0$ in a uniform magnetic field. Perform the limiting transition to classical mechanics.

4. Repeat for electron states with $n = 0$.

5. Find the energy levels and wave functions of the stationary states of a plane harmonic oscillator (with $\omega_1 = \omega_2$) located in a uniform magnetic field perpendicular to its plane [29].

6. Find the spin wave functions of the proton and the electron in a hydrogen atom in the ground state of plane motion in an external magnetic field $\mathcal{H}$.

CHAPTER XI

Theory of Collisions

1. Compute the effective cross section of elastic scattering in the potential

$$U(r) = A\frac{e^{-\varkappa r}}{r}$$

using the Born approximation. Give the condition for applicability of this approximation.

2. In the Born approximation, compute the effective scattering cross section of a "delta-function" potential.

3. In the Born approximation, compute the effective scattering cross section of a spherical "rectangular" well of the form

$$U(r) = \begin{cases} -U_0 & \text{for } r \leqslant a, \\ 0 & \text{for } r \geqslant a \end{cases}$$

and give the condition for applicability of the approximation.

4. In the Born approximation, compute the effective cross section for elastic scattering of electrons by a spherical nucleus with a charge evenly distributed throughout its volume.

5. Compute the effective cross section for scattering of rapid neutrons by a Coulomb field (in the Born approximation).

6. On the basis of dimensional analysis, evaluate the order of magnitude of the scattering cross section of a potential which decreases as $\frac{1}{r^n}$ (in the Born approximation).

7. Show that the scattering amplitude for a particle in an arbitrary external field is connected with the ψ-function by the equation

$$f(\boldsymbol{k}) = -\frac{\mu}{2\pi\hbar^2}\int e^{-i\boldsymbol{k}\boldsymbol{r}}U\psi\, dV.$$

8. Prove that the equation

$$\sigma_s + \sigma_c = \frac{4\pi}{k}\operatorname{Im} f(0)$$

is correct, where σ_s is the total effective cross section for elastic scattering by a center of force, σ_c is the total cross section for nonelastic scattering (including capture), k is the absolute value of the propagation vector of the incident particle, and $f(0) \equiv f(0)|_{\theta=0}$ is the amplitude of elastic scattering through the angle $\theta = 0$.

9. Using the phase theory of scattering, compute the effective scattering cross section of a repelling potential of the form

$$U(r) = \frac{\alpha}{r^2}.$$

10. Compute the effective cross section for scattering of particles by a perfectly reflecting (impenetrable) sphere of radius a.

11. Using the phase theory of scattering and elementary considerations on the magnitude of the phases δ_l for different l, determine the total cross section for scattering by an impenetrable sphere in the limiting cases $ka \ll 1$ and $ka \gg 1$.

12. Compute the effective cross section for scattering by a spherical potential well of depth U_0 and radius a, assuming that a is small relative to the deBroglie wavelength of the particle.

13. Compute the effective cross section for scattering by a potential hill of height U_0 and radius a, assuming that $\lambda\!\!\!^- \gg a$.

14. Compute the effective cross section for scattering of slow particles in an exponentially decreasing, spherically symmetric repelling field.

15. Compute the effective cross section for scattering of slow particles in an exponentially decreasing attracting field, including the case of resonance.

16. Under what conditions will the scattering cross section for the aggregate of a large number of centers of force be equal to the sum of the cross sections for the individual centers?

17. Write the general expression for the effective scattering cross section for mutual scattering of two helium atoms, regarding them approximately as two impenetrable spheres with a given radius, and compute the cross section for the limiting cases of small and large relative velocities of the atoms (consider the cases of collisions of unexcited atoms of the helium isotopes He^4 and He^3).

18. A spherical rotator* in the ground state is hit by a particle interacting with it through Coulomb forces. From perturbation theory, compute the differential effective cross section for scattering through an angle θ with excitation of the rotator to the l-th level.

19. Using the principle of detailed balancing, relate the effective cross section for radiative capture of a neutron by a proton and for photo-disintegration of the deuteron.

---

*In this problem we shall consider the simplest model of the rotator, namely a particle moving on the surface of a sphere at a given radius a.

CHAPTER XII

Parity. Isotopic Spin

1. A system consisting of two mesons, π^+ and π^-, is in a state with a definite orbital angular momentum of the relative motion of the meson l.

Determine the selection rule for the process

$$\pi^- + \pi^+ \rightarrow \pi^0 + \pi^0$$

depending on whether the quantum number l is even or odd.

2. Show that the process

$$\pi^- + d \rightarrow n + n$$

is forbidden for a scalar π-meson (i.e., a meson which has a spin 0 and which is even), assuming that it is captured by the S-level of "mesic deuterium."*

3. Show that from the experimental fact of the extremely small probability of the process

$$\pi^- + d \rightarrow n + n + \pi^0$$

it follows (under the assumption that the capture of π^- takes place from the S-level of "mesic deuterium") that π^- and π^0 have the same internal parity.

4. Show that the reaction of the generation of a pseudoscalar π^0-meson in the collision $p + p$ is forbidden, if the π^0-meson emerges in the P-state. A reaction near the energy threshold is assumed, so that the effective angular momentum of the protons in the final state is equal to 0.

5. What are the eigenfunctions and eigenvalues of the isotropic spin** for a system of two nucleons?

6. Show that

$$\frac{d\sigma(p + d \rightarrow d + n + \pi^+)}{d\sigma(p + d \rightarrow d + p + \pi^0)} = 2,$$

---

*This result was first obtained by Ye. L. Feynberg [24].

**For a presentation of the theory of isotopic spin, see for instance [26], [27].

where the $d\sigma$ are the differential effective cross sections of the corresponding reactions taken at the same relative energies, scattering angles and mutual orientations of the spins.

7. Show that the differential effective cross sections of the reactions of the generation of π-mesons in collisions of pairs of nucleons in which a deuteron is formed

$$p + p \to d + \pi^+ \tag{1}$$

and

$$n + p \to d + \pi^0 \tag{2}$$

are connected by the relationship

$$\frac{d\sigma\,(p + p \to d + \pi^+)}{d\sigma\,(n + p \to d + \pi^0)} = 2.$$

8. Show that the differential effective cross sections of the processes

$$n + p \to p + p + \pi^- \tag{1}$$

and

$$n + p \to n + n + \pi^+, \tag{2}$$

taken for the same relative energies, scattering angles, and mutual orientations of the spins of the particles, are identical.

9. Assuming that the scattering of π-mesons by nucleons takes place chiefly through the intermediate state of the meson-nucleon system with a total isotopic spin of $T = \frac{3}{2}$ $\left(\text{but not through the state with } T = \frac{1}{2}\right)$, compute the relationship of the differential effective cross sections of the following three reactions for the same relative energies, scattering angles, and orientations of the spins:

$$\begin{aligned}
&(\mathrm{I})\ \pi^+ + p \to \pi^+ + p,\\
&\left.\begin{aligned}&(\mathrm{II})\ \pi^- + p \to \pi^0 + n,\\ &(\mathrm{III})\ \pi^- + p \to \pi^- + p.\end{aligned}\right\}
\end{aligned}$$

SOLUTIONS

CHAPTER I

Operators. Constants of Motion

1. $(\hat{A}\hat{B})\hat{C} - \hat{C}(\hat{A}\hat{B}) \equiv \hat{A}\hat{B}\hat{C} - \hat{C}\hat{A}\hat{B} + \hat{A}\hat{C}\hat{B} - \hat{A}\hat{C}\hat{B} = \hat{A}(\hat{B}\hat{C} - \hat{C}\hat{B}) + (\hat{A}\hat{C} - \hat{C}\hat{A})\hat{B}$, or, in more compact form,

$$[\hat{A}\hat{B},\ \hat{C}] = \hat{A}[\hat{B},\ \hat{C}] + [\hat{A},\ \hat{C}]\hat{B}. \tag{1}$$

Since $[\hat{L}_1,\ \hat{L}_2] \equiv -[\hat{L}_2,\ \hat{L}_1]$, identity (1) can be transformed to

$$[\hat{A},\ \hat{B}\hat{C}] = [\hat{A},\ \hat{B}]\hat{C} + \hat{B}[\hat{A},\ \hat{C}]. \tag{2}$$

where we have redefined the operators to preserve the order of the letters A, B and C.

We emphasize the resemblance of these equations [in particular (2)] with the equation for the derivative of the product of two functions. We also note that the sequence of the operators forming the initial product [$\hat{A}$ and $\hat{B}$ in (1), $\hat{B}$ and $\hat{C}$ in (2)] is identical in all the terms.

2. $[\sum\limits_i \hat{A}_i, \sum\limits_k \hat{B}_k] \equiv (\sum\limits_i \hat{A}_i)(\sum\limits_k \hat{B}_k) - (\sum\limits_k \hat{B}_k)(\sum\limits_i \hat{A}_i) = \sum\limits_i \sum\limits_k \hat{A}_i\hat{B}_k - \sum\limits_i \sum\limits_k \hat{B}_k\hat{A}_i = \sum\limits_{i,\,k} [\hat{A}_i,\ \hat{B}_k]$, which is what we had to prove.

3. We denote the operators by $\hat{A}$ and $\hat{B}$, and the Hamiltonian of the system by $\hat{H}$. Then, we have:

$$\frac{d}{dt}(\hat{A}\hat{B}) = \frac{\partial}{\partial t}(\hat{A}\hat{B}) + \frac{i}{\hbar}[\hat{H},\ \hat{A}\hat{B}].$$

By carrying out an obvious transformation on the basis of the results of Problem No. 1 and collecting corresponding terms $\frac{d\hat{A}}{dt} \equiv \dot{\hat{A}}$ and $\frac{d\hat{B}}{dt} \equiv \dot{\hat{B}}$, respectively, we obtain the required differentiation rule:

$$\frac{d}{dt}(\hat{A}\hat{B}) = \dot{\hat{A}}\hat{B} + \hat{A}\dot{\hat{B}}.$$

4. In the equation

$$\overline{L^2} = \frac{\int \psi^* \hat{L}^2 \psi\, d\tau}{\int \psi^* \psi\, d\tau}$$

we know that the denominator is positive. Thus, it is necessary to show that the numerator is positive.

Using the definition of the self-conjugate operator $\hat{L}$, we obtain:

$$\int \psi^* \hat{L}\hat{L}\psi \, d\tau = \int (\hat{L}\psi)(\hat{L}^*\psi^*) \, d\tau = \int |\hat{L}\psi|^2 \, d\tau > 0,$$

5. 1) It is not linear. Indeed, if we denote the complex conjugate operator by $\hat{K}$, we have

$$\hat{K}(c_1\psi_1 + c_2\psi_2) = c_1^*\hat{K}\psi_1 + c_2^*\hat{K}\psi_2 \neq c_1\hat{K}\psi_1 + c_2\hat{K}\psi_2.$$

2) It is not Hermitian.

For a Hermitian operator $\hat{L}$, the condition

$$\int \psi^* \hat{L}\varphi \, d\tau = \int \varphi \hat{L}^* \psi^* \, d\tau \tag{1}$$

must be satisfied.

However, in our case, we have

$$\int \psi^* \hat{K}\varphi \, d\tau = \int \psi^* \varphi^* \, d\tau,$$

$$\int \varphi \hat{K}^* \psi^* \, d\tau = \int \varphi\psi \, d\tau;$$

i.e., condition (1) does not hold.

3) The operator which is the complex conjugate of a complex conjugate operator is equal to the latter (in other words, the operator is real).

Indeed,

$$\hat{K}\psi = \psi^*,$$

Hence,

$$\hat{K}^*\psi^* = \psi.$$

Denoting ψ^* by φ, we have

$$\hat{K}^*\varphi = \varphi^* = \hat{K}\varphi,$$

i.e.,

$$\hat{K}^* = \hat{K}.$$

(The complex conjugate operator changes i to $-i$, while the operator which is its complex conjugate changes $-i$ to i, which is one and the same thing.)

6. We write the required expansion in the form of a series

$$\sum_{n=0}^{\infty} \lambda^n \hat{L}_n,$$

where the $\hat{L}_n$ are operators which must be determined.

Thus,

$$(\hat{A}-\lambda\hat{B})^{-1}=\sum_{n=0}^{\infty}\lambda^n\hat{L}_n.$$

Multiplying (for instance, from the left) by $\hat{A}-\lambda\hat{B}$, we obtain

$$1=\sum_{n=0}^{\infty}\lambda^n(\hat{A}-\lambda\hat{B})\hat{L}_n=A\hat{L}_0+\sum_{n=1}^{\infty}\lambda^n(\hat{A}\hat{L}_n-\hat{B}\hat{L}_{n-1}).$$

By equating the coefficients of identical powers of λ in the left and right members of this equation, we obtain

$$\hat{A}\hat{L}_0=1,\quad \hat{A}\hat{L}_n-\hat{B}\hat{L}_{n-1}=0,$$

whence,

$$\hat{L}_0=\hat{A}^{-1},\quad \hat{L}_n=\hat{A}^{-1}\hat{B}\hat{L}_{n-1}.$$

Thus, we have

$$(\hat{A}-\lambda\hat{B})^{-1}=\hat{A}^{-1}+\lambda\hat{A}^{-1}\hat{B}\hat{A}^{-1}+\lambda^2\hat{A}^{-1}\hat{B}\hat{A}^{-1}\hat{B}\hat{A}^{-1}+\dots$$

For the case where A and B are numbers, this expression becomes the usual series

$$\frac{1}{A-\lambda B}=\frac{1}{A}+\lambda\frac{B}{A^2}+\lambda^2\frac{B^2}{A^3}+\dots$$

7. By writing the Hamiltonian in the form

$$\hat{H}=\frac{1}{2\mu}\left(\hat{p}-\frac{e}{c}\hat{A}\right)\left(\hat{p}-\frac{e}{c}\hat{A}\right),$$

we can convince ourselves that the condition which must be satisfied for it to equal $\hat{H}'$ is that the components of the vector operators $\hat{p}\equiv\frac{\hbar}{i}\nabla$ and $\hat{A}(x, y, z)$ along the same axis commute, i.e., that

$$\nabla A\equiv\operatorname{div}A=0.$$

8. The generalized momentum operator of a particle is $\hat{p}=\frac{\hbar}{i}\nabla$ (it is evident that its components $\hat{p}_x$, $\hat{p}_y$, and $\hat{p}_z$ commute with one another as in the case $\mathcal{H}=0$). The velocity operator is found from the Hamiltonian

$$\hat{H}=\frac{\left(\hat{p}-\frac{e}{c}\hat{A}\right)^2}{2\mu}$$

by using the rule for differentiating operators with respect to time

$$\hat{v} \equiv \dot{\hat{r}} = \frac{i}{\hbar}(\hat{H}\hat{r} - \hat{r}\hat{H}) = \frac{\hat{p} - \frac{e}{c}\hat{A}}{\mu}.$$

The vector potential $\boldsymbol{A}$ is a function of the coordinates (x, y, z). By using commutation relations of the type

$$\hat{p}_y\hat{A}_x - \hat{A}_x\hat{p}_y = \frac{\hbar}{i}\frac{\partial \hat{A}_x}{\partial y},$$

and by using the intensity of the magnetic field $\mathcal{H}$ = rot $\boldsymbol{A}$, we find

$$\hat{v}_x\hat{v}_y - \hat{v}_y\hat{v}_x = \frac{ie\hbar}{\mu^2 c}\mathcal{H}_z,$$
$$\hat{v}_y\hat{v}_z - \hat{v}_z\hat{v}_y = \frac{ie\hbar}{\mu^2 c}\mathcal{H}_x,$$
$$\hat{v}_z\hat{v}_x - \hat{v}_x\hat{v}_z = \frac{ie\hbar}{\mu^2 c}\mathcal{H}_y.$$

These commutation relations can be represented symbolically in vector form

$$\hat{v} \times \hat{v} = \frac{ie\hbar}{\mu^2 c}\mathcal{H}.$$

9. Generally speaking, it is impossible to answer the question asked in this problem simply on the basis of the commutative or noncommutative property of the operators $\hat{A}$ and $\hat{B}$.

Indeed, on the one hand, the commutative property of operators is not, strictly speaking, a necessary condition for the corresponding quantities to have definite values at the same time. Thus, in motion in a centrally symmetric field, in states in which the square of the magnitude of the angular moment is equal to zero, all three components of the angular momentum have definite values simultaneously (zero), although no two of these operators ever commute with each other.

Thus, the noncommutative property of the operators $\hat{A}$ and $\hat{B}$ (first case) is not sufficient to prevent some of their eigenvalues from occurring simultaneously.

On the other hand, from the mere commutative property of the operators $\hat{A}$ and $\hat{B}$ (second case), it is impossible, generally speaking, to conclude that the quality B has a definite value in the state Ψ_A.

Indeed, the commutative property of $\hat{A}$ and $\hat{B}$ is sufficient only for the existence of a complete set of states with simultaneous definite values A and B (we denote the wave functions of these states by Ψ_{AB}). It is not a sufficient condition for any arbitrarily selected wave function Ψ_A to belong to the set of functions Ψ_{AB}. This is connected with the phenomenon of degeneracy, in which a number of values of B correspond to a single value of A. Thus, in the general case, the wave function Ψ_A will be a linear superposition of functions Ψ_{AB} in the form

$$\Psi_A = \sum_{B'} c_{B'} \Psi_{AB'},$$

This reduces to Ψ_{AB} only for a certain set of coefficients ($c_{B'} = \delta_{B'B}$).

We give two simple examples:

1) When a system of particles moves in a centrally symmetric field, in a state where the square of the magnitude of the total angular momentum M^2 has a definite value, the component M_z may or may not have a definite value.

Indeed, all the values of $M^2 \neq 0$ are degenerate, corresponding to different values of M_z (this is connected with the existence of the operators $\hat{M}_x$ and $\hat{M}_y$, which commute with $\hat{M}^2$, but not with $\hat{M}_z$). Therefore, Ψ_{M^2} is a superposition

$$\Psi_{M^2} = \sum_{M_z} c_{M_z} \Psi_{M^2, M_z}.$$

In particular, we can indicate states Ψ_{M^2} in which we know that M_z will have no definite value, despite the fact that the operator $\hat{M}_z$ commutes with $\hat{M}^2$. Instances of this are states with definite values of M_x or M_y (except the state $M^2 = 0$, where $M_x = M_y = M_z = 0$).

2) In the hydrogen atom, several values of the square of the angular momentum M^2 correspond to each energy level E (except for the ground state). Thus, a state with a definite energy is generally not characterized by definite M^2, but it is a superposition of states with different M^2 (reducing to functions Ψ_{E, M^2} only for a definite selection of the coefficients of this superposition). Thus, just because E is definite, it does not follow that M^2 will be definite in the same state, in spite of the fact that $\hat{M}^2$ commutes with the energy operator $\hat{H}$.

Thus, in the general case, the commutative property and nature of $\hat{A}$ and $\hat{B}$ does not make it possible to answer the question asked in the problem. To answer this question, it is necessary to apply the operator $\hat{B}$ to the function Ψ_A. If this operation leads to the equation

$$\hat{B}\Psi_A = \lambda \Psi_A,$$

where λ is a number, Ψ_A will be an eigenfunction of $\hat{B}$, and the variable B will have an eigenvalue (equal to λ) in the state Ψ_A. If this equation is not obtained, B will not have an eigenvalue in this state.

It is only in the special case of no degeneracy (as in one-dimensional motion bound on at least one side) that the commutative property of the operators $\hat{A}$ and $\hat{B}$ will automatically imply that any eigenfunction of $\hat{A}$ is simultaneously an eigenfunction of $\hat{B}$ (and vice versa). Then, in any state, either the variables A and B both have eigenvalues simultaneously, or neither of them has an eigenvalue.

10. The operator which we have to determine (we denote it by $\hat{R}_{\varphi_0}$) must transform an arbitrary function $\Psi(\boldsymbol{r}_1, \boldsymbol{r}_2, \ldots, \boldsymbol{r}_i, \ldots, \boldsymbol{r}_N)$ of the coordinates of the system into the same function Ψ, but in terms of the coordinates rotated through a given angle.

In rotation through an infinitely small angle $d\varphi$ about the $\boldsymbol{n}$-direction ($\boldsymbol{n}$ being a unit vector), the radius vector $\boldsymbol{r}_i$ of the i-th particle changes by an increment $d\boldsymbol{r}_i$. As we know, this increment is

$$d\boldsymbol{r}_i = d\varphi\,(\boldsymbol{n} \times \boldsymbol{r}_i).$$

In rotation through a finite angle $\int d\varphi = \varphi_0$ about the same $\boldsymbol{n}$-axis, $\boldsymbol{r}_i$ will change by a finite increment

$$\int d\boldsymbol{r}_i = \int d\varphi\,(\boldsymbol{n} \times \boldsymbol{r}_i) = \boldsymbol{n} \times \int \boldsymbol{r}_i\, d\varphi \equiv \delta \boldsymbol{r}_i. \tag{1}$$

Let us consider a more general operator $\hat{R}$ — the operator for arbitrary finite displacements of the particles of the system.*

From the definition of $\hat{R}$, we have

$$\hat{R}\Psi(\boldsymbol{r}_1, \ldots, \boldsymbol{r}_i, \ldots, \boldsymbol{r}_N) = \Psi(\boldsymbol{r}_1 + \delta\boldsymbol{r}_1, \ldots, \boldsymbol{r}_i + \delta\boldsymbol{r}_i, \ldots, \boldsymbol{r}_N + \delta\boldsymbol{r}_N). \tag{2}$$

We expand the right hand side of equation (2) into a Taylor's series. This expansion can be written in the form

$$\begin{aligned}\Psi(\boldsymbol{r}_1 + \delta\boldsymbol{r}_1, \ldots, \boldsymbol{r}_i + \delta\boldsymbol{r}_i, \ldots, \boldsymbol{r}_N + \delta\boldsymbol{r}_N) &= \\ = \Psi(\boldsymbol{r}_1, \ldots, \boldsymbol{r}_i, \ldots, \boldsymbol{r}_N) &+ \sum_{i=1}^{N} \delta\boldsymbol{r}_i \frac{\partial \Psi}{\partial \boldsymbol{r}_i} + \\ + \frac{1}{2!}\left(\sum_{i=1}^{N} \delta\boldsymbol{r}_i \frac{\partial}{\partial \boldsymbol{r}_i}\right)^2 \Psi + \ldots &\equiv \left[1 + \sum_{i=1}^{N} \delta\boldsymbol{r}_i \frac{\partial}{\partial \boldsymbol{r}_i} + \right. \\ \left. + \frac{1}{2!}\left(\sum_{i=1}^{N} \delta\boldsymbol{r}_i \frac{\partial}{\partial \boldsymbol{r}_i}\right)^2 + \ldots \right] &\Psi(\boldsymbol{r}_1, \ldots, \boldsymbol{r}_i, \ldots, \boldsymbol{r}_N).\end{aligned} \tag{3}$$

By comparing (3) and (2), we can convince ourselves that the expression in brackets is the operator $\hat{R}$.

---

*Strictly speaking, these displacements must satisfy the condition div $\delta\boldsymbol{r} = 0$.

Since this expression appears as an expansion into a series of exponents, we can write $\hat{R}$ symbolically

$$\hat{R} = e^{\sum_{i=1}^{N} \delta r_i \frac{\partial}{\partial r_i}} = e^{\frac{i}{\hbar} \sum_{i=1}^{N} \delta r_i \cdot \hat{p}_i} \tag{4}$$

(using the momentum operators for the particles $\hat{p}_i = \frac{\hbar}{i} \frac{\partial}{\partial r_i}$).

In the special case of parallel displacement of all the particles over a distance $\boldsymbol{a}$, we have

$$\delta r_1 = \delta r_2 = \ldots = \delta r_i = \ldots = \delta r_N = \boldsymbol{a}.$$

Then, (4) becomes (see [1], p. 58)

$$\hat{R}_a \equiv \hat{T}_a = e^{\frac{i}{\hbar} a \hat{P}},$$

where $\hat{P} = \sum_{i=1}^{N} \hat{p}_i$ is the momentum operator of the system of particles.

Now let us consider the required case of rotation through a finite angle.

Taking the $\boldsymbol{n}$-axis to be the z-axis of a system in cylindrical coordinates (ρ, φ, z), and substituting $\delta\varphi_i = \varphi_0$ and $\delta\rho_i = \delta z_i = 0$, we have

$$\delta r_i \frac{\partial}{\partial r_i} = \delta\varphi_i \frac{\partial}{\partial \varphi_i} + \delta\rho_i \frac{\partial}{\partial \rho_i} + \delta z_i \frac{\partial}{\partial z_i} = \varphi_0 \frac{\partial}{\partial \varphi_i}.$$

By substituting into (4) and remembering that $\frac{\hbar}{i} \frac{\partial}{\partial \varphi_i}$ is the operator for the z-component of the angular momentum of the i-th particle, we obtain

$$\hat{R}_{\varphi_0} = e^{\varphi_0 \sum_i \frac{\partial}{\partial \varphi_i}} = e^{\frac{i}{\hbar} \varphi_0 \hat{M}_z}, \tag{5}$$

where $\hat{M}_z = \sum_{i=1}^{N} \frac{\hbar}{i} \frac{\partial}{\partial \varphi_i}$ is the operator for the component of the angular momentum of the system along the axis of rotation.

Finally, in vector form $(M_z \equiv M_n = \boldsymbol{n}\boldsymbol{M})$, we have

$$\hat{R}_{\varphi_0, n} = e^{\frac{i}{\hbar} \varphi_0 \boldsymbol{n} \hat{\boldsymbol{M}}}.$$

11. Because of the equivalence of the x-, y- and z-axes, we obviously have

$$\overline{M^2} = \overline{M_x^2 + M_y^2 + M_z^2} = \overline{M_x^2} + \overline{M_y^2} + \overline{M_z^2} = 3\overline{M_x^2}.$$

From the definition of the average and the fact that the different possible values of M_x are equally probable, we obtain

$$\overline{M_x^2} = \hbar^2 \overline{m^2} = \hbar^2 \frac{\sum_{m=-l}^{l} m^2}{2l+1} = \hbar^2 \frac{2\sum_{m=1}^{l} m^2}{2l+1}.$$

Using the equation for the sum of the squares of the natural system of numbers

$$\sum_{m=1}^{l} m^2 = \frac{l(l+1)(2l+1)}{6},$$

we obtain

$$\overline{M_x^2} = \frac{\hbar^2 l(l+1)}{3}.$$

Whence,

$$\overline{M^2} = \hbar^2 l(l+1).$$

12. As shown in [1], for example, simple relations connect the linear momentum of a system with the operator for an infinitesimal translation of the system, and the angular momentum with the operator for an infinitesimal rotation. (More accurately, the linear momentum and the angular momentum are each proportional to the difference between the above-mentioned operators and the operator for multiplication by unity.)

Any translation commutes with any other translation, and therefore the operators of the different components of the linear momentum commute. Two rotations about two nonparallel axes do not commute. This corresponds to the noncommutative property of the operators of the different components of the angular momentum.

13. First, let us consider a single particle.

We denote the operators of its coordinates, linear-momentum components, and angular-momentum components by $\hat{x}_i$, $\hat{p}_i$, and $\hbar\hat{l}_i$. We have

$$\hbar\hat{\boldsymbol{l}} = \hat{\boldsymbol{r}} \times \hat{\boldsymbol{p}},$$

or, using the unit skew-symmetric tensor ε_{ikl} ([1], p. 101, or [2], p. 191):

$$\hbar\hat{l}_i = \varepsilon_{iml}\hat{x}_m\hat{p}_l$$

(subscripts occurring twice imply summation).

Using Eq. (1) of Problem No. 1, we find the commutator

$$[\hbar\hat{l}_i, \hat{p}_k] = \varepsilon_{iml}[\hat{x}_m\hat{p}_l, \hat{p}_k] = \varepsilon_{iml}([\hat{x}_m, \hat{p}_k]\hat{p}_l + \hat{x}_m[\hat{p}_l, \hat{p}_k]). \quad (1)$$

Remembering that $[\hat{p}_l, \hat{p}_k] = 0$, while $[\hat{x}_m, \hat{p}_k] = i\hbar\delta_{mk}$, we obtain after substitution into (1) and summation over the dummy index m, the required commutation relation

$$[\hat{l}_i, \hat{p}_k] = i\varepsilon_{iml}\delta_{mk}\hat{p}_l = i\varepsilon_{ikl}\hat{p}_l \tag{2}$$

for a system of particles, $\hat{P} = \sum_a \hat{p}_a$ and $\hat{L} = \sum_a \hat{l}_a$, where a is the number of a particle. Therefore,

$$[\hat{L}_i, \hat{P}_k] = \sum_a \hat{l}_{a_i} \sum_a \hat{p}_{a_k} - \sum_a \hat{p}_{a_k} \sum_a \hat{l}_{a_i} = \sum_a (\hat{l}_{a_i}\hat{p}_{a_k} - \hat{p}_{a_k}\hat{l}_{a_i})$$

(since $\hat{l}_i$ and $\hat{p}_k$, which refer to different particles, certainly commute).

Using equation (2), we find, in complete analogy with (2):

$$[\hat{L}_i, \hat{P}_k] = i\varepsilon_{ikl} \sum_a \hat{p}_{a_l} = i\varepsilon_{ikl}\hat{P}_l.$$

14. From classical mechanics, it is known that the angular momentum of a system consisting of two particles relative to the system's center of mass is perpendicular to the axis passing through the two particles. Indeed, the angular momentum is*

$$\boldsymbol{M} = \boldsymbol{r} \times \boldsymbol{p}. \tag{1}$$

Here $\boldsymbol{r} = \boldsymbol{r}_1 - \boldsymbol{r}_2$ is the relative radius vector of the particles; $\boldsymbol{p} = \mu\boldsymbol{v}$, where $\boldsymbol{v} = \boldsymbol{v}_1 - \boldsymbol{v}_2 = \dot{\boldsymbol{r}}$ is the relative velocity of the particles; and $\mu = \frac{m_1 m_2}{m_1 + m_2}$ is the reduced mass.

According to (1), the vectors $\boldsymbol{M}$ and $\boldsymbol{r}$ are mutually perpendicular.

In quantum mechanics, the assertion that the angular momentum $\boldsymbol{M}$ and the radius vector $\boldsymbol{r}$ are mutually perpendicular should be understood in the sense that, in any state, the eigenvalue of the operator for the component of the angular momentum along the $\boldsymbol{r}$-direction equals zero. This is expressed by the equation

$$\hat{\boldsymbol{r}}\hat{\boldsymbol{M}}\psi = \boldsymbol{r}(\hat{\boldsymbol{r}} \times \hat{\boldsymbol{p}})\psi = 0 \cdot \psi, \tag{2}$$

where $\boldsymbol{p}$ is the momentum of the relative motion $\left(\hat{\boldsymbol{p}} = \frac{\hbar}{i}\frac{\partial}{\partial \boldsymbol{r}}\right)$.

---

*Equation (1) follows directly from the definition of the angular momentum $\boldsymbol{M} = \boldsymbol{r}_1 \times \boldsymbol{p}_1 + \boldsymbol{r}_2 \times \boldsymbol{p}_2$, by expressing $\boldsymbol{r}_1$, and $\boldsymbol{r}_2$ in terms of $\boldsymbol{r}$, using the equations defining center-of-mass system of coordinates $\boldsymbol{r}_1 - \boldsymbol{r}_2 = \boldsymbol{r}$ and $m_1\boldsymbol{r}_1 + m_2\boldsymbol{r}_2 = 0$, as well as the equation $\boldsymbol{p} = \frac{m_1 m_2}{m_1 + m_2}(\boldsymbol{v}_1 - \boldsymbol{v}_2) = \mu\boldsymbol{v}$.

We emphasize that because the pairs of operators $\hat{x}$ and $\hat{M}_x$, $\hat{y}$ and $\hat{M}_y$, and $\hat{z}$ and $\hat{M}_z$ are each commutable, the operators $\hat{x}\hat{M}_x$, $\hat{y}\hat{M}_y$, $\hat{z}\hat{M}_z$, and consequently, $\hat{\mathbf{r}}\hat{\mathbf{M}}$ are Hermitian. Thus, the operator for the component of the angular momentum along the axis of the system has a classical form

$$\frac{\hat{\mathbf{r}}}{r}(\hat{\mathbf{r}} \times \hat{\mathbf{p}})$$

and does not have to be "made Hermitian." This fact is essential for the proof of equation (2).*

Moreover, the operator $\hat{\mathbf{r}}$ commutes with itself. Therefore, we can transform $\hat{\mathbf{r}}(\hat{\mathbf{r}} \times \hat{\mathbf{p}})$ according to the rules of ordinary vector algebra:

$$\hat{\mathbf{r}}(\hat{\mathbf{r}} \times \hat{\mathbf{p}}) = \hat{\mathbf{p}}(\hat{\mathbf{r}} \times \hat{\mathbf{r}}).$$

Since $\hat{\mathbf{r}} \times \hat{\mathbf{r}} \equiv 0$, the assertion expressed by equation (2) is proved.

15. We denote the set of coordinates** of the system by a single letter x, the Hamiltonian of the system by $\hat{H}(x)$, and its wave function by $\psi(x)$. Let the transformation in question change the set of coordinates x into the set of coordinates x':

$$x \to x'. \tag{1}$$

We denote the operator for transformation (1) by $\hat{O}$. The invariance of the Hamiltonian relative to this transformation means that

$$\hat{H}(x') = \hat{H}(x). \tag{2}$$

Let us operate with $\hat{O}$ on the function $\hat{H}\psi$.

From the definition of $\hat{O}$ and according to (2), we have

$$\hat{O}\hat{H}(x)\psi(x) = \hat{H}(x')\psi(x') = \hat{H}(x)\psi(x') = \hat{H}(x)\hat{O}\psi(x).$$

This is equivalent to the operator equation

$$\hat{O}\hat{H} = \hat{H}\hat{O}. \tag{3}$$

We introduce the operator $\hat{O}^{-1}$, the inverse of $\hat{O}$:

$$\hat{O}\hat{O}^{-1} = \hat{1}, \tag{4}$$

where $\hat{1}$ is the unit operator, i.e., the operator for identical transformation. By multiplying equation (3) by $\hat{O}^{-1}$ from the right, we obtain:

$$\hat{O}\hat{H}\hat{O}^{-1} = \hat{H}. \tag{3'}$$

---

*We remember that a non-Hermitian operator, say $\hat{x}\hat{p}_x$, is generally not an operator for an arbitrary physical quantity. An operator of this type is a symmetrical ("Hermitized") expression of the form $\frac{1}{2}(\hat{x}\hat{p}_x + \hat{p}_x\hat{x})$.

**Or, more generally, the set of indepenent variables of the chosen representation.

This relation, which is equivalent to the commutation relation (3), expresses in operator form the invariance of $\hat{H}$ relative to the transformation $\hat{O}$.

16. Here we are required to find the additive constants of the motion (except for parity, which is nonadditive) of a system of interacting particles in denumerable external fields. In classical mechanics, this problem is solved by finding a space (or time) transformation which will leave the Lagrangian function of the given mechanical system invariant [2].

In quantum mechanics, the formal solution of the problem is even somewhat simpler: as we know, the constants of the motion are dynamical variables whose operators commute with the Hamiltonian of the system (and which, moreover, are not explicit functions of time). It is obvious that, with the exception of their commutative property with the Hamiltonian, the commutative property of the operators does not depend, in general, on the type of external field. Thus, the pairs of operators $\hat{M}_x$ and $\hat{M}_y$, $\hat{M}_x$ and $\hat{p}_y$, and $\hat{p}_x$ and $\hat{I}$ ($\hat{I}$ being the parity operator) never commute, while the pairs of operators $\hat{M}_x$ and $\hat{I}$, $\hat{M}_x$ and $\hat{p}_x$, and so on, always commute.

If we restrict ourselves to the case of external potential fields (i.e., nonmagnetic fields, etc.) and number the particles with a subscript $i = 1, 2, \ldots, N$, we can represent the Hamiltonian of the system in the form $(i, k = 1, 2, \ldots, N)$

$$\hat{H}=\sum_{i=1}^{N}\left(-\frac{\hbar^2}{2m_i}\Delta_i\right)+U_{\text{inter}}(\ldots, |\boldsymbol{r}_i-\boldsymbol{r}_k|, \ldots)+$$

$$+U_{\text{ext}}(\boldsymbol{r}_1, \ldots, \boldsymbol{r}_N)\equiv\hat{H}_0+U_{\text{ext}},$$

where U_{inter} is the potential energy of the interaction of the particles of the system.

All the operators with which we are concerned, namely

$$\hat{\boldsymbol{P}}(\hat{P}_x, \hat{P}_y, \hat{P}_z), \quad \hat{\boldsymbol{M}}(\hat{M}_x, \hat{M}_y, \hat{M}_z), \hat{M}^2, \hat{I},$$

evidently commute with the operator $\hat{H}_0$ (which corresponds to a closed system of point masses).* Therefore, all that remains for us to do is to determine whether they commute with the operator for the potential energy of the system in the external field

$$U_{\text{ext}}=\sum_{i=1}^{N}U_{i\,\text{ext}}(\boldsymbol{r}_i).$$

*The noncommutative property of the operators $\hat{M}_x$, $\hat{M}_y$, etc., with one another is responsible for the degeneracy of the eigenvalues of the energy and the square of the angular momentum of a system in terms of the values of the dynamical quantities corresponding to these operators (M_x, etc.).

We shall denote the constants of motion by const. Then, we have

$$1)\ U_{\text{ext}} = 0, \qquad \frac{\partial \hat{H}}{\partial t} = 0.$$

Consequently, the constants of motion of a closed system are: the energy E; the three components of the angular momentum M_x, M_y, and M_z; the square of the absolute value of the momentum M^2; the three components of the linear momentum P_x, P_y, and P_z (i.e., P); and the parity I. Here, the energy levels are degenerate so that each state of the system is characterized by a complex set of the smallest possible number of commuting dynamical variables, for instance:

$$P_x, P_y, P_z$$

or

$$E, M^2, M_z, \text{ etc.}$$

The situation is similar in the case where external fields exist.

2) The axis of the cylinder is the z-axis.

$$U_{\text{ext}} = \sum_{i=1}^{N} U_i(\rho_i).$$

Therefore, the operators

$$\hat{P}_z = \frac{\hbar}{i}\sum_{i=1}^{N}\frac{\partial}{\partial z_i}, \quad \hat{M}_z = \frac{\hbar}{i}\sum_{i=1}^{N}\frac{\partial}{\partial \varphi_i} \text{ and } \hat{I}$$

commute with U_{ext} (and consequently with $\hat{H}$).

Since $\frac{\partial \hat{H}}{\partial t} = 0$, we finally have

$$E = \text{const}, \quad P_z = \text{const}, \quad M_z = \text{const}, \quad I = \text{const}.$$

3) The plane is the (x, y) plane.

$$U_{\text{ext}} = \sum_{i=1}^{N} U_i(|z_i|), \qquad \frac{\partial \hat{H}}{\partial t} = 0.$$

The operators

$$\hat{P}_x = \frac{\hbar}{i}\sum_{i=1}^{N}\frac{\partial}{\partial x_i}, \quad \hat{P}_y = \frac{\hbar}{i}\sum_{i=1}^{N}\frac{\partial}{\partial y_i},$$

$$\hat{M}_z = \frac{\hbar}{i}\sum_{i=1}^{N}\frac{\partial}{\partial \varphi_i} = \frac{\hbar}{i}\sum_{i=1}^{N}\left(x_i\frac{\partial}{\partial y_i} - y_i\frac{\partial}{\partial x_i}\right), \quad \text{and} \quad \hat{I}$$

commute with U_{ext} (and thus with $\hat{H}$). Consequently, E = const, M_z = const, P_x = const, P_y = const, I = const.

4) The center of the sphere is the origin of coordinates.

$$U_{ext} = \sum_{i=1}^{N} U_i(r_i), \qquad \frac{\partial \hat{H}}{\partial t} = 0.$$

The operators $\hat{M}_x$, $\hat{M}_y$, $\hat{M}_z$, and $\hat{M}^2$ in polar form operate only on the variables ϑ_i, and φ_i, and therefore they commute with U_{ext} and $\hat{H}$.

Finally, E = const, M_x = const, M_y = const, M_z = const, M^2 = const, I = const.

5) The half plane is the part of the (x, y) plane limited by the y-axis.

$$U_{ext} = \sum_{i=1}^{N} U_i(x_i, |z_i|), \qquad \hat{P}_y = \frac{\hbar}{i} \sum_{i=1}^{N} \frac{\partial}{\partial y_i}.$$

Consequently,

$$E = \text{const}, \qquad P_y = \text{const}.$$

6) The points lie on the z-axis.

$$U_{ext} = \sum_{i=1}^{N} U_i(\rho_i, z_i), \qquad \hat{M}_z = \frac{\hbar}{i} \sum_{i=1}^{N} \frac{\partial}{\partial \varphi_i}.$$

Consequently, E = const, M_z = const.

In the special case when both points carry charges of identical magnitude and sign, $U_i = U_i(\rho_i, |z_i|)$. Here, therefore, the parity I is also conserved.

7) The field is along the z-axis.

Denoting the intensity of this field by $\mathcal{E}(t)$, and the charges of the particles of the system by e_i, we evidently have

$$U_{ext}(t) = -\mathcal{E}(t) \sum_{i=1}^{N} e_i z_i$$

(a similar expression is obtained for a gravitational field; it is only necessary to replace $\mathcal{E}$ by g, and the charges e_i by the masses m_i).

$$U_{ext} \text{ commutes with } \hat{M}_z = \frac{\hbar}{i} \sum_{i=1}^{N} \left(x_i \frac{\partial}{\partial y_i} - y_i \frac{\partial}{\partial x_i} \right),$$

$$\hat{P}_x = \frac{\hbar}{i} \sum_{i=1}^{N} \frac{\partial}{\partial x_i} \text{ and } \hat{P}_y = \frac{\hbar}{i} \sum_{i=1}^{N} \frac{\partial}{\partial y_i}.$$

Consequently, M_z = const, P_x = const, P_y = const.

8) The axis of the conductor is the z-axis.

$$U_{\text{ext}}(t) = f(t)\sum_{i=1}^{N} U_i(\rho_i), \quad \hat{M}_z = \frac{\hbar}{i}\sum_{i=1}^{N}\frac{\partial}{\partial\varphi_i}, \quad \hat{P}_z = \frac{\hbar}{i}\sum_{i=1}^{N}\frac{\partial}{\partial z_i}.$$

Consequently,

$$M_z = \text{const}, \quad P_z = \text{const}, \quad \text{and} \quad I = \text{const}.$$

9) Selecting the origin of the coordinate system at the center of the ellipsoid, we have

$$U_{\text{ext}} = \sum_{i=1}^{N} U_i(|x_i|, |y_i|, |z_i|),$$

since the ellipsoid has three (mutually perpendicular) planes of symmetry.

Thus, the Hamiltonian $\hat{H}$ commutes with the parity operator $\hat{I}$ (and does not depend explicitly on t).

Consequently,

$$E = \text{const}, \quad I = \text{const}.$$

10) The axis of the helix is the z-axis; the angle of rotation about the axis is φ; and the pitch of the helix is a.

The function $U_{\text{ext}} = \sum_{i=1}^{N} U_i(\rho_i, \varphi_i, z_i)$ is invariant with respect to the transformation

$$\varphi_i \to \varphi_i + \delta\varphi \quad (i = 1, 2, \ldots, N), \qquad z_i \to z_i + \frac{\delta\varphi}{2\pi}a$$

(since, for $\delta\varphi = 2\pi$, the equation $\delta z = a$ necessarily holds). For fixed values of ρ_i:

$$\delta U_{\text{ext}} = \sum_{i=1}^{N}\frac{\partial U_{\text{ext}}}{\partial\varphi_i}\delta\varphi + \sum_{i=1}^{N}\frac{\partial U_{\text{ext}}}{\partial z_i}\delta z =$$

$$= \delta\varphi\left(\sum_{i=1}^{N}\frac{\partial}{\partial\varphi_i} + \frac{a}{2\pi}\sum_{i=1}^{N}\frac{\partial}{\partial z_i}\right)U_{\text{ext}} = 0.$$

In other words, the operator $\hat{U}_{\text{ext}}$ (and, consequently, the Hamiltonian $\hat{H}$) commutes with the operator

$$\sum_i \frac{\partial}{\partial\varphi_i} + \frac{a}{2\pi}\sum_i \frac{\partial}{\partial z_i} = \frac{i}{\hbar}\left(\hat{M}_z + \frac{a}{2\pi}\hat{P}_z\right).$$

Consequently,

$$M_z + \frac{a}{2\pi} P_z = \text{const},$$

and also (since $\frac{\partial \hat{H}}{\partial t} = 0$) $E = \text{const}$.

11) The edges of the prism are parallel to the z-axis.

$$U_{\text{ext}} = \sum_{i=1}^{N} U_i(x_i, y_i), \quad \frac{\partial \hat{H}}{\partial t} = 0, \quad \hat{P}_z = \frac{\hbar}{i} \sum_{i=1}^{N} \frac{\partial}{\partial z_i},$$

Hence,

$$E = \text{const}, \quad P_z = \text{const}.$$

In the special case where the cross section of the prism is a regular polygon with $2n$ sides (n is an integer), the prism will have two longitudinal, mutually perpendicular planes of symmetry. Then, $U_{\text{ext}} = \sum_i U_i (|x_i|, |y_i|)$ (when the z-axis passes through the axis of symmetry of the $2n$-sided polygon), and, because $\hat{I}$ and $\hat{H}$ commute, the parity I will be preserved.

12) The axis of the cone is the z-axis.

If the cone has a single nappe, then

$$U_{\text{ext}} = \sum_{i=1}^{N} U_i(\rho_i, z_i).$$

Thus, evidently, $E = \text{const}$ and $M_z = \text{const}$.

If the cone has two nappes, then, selecting the origin of the coordinates at the vertex, we have

$$U_{\text{ext}} = \sum_i U_i(\rho_i, |z_i|).$$

Accordingly, I will also be constant.

13) The axis of the torus is the z-axis, and the equatorial plane of the torus is the (x, y) plane.

In cylindrical coordinates,

$$U_{\text{ext}} = \sum_{i=1}^{N} U_i(\rho_i, |z_i|).$$

Consequently,

$$E = \text{const}, \quad M_z = \text{const}, \quad I = \text{const}.$$

CHAPTER II

Stationary States. Penetration of Potential Barriers

1. In region I ($x \leq 0$), the Schrödinger equation has the form

$$\frac{d^2\psi}{dx^2} + \frac{2mE}{\hbar^2}\psi = 0, \tag{1}$$

while in the region II ($x \geq 0$),

$$\frac{d^2\psi}{dx^2} + \frac{2m}{\hbar^2}(E - U_0)\psi = 0. \tag{2}$$

Using the notation

$$k^2 = \frac{2mL}{\hbar^2}, \qquad \varkappa^2 = \frac{2m(U_0 - E)}{\hbar^2} \tag{3}$$

we reduce equations (1) and (2) to the form

$$\psi''(x) + k^2\psi(x) = 0, \tag{1'}$$

$$\psi''(x) - \varkappa^2\psi(x) = 0. \tag{2'}$$

The obvious solutions of these equations are the functions

$$\psi_{\mathrm{I}} = c_1 e^{ikx} + c_2 e^{-ikx} \qquad (x \leqslant 0), \tag{4}$$

$$\psi_{\mathrm{II}} = c_3 e^{\varkappa x} + c_4 e^{-\varkappa x} \qquad (x \geqslant 0). \tag{5}$$

The first term in (4) describes a wave incident on the potential wall from the left, while the second term describes the wave reflected from the wall. The first term of (5) (the solution increasing inside the wall) does not satisfy the requirement of finiteness, and therefore c_3 must be equal to zero. Moreover, we shall assume that the ψ-function is normalized in such a way that the c_1 coefficient of the incident wave is equal to unity.

Thus,

$$\psi_{\mathrm{I}}(x) = e^{ikx} + c_2 e^{-ikx} \qquad (x \leqslant 0), \tag{4'}$$

$$\psi_{\mathrm{II}}(x) = c_4 e^{-\varkappa x} \qquad (x \geqslant 0). \tag{5'}$$

To determine the constants c_2 and c_4, we can use the condition that the ψ-function and its derivative are continuous at the boundary regions *I* and *II*, i.e., at $x = 0$

$$\psi_I(0) = \psi_{II}(0), \qquad \psi'_I(0) = \psi'_{II}(0). \tag{6}$$

Substituting (4′) and (5′) into (6), we obtain a system of two equations for the unknowns c_2 and c_4:

$$\left.\begin{aligned} 1 + c_2 &= c_4, \\ ik - ikc_2 &= -\varkappa c_4. \end{aligned}\right\} \tag{7}$$

Since these equations are not homogeneous, system (7) has a solution for any values of k and $\varkappa$. This means [see (3)] that the energy levels E of the particle forms a continuous spectrum (in complete conformity with the fact that the particle moves in an infinite region).*

If we solve the system of equations (7), we find

$$c_2 = -\frac{\varkappa + ik}{\varkappa - ik}, \qquad c_4 = -\frac{2ik}{\varkappa - ik}. \tag{8}$$

We note that $|c_2| = 1$, i.e. [see (4)], the intensities of the incident and reflected waves are equal to each other (total reflection).

The probability density of the particle in the classically forbidden region *II* is, according to (5′), (8) and (3):

$$|\psi_{II}(x)|^2 = \frac{4k^2}{\varkappa^2 + k^2} e^{-2\varkappa x} = \frac{4E}{U_0} e^{-2\sqrt{\frac{2m(U_0 - E)}{\hbar^2}}\, x} \tag{9}$$

Inside region *II*, it decreases exponentially to a negligible value at a distance of the order of

$$\frac{1}{2\varkappa} = \frac{\hbar}{2\sqrt{2m(U_0 - E)}}$$

from its maximum value of $\frac{4E}{U_0}$ (at $x = 0$). In the limiting case where $U_0 \to \infty$, both the maximum value of the function and the distance at which it becomes neglibible approach zero, and we obtain the necessary boundary condition $\psi(0) = 0$.

---

*If on the contrary the motion of the particle is finite (i.e., it takes place in a limited region), then, as can be seen from the simple example of motion in a one-dimensional potential well of finite depth, the condition of the continuity of ψ and ψ' at both edges of the well leads to a system of four homogeneous equations for the four unknown constants c_i. The condition for a nontrivial solution of the system (the requirement that its determinant be equal to zero) appears as an equation for the possible values of the energy E, which thus form a discrete spectrum.

Let us also write out the ψ-function in region I. Using (4′) and (8), and remembering that

$$\varkappa \pm ik = \sqrt{\varkappa^2 + k^2} e^{\pm i \operatorname{arctg} \frac{k}{\varkappa}},$$

we easily find

$$\psi_I(x) = 2ie^{i \operatorname{arctg} \frac{k}{\varkappa}} \sin\left(kx - \operatorname{arctg} \frac{k}{\varkappa}\right). \tag{10}$$

In accordance with the physical picture we obtained above (total reflection from the potential wall), this ψ-function has the form of a standing wave $\sin(kx - \delta)$. Except for the unimportant constant factor $2ie^{i\delta}$, the ψ-function is purely real. Therefore, the probability current density

$$j \equiv j_x = -\frac{i\hbar}{2m}\left(\psi^* \frac{d\psi}{dx} - \psi \frac{d\psi^*}{dx}\right) = 0.$$

This, of course, is equivalent to the assertion that total reflection occurs.

2. The Hamiltonian of a free plane rotator reduces to the kinetic-energy operator, having the form $\frac{\hat{M}_z^2}{2I}$ (where $\hat{M}_z$ is the operator of the component of angular momentum along the axis of rotation, z).

If we replace $\hat{M}_z$ by $\frac{\hbar}{i}\frac{\partial}{\partial \varphi}$, where φ is the angle of rotation of the rotator about the z-axis (the axis of rotation), the Schrödinger equation for stationary states of the rotator takes the form

$$-\frac{\hbar^2}{2I}\frac{d^2\psi}{d\varphi^2} = E\psi.$$

The general solution of this equation which satisfies the requirement of single-valuedness (in this case, the requirement that the solution be periodic in the angle φ) is obtained by equating $\sqrt{\frac{2EI}{\hbar^2}}$ to an integral number m ($m = 0, \pm 1, \pm 2, \ldots$). This general solution is

$$\psi_m(\varphi) = c_1 \sin m\varphi + c_2 \cos m\varphi$$

(where c_1 and c_2 are arbitrary constants).

From the above discussion, the energy level corresponding to this wave function is

$$E_m = \frac{\hbar^2 m^2}{2I}.$$

As should have been expected, all the levels with $m \neq 0$ are two-fold degenerate in terms of the directions of the angular momentum of rotation. Evidently, a normalized wave function for a stationary state, which also corresponds to a definite value of the angular momentum of rotation ($M_z = m\hbar$), is

$$\psi_m(\varphi) = \frac{1}{\sqrt{2\pi}} e^{im\varphi}.$$

3. The Hamiltonian of a rotator in space is simply the operator for its kinetic energy of rotation $\frac{\hat{M}^2}{2I}$ (where $\hat{M}^2$ is the operator for the square of the total angular momentum).

For the two angular coordinates determining the position of the rotator, we select the spherical coordinates ϑ and φ (with the polar axis z). With these variables, the operator $\hat{M}^2$ reduces to the spherical part of the Laplace operator, and the Schrödinger equation for the stationary states

$$\frac{\hat{M}^2}{2I}\psi(\vartheta, \varphi) = E\psi(\vartheta, \varphi)$$

assumes a form known from the theory of spherical harmonics

$$\frac{1}{\sin\vartheta}\frac{\partial}{\partial\vartheta}\left(\sin\vartheta\frac{\partial\psi}{\partial\vartheta}\right) + \frac{1}{\sin^2\vartheta}\frac{\partial^2\psi}{\partial\varphi^2} + \frac{2EI}{\hbar^2}\psi = 0.$$

This equation has solutions which are everywhere finite and single-valued only for

$$\frac{2EI}{\hbar^2} = l(l+1).$$

Hence, for the energy levels, we have

$$E_l = \frac{l(l+1)\hbar^2}{2I} \qquad (l = 0, 1, 2, \ldots).$$

The wave equation describing a state with an energy E_l [i.e., a state with a square of the angular momentum $M^2 = l(l+1)\hbar^2$ and with a component of the angular momentum along the polar axis $M_z = m\hbar$ ($m = -l, \ldots, 0, \ldots, l$)] is a spherical harmonic ([1], p. 109)

$$\psi_{lm}(\vartheta, \varphi) = (-1)^m \sqrt{\frac{2l+1}{4\pi}\frac{(l-m)!}{(l+m)!}} P_l^m(\cos\vartheta)\, e^{im\varphi} \qquad (m \geqslant 0),$$

$$\psi_{lm}(\vartheta, \varphi) = \psi_{l,-|m|}(\vartheta, \varphi) =$$

$$= \sqrt{\frac{2l+1}{4\pi}\frac{(l-|m|)!}{(l+|m|)!}} P_l^{|m|}(\cos\vartheta)\, e^{-i|m|\varphi} \qquad (m < 0),$$

where P_l^m is an associated Legendre function. The functions ψ_{lm} are normalized by the condition

$$\int_0^{2\pi}\int_0^{\pi} \psi_{l'm'}^* \psi_{lm} \sin\vartheta \, d\vartheta \, d\varphi = \delta_{ll'}\delta_{mm'}.$$

4. From the problem, the potential energy of the particle has the form

$$U(z)=\begin{cases}\infty, & z\leqslant 0,\\ mgz, & z\geqslant 0,\end{cases}$$

where the (-g)-direction is taken as usual to be the positive direction of the z-axis, and the reflecting plane to be $z = 0$.

This potential energy, as well as the wave functions and energy levels obtained below, are represented in the drawing. We can confine ourselves to the study of the motion of the particle in the z-direction, since the motion along the x- and y-axes is free and presents no interest in the given case. Then, we can write the time independent Schrödinger equation for the wave function of the particle $\psi(z)$ in the region $z \geq 0$ as

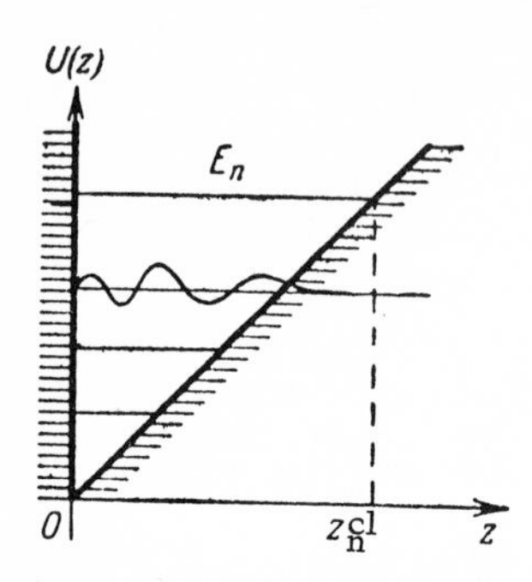

$$-\frac{\hbar^2}{2m}\frac{d^2\psi}{dz^2}+mgz\psi=E\psi, \tag{1}$$

where E is the energy of the particle. This equation must obviously be solved for the boundary conditions

$$\psi\to 0 \quad \text{for} \quad z\to\infty \tag{2}$$

and

$$\psi=0 \quad \text{for} \quad z=0. \tag{3}$$

To reduce equation (1) to its simplest form, we introduce a new independent variable ζ connected with z by the equation

$$\frac{2m^2g}{\hbar^2}z-\frac{2mE}{\hbar^2}=c\zeta, \tag{4}$$

where c is, for the present, an arbitrary constant.

By performing the corresponding substitution in (1), we reduce this equation to the form

$$\frac{d^2\psi}{d\zeta^2}-c^3\left(\frac{\hbar^2}{2m^2g}\right)^2\zeta\psi(\zeta)=0.$$

From this, it is seen that, by setting $c = \left(\frac{2m^2g}{\hbar^2}\right)^{1/3}$, or according to (4),

$$\zeta=\left(\frac{2m^2g}{\hbar^2}\right)^{1/3}\left(z-\frac{E}{mg}\right), \tag{4'}$$

we can reduce (1) to the very simple form

$$\psi''(\zeta)-\zeta\psi(\zeta)=0.$$

The solution of this equation which is finite for all ζ (and thus for all z) is ([1], p. 552)

$$\psi = A\Phi(\zeta) \equiv A\frac{1}{\sqrt{\pi}}\int_0^\infty \cos\left(u\zeta + \frac{1}{3}u^3\right)du, \tag{5}$$

where $\Phi(\zeta)$ is the Airy function, and A is the normalization constant which we shall determine below.

It is clear beforehand that the energy levels of the particle, which according to the problem, is located in the well shown in the drawing, form a discrete spectrum, and that they are infinite in number. To find these levels, we shall use boundary condition (3), which, according to (5) and (4′), reduces to the form

$$\Phi\left(-\frac{2^{1/3}}{m^{1/3}g^{2/3}\hbar^{2/3}}E\right) = 0. \tag{3′}$$

Equating the argument in (3′) to the different roots of the Airy equation, which we denote by $-\alpha_n$ ($n = 1, 2, 3, \ldots$),

$$0 < \alpha_1 < \alpha_2 < \ldots < \alpha_n < \ldots,$$

we find the solutions E_n of this transcendental equation*:

$$-\left(\frac{2}{mg^2\hbar^2}\right)^{1/3} E_n = -\alpha_n.$$

Thus, the energy spectrum of the particle is of the form

$$E_n = \left(\frac{mg^2\hbar^2}{2}\right)^{1/3} \cdot \alpha_n \qquad (n = 1, 2, \ldots). \tag{6}$$

In particular, the ground-state energy ($n = 1$, $\alpha_1 \approx 2.34$) is

$$E_1 \approx 2.34\left(\frac{mg^2\hbar^2}{2}\right)^{1/3}. \tag{6′}$$

As we expect in the case of one-dimensional finite motion, the energy levels are not degenerate. The wave functions of the stationary states corresponding to these energy levels are, according to (5), (4′) and (6), of the form

$$\psi_n(z) = A_n\Phi(\zeta_n) = A_n\Phi\left(\frac{z}{a} - \alpha_n\right), \tag{7}$$

where a denotes the characteristic length

$$a = \left(\frac{\hbar^2}{2m^2g}\right)^{1/3}. \tag{8}$$

The normalization constant A depends on n and a.

---

*The first few roots ($-\alpha_n$) are given in [3].

These functions oscillate in the classical region, the number of nodes of the function ψ_n being equal to n (including the node at the edge of the region, at $z = 0$). The distance between neighboring nodes, which is equal to*

$$\pi\bar{\lambda} = \frac{\pi\hbar}{\sqrt{2m\,[E - U(z)]}}, \tag{9}$$

decreases toward $z = 0$ (i.e., with increasing kinetic energy, see figure).

The constant coefficient in (7) is determined from the condition that the ψ-function is normalized to unity. If the function is normalized in terms of ζ, then obviously the coefficient is equal to**

$$A_n = \frac{1}{\sqrt{\int\limits_{-\alpha_n}^{\infty} [\Phi(\zeta)]^2\, d\zeta}}. \tag{10}$$

If, on the other hand, the function is normalized in terms of z, then [see (4′), (8)]

$$A_n = \frac{1}{\sqrt{a}} \cdot \frac{1}{\sqrt{\int\limits_{-\alpha_n}^{\infty} [\Phi(\zeta)]^2\, d\zeta}}. \tag{10′}$$

Let us now study the asymptotic behavior of the wave function $\psi_n(z)$ at a sufficient distance from the classical point of return***

$$z_n^{\mathrm{cl}} = \frac{E_n}{mg}, \tag{11}$$

as well as the form of the energy spectrum E_n for $n \gg 1$, i.e., in the quasi-classical case.

According to (6) and (8), the lengths z_n^{cl} and a are connected by the equation

$$z_n^{\mathrm{cl}} = a \cdot \alpha_n. \tag{11′}$$

---

*Obviously, quantity (9) has the meaning of the distance between neighboring nodes only for $n \gg 1$. In this case, the bar indicates the average over a segment Δz containing a large number of wavelengths $2\pi\lambda$, but which is small relative to the distance over which $U(z)$ changes appreciably.

**Because the Airy function is real, for real values of the argument

$$|\Phi(\zeta)|^2 = [\Phi(\zeta)]^2.$$

***z_n^{cl} is evidently the greatest height which can be attained (classically) by a particle of mass mg having a given energy E_n.

We rewrite (4′) in the form [see (8), (11), (11′)]

$$\zeta = \frac{z - z_n^{cl}}{a} = \frac{z}{a} - \alpha_n$$

and consider the asymptotic expressions for the function $\psi_n(z)$.

1) The classically forbidden region, and values of z which are not too close to z_n^{cl}:

$$z - z_n^{cl} \gg a, \text{ i.e., } \zeta \gg 1 .^*$$

Using the corresponding asymptotic expression for the Airy function [1]

$$\Phi(\zeta) \approx \frac{1}{2\zeta^{1/4}} e^{-2/3\,\zeta^{3/2}},$$

we find

$$\psi_n(z) \approx \frac{A_n}{2}\left(\frac{a}{z - z_n^{cl}}\right)^{1/4} e^{-\frac{2}{3}\left(\frac{z - z_n^{cl}}{a}\right)^{3/2}} \tag{12}$$

(exponential decrease of the probability density $|\psi_n|^2$ in the classically forbidden region).

2) The region of classical motion and values of z not too close to z_n^{cl}:

$$0 < z < z_n^{cl} \text{ and } |z - z_n^{cl}| \gg a,$$

i.e.,

$$-\alpha_n < \zeta < 0 \text{ and } |\zeta| \gg 1.$$

Evidently, for the second of these conditions to be met, it is in every case necessary that $\alpha_n \gg 1$. Since $\alpha_n \sim n^{2/3}$, in this case, as will be shown below, the region of values of ζ under consideration exists only for highly excited (quasi-classical) energy levels, i.e., for $n \gg 1$.

The required asymptotic expression for $\Phi(\zeta)$ has the form

$$\Phi(\zeta) \approx \frac{1}{|\zeta|^{1/4}} \sin\left(\frac{2}{3}|\zeta|^{3/2} + \frac{\pi}{4}\right), \tag{13}$$

Whence,

$$\psi_n(z) \approx A_n\left(\frac{a}{|z - z_n^{cl}|}\right)^{1/4} \sin\left[\frac{2}{3}\left(\frac{|z - z_n^{cl}|}{a}\right)^{3/2} + \frac{\pi}{4}\right]. \tag{14}$$

---

*It is not difficult to verify that, because of (9) and (4′), the inequality $|\zeta| \gg 1$ is equivalent to the condition for the quasi-classical case

$$\left|\frac{d\lambda}{dz}\right| \ll 1.$$

Thus, the asymptotic expressions (12) and (14) represent quasi-classical wave functions. Using (14), it is possible to find an explicit equation for the roots of the Airy equation $\zeta_n \equiv -\alpha_n$, and consequently for the energy levels (6) in the quasi-classical case. For this, it is obviously necessary to equate the argument of the sine to an integral multiple of π:

$$\frac{2}{3}|\zeta|^{3/2}+\frac{\pi}{4}=(n+1)\pi \qquad (n=0,\ 1,\ 2,\ \ldots),$$

Whence,

$$\alpha_n=|\zeta_n|=\left[\frac{3}{2}\left(n\pi+\frac{3\pi}{4}\right)\right]^{2/3}. \tag{15}$$

Thus [compare with (6)]

$$E_n=\frac{1}{2}(9\pi^2 mg^2\hbar^2)^{1/3}\left(n+\frac{3}{4}\right)^{2/3}. \tag{16}$$

This result can of course be obtained without any knowledge of the wave function, simply by using one of Bohr's quantization rules (see Problem No. 2, Chapter VII).

In the quasi-classical case, it is likewise possible to obtain a simple expression for the normalization constant A_n.

Indeed, since for $n \gg 1$ the wave function (7) oscillates rapidly in the classical region $0 < z < z_n^{\mathrm{cl}}$ [see (14)] and decreases exponentially outside of this region in the integral in (10) we can replace the $\sin^2$ by its average value $\frac{1}{2}$ and confine ourselves to integrating over ζ down to $\zeta = 0$. Considering that $n \gg 1$, this gives

$$A_n \approx (\alpha_n)^{-1/4} \approx \left(\frac{2}{3\pi n}\right)^{1/6}$$

and correspondingly [see (10) and (10′)]

$$A_n \approx \frac{1}{\sqrt{a}}\left(\frac{2}{3\pi n}\right)^{1/6}. \tag{17}$$

We shall also write out the expression for the average distance $\pi\lambda\!\!\!^{-}$ between adjacent nodes of the quasi-classical ψ-function [see (9)]. Using (4′) and (8), we find*

---

*The same result can be obtained with the help of (13) from the obvious condition

$$\Delta\left(\frac{2}{3}|\zeta|^{3/2}\right)\approx|\zeta|^{1/2}\Delta\zeta=\pi,$$

by considering that $\pi\lambda\!\!\!^{-} \equiv \Delta z = a\Delta\zeta$.

$$\overline{\pi\lambda} = \frac{\pi a}{\sqrt{|\zeta_n|}} = \frac{\pi a}{\sqrt{\left|\frac{z}{a} - \alpha_n\right|}}. \tag{18}$$

Since $|\zeta_n| \gg 1$ in the quasi-classical region, $\overline{\pi\lambda} \ll a$.

Nearing the reflecting plane, i.e., for $\frac{z}{a} \ll \alpha_n$, this "half-wavelength" is minimum, and since

$$\alpha_n \approx \left(\frac{3\pi}{2} n\right)^{2/3},$$

it is equal to

$$\left(\overline{\pi\lambda}\right)_{\min} \approx \left(\frac{2\pi^2}{3}\right)^{1/3} \frac{a}{n^{1/3}}. \tag{18'}$$

Finally, we find the distance between two successive levels from (16), using the equation

$$\Delta \ln E_n = \frac{\Delta E_n}{E_n} = \frac{2}{3}\frac{\Delta n}{n}.$$

Substituting $\Delta n = 1$ into this, we obtain

$$\Delta E_n = \frac{2}{3}\frac{E_n}{n}. \tag{19}$$

We shall not demonstrate the limiting transition to classical mechanics (see the footnote to the formulation of the problem).

This limiting transition is carried out by averaging out the quantum-mechanical probability density $|\psi_n(z)|^2$ over an interval Δz which is small relative to the dimensions of the classical region of motion, but which contains a large number of wavelengths, i.e., an interval satisfying the inequality

$$2\pi\bar{\lambda} \ll \Delta z \ll z_n^{\text{cl}}.$$

According to (14) and (17), we have

$$|\psi_n(z)|^2 = \frac{1}{a}\left(\frac{2}{3\pi n}\right)^{1/3} \sqrt{\frac{a}{|z - z_n^{\text{cl}}|}} \sin^2\left[\frac{2}{3}\left(\frac{|z - z_n^{\text{cl}}|}{a}\right)^{3/2} + \frac{\pi}{4}\right].$$

In averaging this expression over the interval Δz, we are entitled to replace the square of the sine, which oscillates many times over this interval, by its average value $\frac{1}{2}$. After multiplication by Δz, this gives

$$\overline{|\psi_n(z)|^2}\,\Delta z = \left(\frac{2}{3\pi n}\right)^{1/3} \frac{1}{2\sqrt{a|z - z_n^{\text{cl}}|}}\,\Delta z. \tag{20}$$

In the classical limit ($\hbar \to 0$, $n \to \infty$), this probability must become $\frac{\Delta t}{\frac{1}{2}T}$ (since it is normalized to unity), i.e., the relation of the time spent in the interval Δz to the half-period of the classical motion. Thus, in the limit, we have

$$\overline{|\psi(z)|^2}\,\Delta z = \frac{\Delta t}{\frac{1}{2}T}.$$

Eliminating $a^{1/2}n^{1/3} \sim (n\hbar)^{1/3}$ from (20) by means of (16) and omitting the sign of n everywhere, we obtain

$$\frac{\Delta z}{\Delta t} = \frac{2}{\frac{1}{2}T}\sqrt{\frac{EH}{mg}}, \tag{21}$$

where H denotes $|z - z^{\text{cl}}|$. Obviously, this relation must be equal to the classical velocity of the particle

$$\left|\frac{dz}{dt}\right| \equiv v_{\text{cl}} = \sqrt{2gH}.$$

Since

$$\frac{1}{2}T = \int_0^{H_{\max}} \frac{dH}{v} = \int_0^{\frac{E}{mg}} \frac{dH}{\sqrt{2gH}} = \sqrt{\frac{2E}{mg^2}}, \tag{22}$$

the equation $\frac{\Delta z}{\Delta t} = \sqrt{2gH}$ is indeed satisfied.

In conclusion, it will be useful for us to evaluate the orders of magnitude which we encounter in applying the results we have obtained to a macroscopic particle, for example a sphere of mass $m = 1$ g, which falls freely from a height $H = 100$ *cм* in the field of terrestrial gravity ($g \approx 10^3$ cm/sec^2) onto a solid slab.

The order of magnitude of the characteristic "zero-point" energy $\varepsilon \sim (mg^2\hbar^2)^{1/3}$ [see (6′)] is

$$\varepsilon \sim (1 \cdot 10^6 \cdot 10^{-54})^{1/3} = 10^{-16} \text{ erg},$$

while the energy of the ball is $E = mgH \approx 1 \cdot 10^3 \cdot 100 = 10^5$ ergs. Hence, for the number of the energy level n (the number of nodes of the ψ-function) and the distance ΔE_n between adjacent energy levels, we obtain [see (16), (19)]:

$$n \sim \left(\frac{E}{\varepsilon}\right)^{3/2} \sim 10^{32},$$

$$\Delta E_n \sim \frac{E}{n} \sim 10^{-27} \text{ erg}.$$

The characteristic length $a \sim \left(\frac{\hbar^2}{m^2 g}\right)^{1/3}$ [see (8)] is equal to

$$a \sim \left(\frac{10^{-54}}{1 \cdot 10^3}\right)^{1/3} = 10^{-19} \text{ cm},$$

while the wavelength (minimum) of the ball is

$$\lambdabar \sim \frac{a}{n^{1/3}} \sim 10^{-30} \text{ cm}$$

($\lambdabar \cdot n \sim H$, as we expect).

The scales of these quantities give an idea of the tremendous accuracy with which the motion of a macroscopic body is described by the laws of classical mechanics.

5. The Hamiltonian of a three-dimensional harmonic oscillator

$$\hat{H} = \frac{1}{2\mu}(\hat{p}_x^2 + \hat{p}_y^2 + \hat{p}_z^2) + \frac{\mu}{2}(\omega_1^2 x^2 + \omega_2^2 y^2 + \omega_3^2 z^2)$$

decomposes into three Hamiltonians for one-dimensional oscillators. Therefore, the Schrödinger equation

$$H\psi(r) = E\psi(r)$$

is solved by separating the variables x, y and z. Thus, the ψ-function takes the form

$$\psi_{n_1 n_2 n_3}(r) = \psi_{n_1}(x)\,\psi_{n_2}(y)\,\psi_{n_3}(z),$$

where the $\psi_{n_1}(x)$, ... are the wave functions of one-dimensional oscillators (with a frequency of ω_1, ω_2, and ω_3, respectively), and the quantum numbers n_1, n_2, and n_3 assume values 0, 1, 2, ... The energy levels of an oscillator in space are obviously equal to

$$E_{n_1 n_2 n_3} = \left(n_1 + \frac{1}{2}\right)\hbar\omega_1 + \left(n_2 + \frac{1}{2}\right)\hbar\omega_2 + \left(n_3 + \frac{1}{2}\right)\hbar\omega_3.$$

In the case of an isotropic oscillator, we obtain

$$E_{n_1 n_2 n_3} = \hbar\omega\left(n_1 + n_2 + n_3 + \frac{3}{2}\right).$$

The energy levels depend only on the sum $n_1 + n_2 + n_3 \equiv n$, while the number of independent wave functions $\psi_{n_1 n_2 n_3}(x, y, z)$ is equal to the number of different sets of the three numbers n_1, n_2, and n_3. In other words, the energy levels are degenerate.

To compute the degree of degeneracy of a level with a given n, we note that, if n_1 is also fixed, the number of sets of

$$n_1, \ n_2, \ n_3$$

is simply equal to the number of different permissible n_2, i.e., $(n - n_1 + 1)$. Summing this number over all permissible values of n_1

(for a given n), we obtain the total number of different combinations of n_1, n_2, and n_3. This is the degree of degeneracy (statistical weight) g_n of the level $E_n = \left(n + \frac{3}{2}\right)\hbar\omega$:

$$g_n = \sum_{n_1=0}^{n} (n - n_1 + 1) = \frac{(n+1)(n+2)}{2}.$$

As should be expected, the lowest level ($n = 0$) is nondegenerate ($g_0 = 1$).

6. It is necessary to find a solution of the Schrödinger equation

$$\Delta\psi + k^2\psi = 0 \tag{1}$$

($k^2 = \frac{2\mu E}{\hbar^2}$, where μ is the mass of the particle and E its energy) inside a circle of radius a ($\rho \leqslant a$) with the boundary condition

$$[\psi(\rho, \varphi)]_{\rho=a} = 0 \text{ (where } \varphi \text{ is the azimuth).}$$

Equation (1) is solved by separating the variables in terms of the polar coordinates (ρ, φ). Substituting $\psi = R(\rho)\,\Phi(\varphi)$, we obtain

$$\rho^2\left(\frac{R'' + \frac{1}{\rho}R'}{R} + k^2\right) + \frac{\Phi''}{\Phi} = 0.$$

Whence

$$\frac{\Phi''}{\Phi} = \text{const} = -m^2,$$

where

$$m = 0, \pm 1, \pm 2, \ldots$$

because of the conditions that $\Phi(\varphi)$ be finite and single-valued. Consequently,

$$\rho^2 R'' + \rho R' + (k^2\rho^2 - m^2) R = 0. \tag{2}$$

Thus, the azimuthal function $\Phi(\varphi)$ describing a state with a definite value of the angular momentum $M_z = m\hbar$ and normalized to unity has the form

$$\Phi_m(\varphi) = \frac{1}{\sqrt{2\pi}} e^{im\varphi},$$

while the solution of the radial equation is

$$R(\rho) = c_1 J_m(k\rho) + c_2 N_m(k\rho),$$

where $J_m(k\rho)$ and $N_m(k\rho)$ are Bessel functions of the first and second kind respectively. For the wave function to be finite at $\rho = 0$, it is obviously necessary that $c_2 = 0$.

The boundary condition at $\rho = a$ leads to an equation for the energy levels of the particle

$$J_m(ka) = 0. \tag{3}$$

Hence $ka = \lambda_n^{(m)}$ (where $\lambda_n^{(m)}$ is the n-th root of the m-th Bessel function of the first kind), and, finally,

$$E_{mn} = \frac{\hbar^2}{2\mu a^2}[\lambda_n^{(m)}]^2.$$

We can determine the constant c_1 from the normalization condition

$$\int_0^a |R|^2 \rho\, d\rho = 1.$$

For this, we shall use the integration formula ([4], p. 237)

$$\int [J_m(k\rho)]^2 \rho\, d\rho = \frac{\rho^2}{2}\{[J_m(k\rho)]^2 - J_{m-1}(k\rho)\, J_{m+1}(k\rho)\}, \tag{4}$$

and the well-known recursion formula

$$J_{m-1}(x) + J_{m+1}(x) = \frac{2m}{x} J_m(x). \tag{5}$$

Substituting the limits of integration 0 and a into (4), we find, using (3) and (5):

$$\frac{1}{c_1^2} = \int_0^a [J_m(k\rho)]^2 \rho\, d\rho = -\frac{a^2}{2} J_{m-1}(\lambda_n^{(m)})\, J_{m+1}(\lambda_n^{(m)}) =$$

$$= \frac{a^2}{2}[J_{m\pm 1}(\lambda_n^{(m)})]^2$$

(the + or − signs obviously make no difference).

Thus, the complete wave function, normalized to unity, has the form

$$\psi_{mn}(\rho, \varphi) = R_{mn}(\rho)\, \Phi_m(\varphi) =$$

$$= \frac{1}{a\sqrt{\pi}\, J_{m\pm 1}(\lambda_n^{(m)})} J_m\left(\lambda_n^{(m)} \frac{\rho}{a}\right) e^{im\varphi}.$$

7. By separating variables in the Schrödinger equation for a spherically symmetric potential

$$U(r) = 0 \qquad (r \leqslant a),$$

$$U(r) = \infty \qquad (r > a),$$

we obtain for the wave function

$$\psi(r, \theta, \varphi) = R(r) P_l^{(m)}(\cos\theta) e^{im\varphi},$$

where, for $r \leqslant a$, $R(r)$ satisfies the equation

$$R'' + \frac{2}{r} R' + \left(k^2 - \frac{l(l+1)}{r^2}\right) R = 0 \qquad (l = 0, 1, 2, \ldots) \qquad (1)$$

and $R(r) \equiv 0$ for $r > a$. Here

$$k^2 = \frac{2mE}{\hbar^2},$$

where E is the energy level measured from the bottom of the well. Thus, it is necessary to find a solution of equation (1) which satisfies the boundary condition $R(a) = 0$ and which is everywhere finite.

Introducing a new unknown function

$$\chi(r) = \sqrt{r} R(r),$$

we obtain for it Bessel's differential equation

$$\chi'' + \frac{1}{r} \chi' + \left[k^2 - \frac{\left(l + \frac{1}{2}\right)^2}{r^2}\right] \chi = 0.$$

Solutions of this equation which are regular (and equal to zero) at $r = 0$ are Bessel functions of the first kind and of semi-integral order $J_{l+\frac{1}{2}}(kr)$. From the boundary condition $R(a) = 0$, we obtain an equation (generally transcendental) for finding the possible values of k, and consequently the possible radial functions and energy levels:

$$J_{l+\frac{1}{2}}(ka) = 0.$$

For each given l, this equation has an infinite number of roots:

$$k_n^{(l)} a \equiv \lambda_{nl} \qquad (n = 0, 1, 2, \ldots).$$

Finally, the radial functions and energy levels of a particle are given by the equations

$$R_{nl}(r) = \frac{1}{\sqrt{r}} J_{l+\frac{1}{2}}\left(\lambda_{nl} \frac{r}{a}\right),$$

$$E_n^{(l)} = \frac{\hbar^2 \left[k_n^{(l)}\right]^2}{2m} = \frac{\hbar^2 \lambda_{nl}^2}{2ma^2}.$$

We note that the lowest level corresponds to $l = 0$, $n = 1$ (and not to $n = 0$, since then $k_0^{(0)} = 0$, and the corresponding ψ-function becomes identically equal to zero). The fact that the lowest level is different from zero could have been established beforehand on the basis of the uncertainty principle.

Using the well-known equations

$$J_{1/2}(x)=\sqrt{\frac{2}{\pi x}}\sin x,$$

$$J_{3/2}(x)=\sqrt{\frac{2}{\pi x}}\left(\frac{\sin x}{x}-\cos x\right), \text{ etc.},$$

we obtain equations for finding the energy levels with different l:

$$l=0: \qquad ka=n\pi,$$

$$l=1: \qquad \operatorname{tg} ka=ka, \text{ etc.}$$

Finally, using the asymptotic equation

$$J_{l+\frac{1}{2}}(x)\approx\sqrt{\frac{2}{\pi x}}\sin\left(x-\frac{l\pi}{2}\right) \qquad (x\gg 1,\ x\gg l)$$

we obtain a simple relation for high (quasi-classical) energy levels with any l:

$$k_n^{(l)}a\approx n\pi+\frac{l\pi}{2} \qquad (n\gg 1).$$

8. The required solution of the Schrödinger equation is spherically symmetrical:

$$\psi(r)=R(r).$$

We substitute a new unknown function $f(r)$ which satisfies the equation

$$R(r)=\frac{1}{r}f(r),$$

obtaining for it the equation

$$f''+\frac{2\mu}{\hbar^2}\left(E+U_0e^{-\frac{r}{a}}\right)f=0, \tag{1}$$

where μ is the mass of the particle, and E is the energy level.

By substituting the variable

$$\xi=e^{-\frac{r}{2a}}$$

and using the notation

$$\lambda^2 = \frac{8\mu}{\hbar^2} U_0 a^2, \tag{2}$$

$$p^2 = -\frac{8\mu}{\hbar^2} E a^2 > 0, \tag{2'}$$

we arrive at the equation

$$f'' + \frac{1}{\xi} f' + \left(\lambda^2 - \frac{p^2}{\xi^2}\right) f = 0,$$

where the primes indicate differentiation with respect to ξ.

This equation is Bessel's differential equation. Its general solution is

$$f(\xi) = C_1 J_p(\lambda\xi) + C_2 N_p(\lambda\xi) \qquad (p > 0,\ \lambda > 0).$$

The isolated singular point of this solution $\xi = 0$ corresponds to $r = \infty$, where the function f must decrease to zero exponentially (for a bound state, i.e., a state with $E < 0$). This condition is satisfied only if $C_2 = 0$.

Thus, the wave function has the form

$$R(r) = \frac{C_1}{r} J_p\left(\lambda e^{-\frac{r}{2a}}\right).$$

The requirement that this function be finite at $r = 0$ yields a transcendental equation for the energy levels of bound states:

$$J_p(\lambda) = 0. \tag{3}$$

If the well parameters a and U_0 are given, it is necessary to compute λ from (2) and to substitute it into (3). After this, the possible values of p are found from tables, and from them we can compute the values of E [see (2')]. The ground state will correspond to the first root of a certain Bessel function, the first excited level to the second root of another Bessel function, and so on.

It is easily seen that, in a well with a sufficiently small "volume" (such that $\lambda \leq 2.4$, i.e., $U_0 a^2$ is less than or equal to the first root of the function J_0), no level exists, since equation (3) is not satisfied for any p.

We note that the problem can be reversed: from a given depth of a level $|E|$, establish the relationship of the well parameters a and U_0. In this case, it is necessary to assume a certain a, to find p from (2'), and to compute λ from (3), and finally U_0 from (2).

9. Like the ψ-function of any ground state, the wave function of a particle in the only level existing in the well cannot have any nodes; i.e., it must be even (relative to the center of the well).

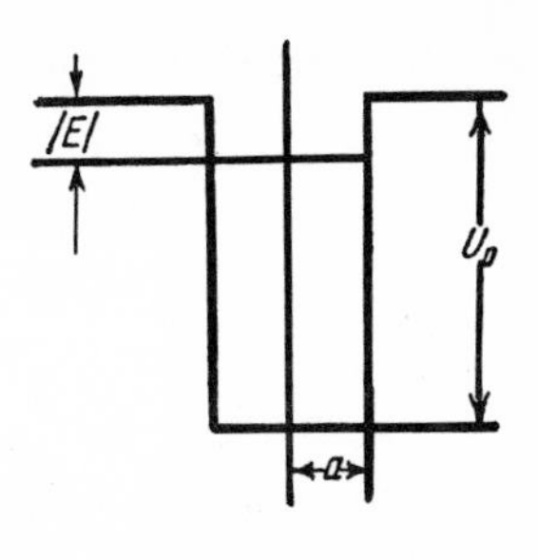

Inside the well, the ψ-function is

$$\psi_{\text{in}} = c_1 \cos kx$$
$$\left(k^2 = \frac{2\mu(E-U)}{\hbar^2} = \frac{2\mu(-|E|+U_0)}{\hbar^2}\right),$$

while outside, on the right, it is

$$\psi_{\text{r}} = c_2 e^{-\varkappa x}$$
$$\left(\varkappa^2 = -\frac{2\mu E}{\hbar^2} = \frac{2\mu|E|}{\hbar^2}\right).$$

By equating these two functions and their derivatives at the right boundary, we obtain the following condition

$$k \operatorname{tg} ka = \varkappa.$$

Now, let U_0 approach infinity and a approach zero. At the same time, k will approach infinity. But, from the above condition, $\varkappa$ remains constant and consequently $\operatorname{tg} ka$ must approach zero. Replacing the value of the tangent by the value of the argument, we find

$$k^2 a = \varkappa, \quad \text{i.e.,} \quad \frac{2\mu U_0 a}{\hbar^2} = \varkappa.$$

Thus, as a approaches zero and U_0 approaches infinity, their product remains constant:

$$aU_0 = \text{const.}$$

Let us find the boundary conditions for the functions outside a well of this type.

Let the solution to the left of the well be u, and the solution to the right be v (outside the well, there can be an arbitrary additional potential).

The solution inside the well is

$$\psi_{\text{in}} = c_1 \sin kx + c_2 \cos kx,$$

where, as formerly,

$$k^2 = \frac{2\mu(E-U)}{\hbar^2} = \frac{2\mu(E+U_0)}{\hbar^2}.$$

The boundary conditions to the left of the well ($x \to -a$) have the form

$$u = -c_1 \sin ka + c_2 \cos ka,$$
$$u' = kc_1 \cos ka + kc_2 \sin ka.$$

Solving these equations for c_1 and c_2, we have

$$c_1 = -u \sin ka + u' \frac{\cos ka}{k},$$

$$c_2 = u \cos ka + u' \frac{\sin ka}{k}.$$

The boundary condition to the right of the well ($x \to +a$) are

$$v = c_1 \sin ka + c_2 \cos ka,$$

$$v' = kc_1 \cos ka - kc_2 \sin ka.$$

By substituting into this the previously found values of c_1 and c_2, we can express v and v' in terms of u and u':

$$v = u \cos 2ka + u' \frac{\sin 2ka}{k},$$

$$v' = -ku \sin 2ka + u' \cos 2ka.$$

Taking the limit

$$a \to 0, \quad k^2 = \frac{\varkappa}{a} \to \infty \qquad (\text{i.e.,} \quad ka = \sqrt{\varkappa a} \to 0),$$

we obtain

$$v = u, \qquad v' = -2k^2 au + u'$$

Replacing $k^2 a$ by $\varkappa$, this becomes

$$u = v,$$

$$\frac{u'}{u} - \frac{v'}{v} = 2\varkappa, \qquad u' - v' = 2\varkappa u, \tag{1}$$

where $\varkappa$ is the only constant which characterizes the well and which is directly connected with the value of its energy level:

$$E = -\frac{\hbar^2 \varkappa^2}{2\mu}.$$

Condition (1) can be expressed in the form of a δ-function potential

$$U = -\frac{\hbar^2 \varkappa}{\mu} \delta(x).$$

Indeed, integrating the Schrödinger equation

$$-\frac{\hbar^2}{2\mu} \frac{d^2\psi}{dx^2} + U_1(x)\psi - \frac{\hbar^2 \varkappa}{\mu} \delta(x)\psi = E\psi$$

[where $U_1(x)$ is an arbitrary but continuous additional potential] over the small interval of x near $x = 0$, we obviously have

$$-\frac{\hbar^2}{2\mu}\left[\frac{d\psi}{dx}(+0)-\frac{d\psi}{dx}(-0)\right]-\frac{\hbar^2\varkappa}{\mu}\psi(0)=0$$

or

$$\frac{d\psi}{dx}(+0)-\frac{d\psi}{dx}(-0)=-2\varkappa\psi(0),$$

which is identical with condition (1).

The "delta-function" property of the potential is also shown by the following considerations. If U_0 approaches infinity and the condition

$$2U_0a=\frac{\hbar^2\varkappa}{\mu}=\text{const}$$

is satisfied (i.e., the sectional area of the well shown in the diagram remains constant), the potential describing the rectangular well will converge to a δ-function with a coefficient $-\frac{\hbar^2\varkappa}{\mu}$, whose absolute value is equal to the area of the rectangle in the diagram.

10. The ψ-function of the ground state must be even, i.e.,

$$\psi_0(-x)=\psi_0(x) \quad \text{or} \quad u(-x)=v(x).$$

The function v satisfies the Schrödinger equation with a negative energy $-\epsilon$

$$-\frac{\hbar^2}{2\mu}\frac{d^2v}{dx^2}=-\varepsilon v$$

and with the boundary condition found in the previous problem

$$\frac{u'}{u}-\frac{v'}{v}=2\varkappa,$$

where $\varkappa$ characterizes the potential well.

Because the ψ-function is even, we have

$$\frac{v'}{v}=-\varkappa.$$

The solution of the equation has the form

$$v=c_1e^{-x\sqrt{\frac{2\mu\varepsilon}{\hbar^2}}}+c_2e^{x\sqrt{\frac{2\mu\varepsilon}{\hbar^2}}}.$$

From the requirement that v be finite as $x\to\infty$, it is necessary that $c_2 = 0$, i.e.,

$$v=ce^{-x\sqrt{\frac{2\mu\varepsilon}{\hbar^2}}}.$$

From the normalization condition, $c = \sqrt{\varkappa}$. Therefore,

$$\psi_0(x) = \sqrt{\varkappa} e^{-\varkappa |x|}.$$

The energy levels of the continuous spectrum are twofold degenerate, in accordance with the fact that a particle can hit the well from the left or from the right. The functions of the first type obviously have the form

$$u = e^{ikx} + c_1 e^{-ikx},$$
$$v = c_2 e^{ikx} \qquad \left(k^2 \equiv \frac{2\mu E}{\hbar^2}\right)$$

Using the boundary conditions at the well, we obtain

$$c_1 = -\frac{1}{1 + i\frac{k}{\varkappa}} \text{ and } c_2 = \frac{i\frac{k}{\varkappa}}{1 + i\frac{k}{\varkappa}}.$$

It is convenient to write this solution in the form

$$u_{\text{I}} = e^{ikx} - \frac{e^{-ikx}}{1 + i\frac{k}{\varkappa}},$$

$$v_{\text{I}} = e^{ikx} - \frac{e^{ikx}}{1 + i\frac{k}{\varkappa}}.$$

The solutions of the second type (for which the particle hits the well from the right) can be obtained from the substitution

$$u_{\text{II}}(x) = v_{\text{I}}(-x),$$
$$v_{\text{II}}(x) = u_{\text{I}}(-x).$$

It is easily seen that the boundary conditions are observed in this substitution.

11. From the problem, the potential energy of the oscillator is

$$U(x, y, z) = \frac{1}{2}\mu\omega^2 x^2 + \frac{1}{2}\mu\omega^2 y^2 + \frac{1}{2}\mu\omega^2 z^2 = \frac{1}{2}\mu\omega^2 r^2.$$

Because of the conditions given in the problem and since U depends only on r, we shall solve the Schrödinger equation for the oscillator by separation of the variables in terms of the spherical coordinates (r, θ, φ).

The Schrödinger equation for this problem is

$$\frac{1}{r^2}\frac{\partial}{\partial r}\left(r^2 \frac{\partial\psi}{\partial r}\right) + \frac{1}{r^2}\left[\frac{1}{\sin\theta}\frac{\partial}{\partial\theta}\left(\sin\theta \frac{\partial\psi}{\partial\theta}\right) + \frac{1}{\sin^2\theta}\frac{\partial^2\psi}{\partial\varphi^2}\right] +$$
$$+ \frac{2\mu}{\hbar^2}\left(E - \frac{\mu\omega^2 r^2}{2}\right)\psi = 0,$$

where E is the energy of the oscillator.

Separating the variables, we have

$$\psi(r, \theta, \varphi) = R(r)\, Y(\theta, \varphi). \tag{1}$$

In this separation, as we know, we obtain the spherical harmonic Y_{lm} (θ, φ) for the angular function $Y(\theta, \varphi)$. This spherical harmonic is given in Problem No. 3 of this chapter, and we shall not write it out. This angular property of the wave function (1) is a necessary and sufficient condition for the square of the angular momentum M^2 and its component along the polar z-axis to have definite values in a state described by the wave function. The corresponding eigenvalues are

$$M^2 = \hbar^2 l(l+1), \quad M_z = m\hbar \quad (l = 0,\ 1,\ 2, \ldots, \ -l \leqslant m \leqslant l).$$

For the radial function $R(r)$, we obtain the equation

$$\frac{d^2R}{dr^2} + \frac{2}{r}\frac{dR}{dr} + \frac{2\mu}{\hbar^2}\left[E - \frac{\hbar^2}{2\mu}\frac{l(l+1)}{r^2} - \frac{\mu\omega^2 r^2}{2}\right] R = 0.$$

By substituting the new variable

$$\xi = \frac{\mu\omega}{\hbar} r^2, \tag{2}$$

we transform this equation to the form

$$\xi \frac{d^2R}{d\xi^2} + \frac{3}{2}\frac{dR}{d\xi} + \left[\frac{E}{2\hbar\omega} - \frac{l(l+1)}{4\xi} - \frac{\xi}{4}\right] R = 0. \tag{3}$$

Let us study the behavior of the function $R(\xi)$ for large and small ξ.

As $\xi \to \infty$, if we neglect all quantitites which are not proportional to ξ, we obtain (after cancelling ξ)

$$\frac{d^2R}{d\xi^2} - \frac{1}{4} R = 0.$$

From this, after rejecting the solution which increases without limit to infinity, we have

$$R \sim e^{-\frac{\xi}{2}} \qquad (\xi \to \infty). \tag{4}$$

As $\xi \to 0$, retaining in the parentheses only the term which is the lowest power of ξ, we obtain

$$\frac{d^2R}{d\xi^2} + \frac{3}{2\xi}\frac{dR}{d\xi} - \frac{l(l+1)}{4\xi^2} R = 0. \tag{5}$$

Let us look for a solution to this equation in the form

$$R \sim \xi^s \qquad (\xi \to 0). \tag{6}$$

Substituting (6) into (5), we obtain

$$s(s-1)+\frac{3}{2}s-\frac{l(l+1)}{4}=0.$$

Because of the requirement that the function R be finite at $\xi = 0$, we select only the nonnegative root of this quadratic equation, namely,

$$s=\frac{1}{2}l. \tag{7}$$

In accordance with (4), (6) and (7), let us look for a solution to equation (3) in the form

$$R(\xi)=e^{-\frac{\xi}{2}}\xi^{\frac{l}{2}}w(\xi). \tag{8}$$

Substituting (8) into (3), we obtain, after simplification, the following equation for the function $\omega(\xi)$:

$$\xi\frac{d^2w}{d\xi^2}+\left(l+\frac{3}{2}-\xi\right)\frac{dw}{d\xi}+\left(\frac{E}{2\hbar\omega}-\frac{l}{2}-\frac{3}{4}\right)w=0. \tag{9}$$

In view of equation (8) and the requirement that $R(\xi)$ be finite for all ξ, we conclude that as $\xi \to \infty$, the required solution of equation (9) must not diverge any more rapidly than a finite power of ξ, while at $\xi = 0$, it must be finite.

A solution satisfying the later condition is a confluent hypergeometric function ([1], pp. 557-561):

$$w(\xi)=F\left(-\frac{E}{2\hbar\omega}+\frac{l}{2}+\frac{3}{4},\quad l+\frac{3}{2},\ \xi\right). \tag{10}$$

A solution satisfying the condition at infinity is obtained only when the first argument of the function F assumes values which are negative integers or zero. In this case, the function reduces to a polynomial (whereas in the opposite case, it diverges as e^{ξ} when $\xi \to \infty$).

Thus, it is necessary that

$$-\frac{E}{2\hbar\omega}+\frac{l}{2}+\frac{3}{4}=-p \qquad (p=0,\ 1,\ 2,\ldots) \tag{11}$$

or

$$E=\hbar\omega\left(l+2p+\frac{3}{2}\right). \tag{12}$$

Designating the integer $(l+2p)$ by n, we finally obtain

$$E_n=\hbar\omega\left(n+\frac{3}{2}\right), \tag{12'}$$

where, obviously, $n = 0, 1, 2, 3, \ldots$.

Thus, the isotropic oscillator has an infinite set of equally spaced levels. These levels are degenerate (their degree of degeneracy is computed in Problem No. 5 of this chapter).

According to (8), (10) and (11), the radial function is of the form

$$R_{pl}(\xi) = Ce^{-\frac{\xi}{2}}\xi^{\frac{l}{2}}F\left(-p,\ l+\frac{3}{2},\ \xi\right), \tag{13}$$

where C is a constant.

Considering equation (2) and the fact that $F(\alpha, \beta, 0) = 1$, we can satisfy ourselves that as $r \to 0$,

$$R_{pl}(r) \sim r^l, \tag{14}$$

as required.*

We can find the constant C from the normalization condition

$$\int_0^\infty R_{pl}^2 r^2\, dr = 1, \tag{15}$$

i.e., according to equation (2) and (13)

$$C^2 \cdot \frac{1}{2}\left(\frac{\hbar}{\mu\omega}\right)^{3/2} \int_0^\infty e^{-\xi}\xi^{l+\frac{1}{2}}\left[F\left(-p,\ l+\frac{3}{2},\ \xi\right)\right]^2 d\xi = 1. \tag{15'}$$

We compute the normalization integral appearing in (15′) for $p = 1, 2, 3, \ldots$ by the method presented in [1], p. 565. This yields

$$C^2 \cdot \frac{1}{2}\left(\frac{\hbar}{\mu\omega}\right)^{3/2} \cdot \frac{\Gamma\left(l+\frac{3}{2}\right)p!}{\left(l+\frac{3}{2}\right)\left(l+\frac{5}{2}\right)\cdots\left(l+p+\frac{1}{2}\right)} = 1 \tag{16}$$

$$(p = 1,\ 2, \ldots).$$

For $p = 0$, the function F becomes unity, and obviously the normalization integral in (15) becomes equal to $\Gamma\left(l+\frac{3}{2}\right)$. Using (13), (2)

---

*In [1], pp. 154-155, a similar problem is considered, with a more general potential

$$U = \frac{A}{r^2} + Br^2.$$

However, it is easily verified that the function $R(r)$ found there does not satisfy condition (14), which is necessary for $A = 0$ (there, the function is proportional to r^{l+1} as $r \to 0$). Consequently, the function given there is incorrect. The reason for this is a computational error in the derivation of the equation corresponding to our equation (3). Nonetheless, the correct energy levels were obtained in this problem.

and (16), we finally obtain the following radial functions, normalized to unity: for $p = 1, 2, 3, \ldots$

$$R_{pl}(r) = \sqrt{2}\left(\frac{\mu\omega}{\hbar}\right)^{\frac{l}{2}+\frac{3}{4}} \sqrt{\frac{\left(l+\frac{3}{2}\right)\left(l+\frac{5}{2}\right)\cdots\left(l+p+\frac{1}{2}\right)}{\Gamma\left(l+\frac{3}{2}\right)p!}} \times \tag{17}$$

$$\times e^{-\frac{\mu\omega}{2\hbar}r^2} r^l F\left(-p,\ l+\frac{3}{2},\ \frac{\mu\omega r^2}{\hbar}\right),$$

and, for $p = 0$,

$$R_{0l}(r) = \sqrt{\frac{2}{\Gamma\left(l+\frac{3}{2}\right)}}\left(\frac{\mu\omega}{\hbar}\right)^{\frac{l}{2}+\frac{3}{4}} e^{-\frac{\mu\omega}{2\hbar}r^2} r^l. \tag{18}$$

In particular, the radial function of the ground state of a spherical isotropic oscillator, corresponding to the value $n=0$, i.e., $p = l = 0$, has the form

$$R_{00}(r) = \frac{2}{\pi^{1/4}}\left(\frac{\mu\omega}{\hbar}\right)^{3/4} e^{-\frac{\mu\omega}{2\hbar}r^2}. \tag{19}$$

The complete ψ-function of the ground state is obtained according to (1), by multiplying $R_{00}(r)$ by $Y_{00}(\theta, \varphi) = \frac{1}{\sqrt{4\pi}}$:

$$\psi_{000}(r) = \left(\frac{\mu\omega}{\pi\hbar}\right)^{3/4} e^{-\frac{\mu\omega r^2}{2\hbar}}. \tag{19'}$$

In conclusion, let us establish the asymptotic behavior of the radial function $R_{pl}(r)$ as $r \to \infty$.

In our case, the confluent hypergeometric function has reduced to a polynomial in $\xi \sim r^2$ of degree p. Consequently, as $r \to \infty$, we have, considering (12):

$$R_{pl}(r) \sim e^{-\frac{\mu\omega}{2\hbar}r^2} r^{l+2p} = e^{-\frac{\mu\omega}{2\hbar}r^2} r^n \qquad (n = 0,\ 1,\ 2, \ldots),$$

Thus, the asymptotic behavior is identical for all radial functions belonging to the same energy level (12').

12. Let m, e and ω represent the oscillator's mass, charge and angular frequency respectively, and let $\mathcal{E}$ be the intensity of the external electric field. We select the origin of coordinates ($x = 0$) at the equilibrium point of the oscillator in the absence of an electric field.

The "electrical" part of the potential energy of the oscillator is equal to $-e\mathscr{E}x$ (in this problem, we define potential energy as zero at $x = 0$). Thus, the Hamiltonian of the problem has the form

$$\hat{H} = -\frac{\hbar^2}{2m}\frac{d^2}{dx^2} + \frac{m\omega^2 x^2}{2} - e\mathscr{E}x. \tag{1}$$

Performing the following change of variables

$$x_1 = x - \frac{e\mathscr{E}}{m\omega^2}, \tag{2}$$

in Hamiltonian (1), we obtain

$$\hat{H} = -\frac{\hbar^2}{2m}\frac{d^2}{dx_1^2} + \frac{m\omega^2 x_1^2}{2} - \frac{(e\mathscr{E})^2}{2m\omega^2}. \tag{3}$$

Except for the unimportant additive constant $-\frac{(e\mathscr{E})^2}{2m\omega^2}$, the Hamiltonian (3) is exactly the same as the Hamiltonian for an oscillator in the absence of an electric field. This oscillator has the same frequency ω, but its equilibrium position is shifted to the point $x_1 = 0$, i.e., according to (2), to the point

$$x = \frac{e\mathscr{E}}{m\omega^2}. \tag{4}$$

As we could easily have predicted, this point of equilibrium corresponds to the mutual balancing of the electric and elastic forces, i.e., to the potential-energy minimum in (1)

$$f_{\text{elec}} + f_{\text{elas}} = e\mathscr{E} - m\omega^2 x = 0.$$

From our discussion, it is evident that the system of the energy levels of the oscillator in a uniform field $\mathscr{E}$ remains the same as in the absence of a field:

$$E_n = \hbar\omega\left(n + \frac{1}{2}\right) \qquad (n = 0,\ 1,\ 2, \ldots).$$

These levels are measured from the potential-energy minimum in (1) or in (3).

The wave functions of the stationary states have the same form as in the absence of a field [1], but they are expressed in terms of the "shifted" variable $x_1 = x - \frac{e\mathscr{E}}{m\omega^2}$:

$$\psi_n(x) = \left(\frac{m\omega}{\pi\hbar}\right)^{1/4} \frac{1}{\sqrt{2^n n!}} e^{-\frac{m\omega}{2\hbar}\left(x - \frac{e\mathscr{E}}{m\omega^2}\right)^2} H_n\left[\sqrt{\frac{m\omega}{\hbar}}\left(x - \frac{e\mathscr{E}}{m\omega^2}\right)\right],$$

where H_n is a Hermite polynomial.

13. Let us write the Schrödinger equation for the stationary state of a μ-meson* in the field of a nucleus with charge $+Ze$ (we ignore, as usual, the motion of the center of mass of the system, which presents no interest):

$$\Delta\psi(r)+\frac{2\mu'}{\hbar^2}[E-U(r)]\psi(r)=0. \tag{1}$$

Here $\boldsymbol{r}$ is the radius vector of the meson relative to the center of the nucleus; $\mu'=\frac{\mu M}{\mu+M}$ is the reduced mass of the meson + nucleus system; and E is the energy of their relative motion (since $\frac{M}{\mu}\gtrsim 10$ even for the slightest nuclei, μ' is close to the mass of the meson μ, and accordingly from now on we shall drop the prime).

From the conditions specified in the problem, the potential energy $U(r)$, which, in this problem, we define as 0 at $r=\infty$, has the form**

$$U(r)=\begin{cases} -\frac{Ze^2}{R}\left(\frac{3}{2}-\frac{1}{2}\frac{r^2}{R^2}\right) & \text{for } r\leqslant R, \\ -\frac{Ze^2}{r} & \text{for } r\geqslant R. \end{cases} \tag{2}$$

The potential diagram $U(r)$ and the energy levels of the meson are shown in the figure.

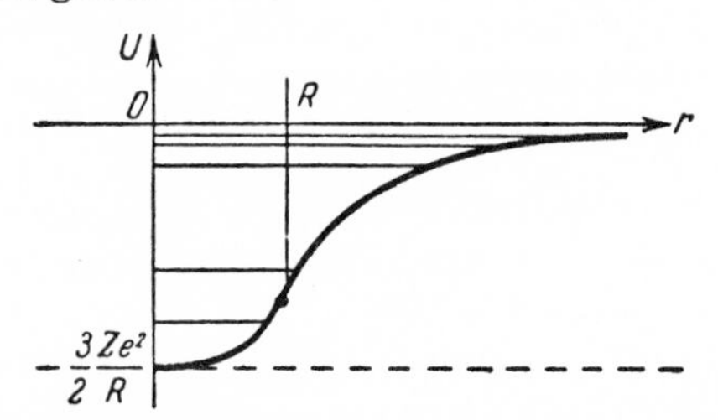

As can be seen from (2), outside the nucleus, the μ-meson moves in an attractive Coulomb field produced by the charge $+Ze$, whereas

*We note that the use of the non-relativistic wave equation is justified, since, as we shall see below, the order of magnitude of the kinetic energy of the meson is 10 Mev, which is small relative to its rest-mass energy $\mu c^2\sim 100$ Mev.

**Expression (2) follows immediately from the equation and from the solution of the elementary electrostatic problem of finding the potential

$$U(r)=-e\varphi(r)$$

inside and outside a sphere having a charge uniformly distributed throughout its volume ([5], p. 49).

inside the nucleus, it moves in the potential of an isotropic harmonic oscillator having a frequency of

$$\omega = \sqrt{\frac{Ze^2}{\mu R^3}}. \tag{3}$$

This follows directly from a comparison of the oscillator potential $\frac{\mu\omega^2 r^2}{2}$ with the part of the potential in (2) which depends on the coordinates $\frac{Ze^2 r^2}{2R^3}$ (the term $-\frac{3}{2}\,\frac{Ze^2}{R}$ in this potential is obviously an unimportant constant component).

We note that for all real nuclei this characteristic frequency is approximately the same. Indeed, as we know,

$$R \approx r_0 A^{1/3}, \tag{4}$$

where $r_0 \approx 1.2 \cdot 10^{-13}$ cm, and A is the mass number of the nucleus. Thus,

$$\frac{Z}{R^3} \sim \frac{Z}{A}.$$

However, for all nuclei, this relationship is approximately constant (and close to 1/2). Accordingly, when we consider the limits $Z \to 0$ and $Z \to \infty$ below, we shall regard the relation $\frac{Z}{R^3}$ as fixed.

The solution of equation (1) for arbitrary R turns out to be fairly awkward. We shall not give this solution, confining ourselves to the consideration of the two limiting cases

a) $R \to 0$ and b) $R \to \infty$ (for $\frac{Z}{R^3}$ = const!)

(and this only for bound states of the meson, which present the greatest interest and which obviously correspond to a discrete spectrum of negative energies E).

Case (a) corresponds to a "hydrogenlike" nucleus + meson system. Therefore, the energy levels are given by the Balmer formula

$$E_n^{\text{Coul}} = -\frac{Z^2 \mu e^4}{2\hbar^2 n^2} \qquad (n = 1,\ 2,\ 3, \ldots), \tag{5}$$

and the wave functions have a "hydrogenlike" form (the electron mass m being replaced by the meson mass μ).

In case (b), the system forms an isotropic harmonic oscillator, whose energy levels are given by the formula (see Problems No. 5 and No. 11)

$$E_n^{\text{osc}} = \hbar\omega\left(n + \frac{3}{2}\right) \qquad (n = 0,\ 1,\ 2,\ 3, \ldots), \tag{6}$$

where ω is determined from equation (3).

For our subsequent discussion, we give the wave function for the ground state of the oscillator (normalized to unity)

$$\psi_0 = \left(\frac{\mu\omega}{\pi\hbar}\right)^{3/4} \exp\left(-\frac{\mu\omega r^2}{2\hbar}\right),$$

and also the expectation value of the radius r in this state

$$\bar{r} = \int_0^\infty r\,|\psi_0|^2\, 4\pi r^2\, dr = \frac{2}{\sqrt{\pi}}\sqrt{\frac{\hbar}{\mu\omega}}. \tag{7}$$

It is easily seen that, for actual nuclei (nuclei with finite R), the range of validity of case (a) is given by the inequality $R \ll a$, where

$$a = \frac{\hbar^2}{Z\mu e^2} \tag{8}$$

is the radius of the first Bohr orbit of a meson of mass μ in the field of a nucleus with a charge Ze, The range of validity of case (b) is given by the inequality $R \gg a$.

The first of these statements is obvious. It implies the smallness of the dimensions of the "oscillatory" region relative to the distances which are significant in the motion in a Coulomb attracting field. The second statement can be explained as follows. An "oscillatory" system implies that the boundary radius R is large relative to the dimensions of the region of motion $\sim\sqrt{\frac{\hbar}{\mu\omega}}$.* But the inequality $R \gg \sqrt{\frac{\hbar}{\mu\omega}}$ leads, according to (3) and (8), to the inequality $R \gg a$.

Let us determine to what extent each of the limiting cases (a) and (b) is applicable to actual nuclei. For this purpose, let us compute the ratio $\frac{R}{a}$.

According to (4) and (8), we have

$$\frac{R}{a} = \frac{r_0 A^{1/3} Z\mu e^2}{\hbar^2} \approx 2^{1/3}\frac{\mu}{m}\cdot\frac{r_0}{a_0} Z^{4/3}, \tag{9}$$

---

*This characteristic magnitude (frequently called the amplitude of the zero-order oscillations of the oscillator) is, as appears from its definition, the distance r at which the potential energy $\frac{1}{2}\mu\omega^2 r^2$ is comparable with the zero-order energy of the oscillator $\frac{3}{2}\hbar\omega$:

$$r = \sqrt{\frac{3\hbar}{\mu\omega}} \sim \sqrt{\frac{\hbar}{\mu\omega}}.$$

Naturally, $\bar{r}$ is of the same order of magnitude [see (7)].

where, for convenience, we have used the electron mass m and

$$a_0 = \frac{\hbar^2}{me^2} \approx 0.53 \cdot 10^{-8} \text{ cm},$$

and where we have set $A \approx 2Z$, which is accurate enough for our purpose.

Substituting $\frac{r_0}{a_0} \approx 2.3 \cdot 10^{-5}$ and $\frac{\mu}{m} \approx 210$, we see that

$$\frac{R}{a} = 1 \quad \text{for} \quad Z \approx 45.$$

Thus, for $Z \ll 45$, i.e., for light nuclei, the "hydrogenlike" case holds for the motion of the μ-meson. The other limiting case, $Z \gg 45$ (oscillatory motion), begins to hold, and then only in a rough approximation, only for the heaviest nuclei with $Z \approx 80$-100.

Indeed, if we compute $\bar{r}$ from equations (7) and (8), we find (setting $A = 2Z$) $\bar{r} \approx 7 \cdot 10^{-13}$ cm. However, this quantity is not small, but is close to the radius of heavy nuclei. Hence, it is clear that we are dealing with an intermediate case rather than with a limiting case.

We know, moreover, that, for nuclei with $Z \approx 80$-90, a numerical solution of the problem (without any approximations) yields a characteristic distance between the lowest levels of about 6 Mev, while the oscillator energy level spacing $\hbar\omega$, computed from the limiting formula (3), is equal to approximately 10 Mev. The part of the normalization integral $\int |\psi_0|^2 \, dV = 1$ (for the ground state) corresponding to the region $r \le R$ amounts to about 0.55. Thus, in the heaviest nuclei, the μ^--meson spends roughly speaking about 55% of its time inside the nucleus.

Finally, from the energy level diagram, we can convince ourselves of the correctness of our initial assumption that the motion of the meson is nonrelativistic (see the first footnote to this problem).

14. In accordance with the condition specified in the problem, we shall start in all cases from the equation

$$E_n = \frac{\pi^2\hbar^2}{2\mu a^2} n^2. \tag{1}$$

To obtain equations for the order of magnitude of the energy levels in the given cases, we must replace in (1) the width of the rectangular well a by the distance l_{cl} between the return points for motion in the corresponding nonrectangular well, expressing this distance in terms of the particle energy E.

1) The potential energy U is equal to $\frac{1}{2}\mu\omega^2x^2$. We find the value of $l_{cl} \equiv l$ from the equation $U\left(\frac{1}{2}l\right) = E$. Hence,

$$l=\sqrt{\frac{8E}{\mu\omega^2}}. \tag{2}$$

Substituting (2) into (1) and replacing E by E_n, we obtain

$$E_n=\frac{\pi}{4}\hbar\omega n.^* \tag{3}$$

On the whole (for $n \gg 1$), this formula differs from the true formula by a factor of $\frac{\pi}{4}\approx 0.79$.

2) We take the direction of the field $\mathcal{E}$ as the x-axis, and the reflecting wall as the plane $x = 0$. The conditions of the problem imply that the motion of the particle takes place in the half-space $x \leq 0$, where the potential energy U is equal to $(-e\mathcal{E}x)$. For $x \geq 0$, we have $U = \infty$. From the equation $U(-l) = E$, we find

$$l=\frac{E}{e\mathcal{E}}, \tag{4}$$

After substituting this into (1) and replacing E by E_n, we obtain

$$E_n=\left(\frac{\pi^2\hbar^2e^2\mathcal{E}^2}{2\mu}\right)^{1/3}n^{2/3}. \tag{5}$$

The exact equation and the quasi-classical equation for the energy levels were obtained in Problem No. 4. This equation for the order of magnitude resembles the quasi-classical equation, differing from it basically only by the factor $\left(\frac{1}{2}\cdot\frac{8}{9}\right)^{1/3}\approx 0.76$.

It is quite natural that (5) should be so close to the quasi-classical formula. Indeed, the method we have used to estimate the energy spectrum is based on formula (1) for a potential box. In other words, it is based on equating the dimension of the region of classical motion l_{cl} to an integral number of de Broglie half-wavelengths. Thus, our method amounts simply to a cruder form of Bohr's quantization rule.

3) The potential energy U has the form $\left(-\frac{Ze^2}{r}\right)$. Therefore l, obtained from $U(l) = E$, is equal to

$$l=-\frac{Ze^2}{E}>0. \tag{6}$$

---

*In exactly the same way, it is possible to estimate the energy spectrum of a charged particle in a uniform magnetic field, by setting l_{cl} equal to $2\frac{c\mu v_t}{|e|\mathcal{H}}$ the diameter of the first Larmor orbit. The result is of the form (3), where $\omega\equiv\frac{|e|\mathcal{H}}{\mu c}$.

In this case, we cannot use equation (1) directly since $E < 0$ as a consequence of the different definition of U (zero at infinity). However, since the left member of (1) is equal to the kinetic energy T, and in motion in a Coulomb field the moduli of the average values of T and E are equal (the virial theorem [2]), it is still possible to combine equations (1) and (6) by replacing $E = E_n$ by $|E_n|$. This yields

$$|E_n| = \frac{2}{\pi^2} \frac{Z^2 \mu e^4}{\hbar^2 n^2},$$

which differs from the true formula by a factor of $\frac{4}{\pi^2} \approx 0.41$.

We emphasize that the method we have used to find the energy levels is not simply a dimensional estimate. Actually, in addition to the factor giving the dimensions of the energy (which can indeed be obtained from dimensional analysis), we have obtained in all cases the correct relationship of E_n to the quantum number n.

15. Let us consider a one-dimensional barrier of arbitrary shape (see figure). Let a particle with an energy $E > U_0$ (U_0 being the

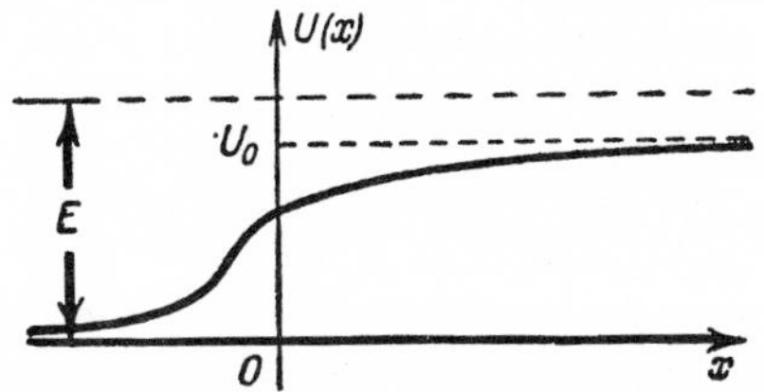

height of the barrier) hit the barrier from the left. Then, for $x \to +\infty$, there is only the transmitted wave

$$\psi = Ae^{ik_2 x} \quad \left(k_2 = \frac{1}{\hbar}\sqrt{2m(E - U_0)}\right), \tag{1}$$

while for $x \to -\infty$, there is a superposition of the incident and reflected waves

$$\psi = e^{ik_1 x} + Be^{-ik_1 x} \qquad \left(k_1 = \frac{1}{\hbar}\sqrt{2mE}\right). \tag{2}$$

To prove the given equation, we shall use the law of the conservation of the number of particles (the equation of continuity)

$$\frac{\partial |\psi|^2}{\partial t} + \operatorname{div} \mathbf{j} = 0, \tag{3}$$

where

$$\mathbf{j} = -\frac{i\hbar}{2m}(\psi^* \nabla\psi - \psi \nabla\psi^*) \tag{4}$$

is the probability current density.

In the stationary problem we are considering $\frac{\partial |\psi|^2}{\partial t} = 0$. Therefore, div $j = 0$. Because of the one-dimensionality of the motion, the latest equation becomes

$$\frac{dj_x}{dx} = 0 \quad \text{or} \quad j \equiv j_x = \text{const.} \tag{5}$$

Thus, the law of the conservation of the number of particles implies that the current density $j \equiv j_x$ is identical for all x.

Let us compute j for $x = +\infty$ and $x = -\infty$. Using (1), (2) and (4), we easily find

$$j(+\infty) = \frac{\hbar k_2 |A|^2}{m}, \quad j(-\infty) = \frac{\hbar k_1}{m}(1 - |B|^2).$$

According to (5), we can equate these two quantities to one another. Then we have

$$\frac{k_2}{k_1}|A|^2 + |B|^2 = 1. \tag{6}$$

However, the first term in (6) is nothing other than the ratio of the probability current density j in transmitted and incident waves; i.e., by definition it is the transmission coefficient D. The second term is equal to the ratio of the quantities j for the reflected and incident waves; i.e., it represents the reflection coefficient R. Thus, the required equation is proved.

16. We designate the three regions in the order of increasing x by I, II, and III. In regions I and III the Schrödinger equation is

$$\psi'' + k^2\psi = 0, \tag{1}$$

where $k^2 = \frac{2mE}{\hbar^2}$ (E is the energy of the particle). In region II, the Schrödinger equation is

$$\psi'' + k'^2\psi = 0, \tag{1'}$$

where

$$k'^2 = \frac{2m(E + U_0)}{\hbar^2}.$$

Let the incident particle move along the positive direction of the x-axis. This means that in region III there is only the transmitted wave. If we normalize the ψ-function in such a way that the coefficient of the incident wave is equal to unity, we have the following solutions for the Schrödinger equation in the different regions:

$$\psi = e^{ikx} + Ae^{-ikx} \qquad (x \leqslant 0), \tag{2}$$

$$\psi = Be^{ik'x} + Ce^{-ik'x} \qquad (0 \leqslant x \leqslant a), \tag{2'}$$

$$\psi = De^{ikx} \qquad (x \geqslant a). \tag{2''}$$

The constants A, B, C and D are found from the condition that ψ and $\frac{d\psi}{dx}$ are continuous at $x=0$ and $x=a$:

$$1+A=B+C, \qquad k(1-A)=k'(B-C);$$
$$Be^{ik'a}+Ce^{-ik'a}=De^{ika}, \qquad k'(Be^{ik'a}-Ce^{-ik'a})=kDe^{ika}.$$

Hence,

$$A=\frac{\left[\left(\frac{k'}{k}\right)^2-1\right]2i\sin k'a}{\left(\frac{k'}{k}+1\right)^2 e^{-ik'a}-\left(\frac{k'}{k}-1\right)^2 e^{ik'a}}, \tag{3}$$

$$B=\frac{\left(1+\frac{k'}{k}\right)}{\left(\frac{k'}{k}+1\right)^2-\left(\frac{k'}{k}-1\right)^2 e^{2ik'a}}, \tag{4}$$

$$C=\frac{2\left(\frac{k'}{k}-1\right)}{\left(\frac{k'}{k}+1\right)^2 e^{-2ik'a}-\left(\frac{k'}{k}-1\right)^2}, \tag{5}$$

$$D=\frac{4\frac{k'}{k}e^{-ika}}{\left(\frac{k'}{k}+1\right)^2 e^{-ik'a}-\left(\frac{k'}{k}-1\right)^2 e^{ik'a}}. \tag{6}$$

The transmission coefficient T is defined as the ratio of the current density of the transmitted wave to the current density of the incident wave

$$T=\frac{k|D|^2}{k}=|D|^2, \tag{7}$$

while the reflection coefficient R is defined as the ratio of the current density of the reflected wave (in region I) to that of the incident wave

$$R=\frac{k|A|^2}{k}=|A|^2. \tag{8}$$

We have finally

$$T=\frac{4k^2k'^2}{4k^2k'^2+(k'^2-k^2)^2\sin^2 k'a}, \tag{9}$$

$$R=\frac{(k'^2-k^2)^2\sin^2 k'a}{4k^2k'^2+(k'^2-k^2)^2\sin^2 k'a}. \tag{10}$$

As we would expect on the basis of the law of the conservation of the number of particles, the equation $T+R=1$ is automatically satisfied.

From (9) and (10), we see that for particles with an energy satisfying the condition $k'a = n\pi$ ($n = 1, 2, 3, \ldots$), the well is perfectly transparent ($T = 1$, $R = 0$).

We note the following important factor.* The coefficients T and R, which are regarded formally as functions of complex k, have isolated singular points (poles) for the purely imaginary k corresponding to the discrete energy levels in the potential well under consideration.

Indeed, as we can easily verify with (1) and (1′), the condition for T and R to go to infinity is

$$4k^2k'^2 + (k'^2 - k^2)^2 \sin^2 k'a = 0,$$

which is completely equivalent to the equation for discrete energy levels. Let us use this equation from the solution of the well-known problem of a potential well of finite depth ([1], p. 82). Since, in our problem, the energy is measured from the top of the well, while, in the solution we have referred to, the energy is measured from the bottom of the well, we write out equation (3) from this solution, replacing k by k':

$$\arcsin \frac{\hbar k'}{\sqrt{2mU_0}} = \frac{n\pi - k'a}{2} \qquad (n = 1, 2, 3, \ldots).$$

The equivalence of the two equations becomes clear, if it is noted that, according to equations (3)-(8), when $|T| = |R| = \infty$, we also have $|A| = |B| = |C| = |D| = \infty$. But this means that in (2) we can neglect the term e^{ikx}. As a consequence (for $k = i|k|$) the solutions (2) and (2′) assume the form $Ae^{|k|x}$ and $De^{-|k|x}$ (attenuation of the ψ-function outside the well!). Thus, we evidently arrive at the problem of finding the energy levels inside the well.

17. The potential energy $U(x)$ is equal to $U_0\left(1 + \frac{x}{a}\right)$ for $-a \le x \le 0$, to $U_0\left(1 - \frac{x}{a}\right)$ for $0 \le x \le a$, and to zero for $|x| \geqslant a$. Defining

$$k_0^2 = \frac{2mE}{\hbar^2}, \qquad \varkappa_0^2 = \frac{2mU_0}{\hbar^2} \tag{1}$$

(where E is the energy of the particle), we can write the Schrödinger equation in these regions

$$\frac{d^2\psi}{dx^2} + k_0^2\psi = 0 \qquad (|x| \geqslant a), \tag{2}$$

*This factor is directly connected with the general relation between the scattering law and the discrete energy levels which appears in the theory of elastic scattering ([1], Section 107, or [6], pp. 321-322).

$$\frac{d^2\psi}{dx^2}-\left(\varkappa_0^2-k_0^2+\varkappa_0^2\frac{x}{a}\right)\psi=0 \qquad (-a\leqslant x\leqslant 0), \tag{3}$$

$$\frac{d^2\psi}{dx^2}-\left(\varkappa_0^2-k_0^2-\varkappa_0^2\frac{x}{a}\right)\psi=0 \qquad (0\leqslant x\leqslant a). \tag{4}$$

Carrying out the following substitutions of variables in equations (3) and (4) respectively:

$$\zeta=\left(\frac{a}{\varkappa_0^2}\right)^{2/3}\left(\varkappa_0^2-k_0^2+\varkappa_0^2\frac{x}{a}\right), \tag{5}$$

$$\eta=\left(\frac{a}{\varkappa_0^2}\right)^{2/3}\left(\varkappa_0^2-k_0^2-\varkappa_0^2\frac{x}{a}\right), \tag{6}$$

we reduce them to the form

$$\frac{d^2\psi}{d\zeta^2}-\zeta\psi=0, \tag{3'}$$

$$\frac{d^2\psi}{d\eta^2}-\eta\psi=0. \tag{4'}$$

The general solution of an equation of type (3′) or (4′) is a linear combination of the two Airy functions v and u.*

Assuming that the particle arrives at the barrier from the negative side of x (i.e., for $x \geq a$, there is only a transmitted wave) and taking the coefficient of the incident wave to be equal to unity, we obtain for the wave function

$$\left.\begin{aligned}
\psi &= e^{ik_0x}+Ae^{-ik_0x} && (x\leqslant -a),\\
\psi &= Bu(\zeta)+Cv(\zeta) && (-a\leqslant x\leqslant 0),\\
\psi &= Du(\eta)+Ev(\eta) && (0\leqslant x\leqslant a),\\
\psi &= Fe^{ik_0x} && (x\geqslant a).
\end{aligned}\right\} \tag{7}$$

From the continuity of $\psi(x)$ and $\frac{d\psi}{dx}$ at the points $x = -a$, $x = 0$, $x = a$, we obtain a system of six equations for the six unknown constants A, B, C, D, E, and F:

---

*See for instance [1], p. 552, where the properties of one of the Airy functions $[\Phi(x) \equiv v(x)]$ are described. In the future, we shall use the formulas for both Airy functions $v(x)$ and $u(x)$ given in [3].

$$\left.\begin{aligned} &e^{-ik_0a}+Ae^{ik_0a}=Bu(-\lambda)+Cv(-\lambda),\\ &i\sqrt{\lambda}\,(e^{-ik_0a}-Ae^{ik_0a})=Bu'(-\lambda)+Cv'(-\lambda),\\ &Bu(\mu)+Cv(\mu)=Du(\mu)+Ev(\mu),\\ &Bu'(\mu)+Cv'(\mu)=-Du'(\mu)-Ev'(\mu),\\ &Du(-\lambda)+Ev(-\lambda)=Fe^{ik_0a},\\ &Du'(-\lambda)+Ev'(-\lambda)=-i\sqrt{\lambda}\,Fe^{ik_0a}. \end{aligned}\right\} \tag{8}$$

In equations (8), we have used the notation

$$\lambda\equiv k_0^2a^{2/3}\varkappa_0^{-4/3}=(\varkappa_0a)^{2/3}\left(\frac{k_0}{\varkappa_0}\right)^2, \tag{9}$$

$$\mu\equiv a^{2/3}\varkappa_0^{-4/3}(\varkappa_0^2-k_0^2)=(\varkappa_0a)^{2/3}\left(1-\frac{k_0^2}{\varkappa_0^2}\right). \tag{10}$$

Since the velocity of the particle outside the barrier is the same to the left and to the right, the transmission coefficient γ, defined as the ratio of the current densities for $x > a$ and $x < -a$, is obviously equal to $|F|^2$. Solving the system (8) and assuming that the Airy functions u and v are normalized according to [3] by the requirement

$$u'(t)\,v(t)-u(t)\,v'(t)=1,$$

we find

$$\gamma=|F|^2=$$

$$=\frac{\lambda}{\{[v(\mu)u'(-\lambda)-u(\mu)v'(-\lambda)]^2+\lambda[v(\mu)u(-\lambda)-u(\mu)v(-\lambda)]^2\}}\times$$

$$\times\frac{1}{\{[v'(\mu)u'(-\lambda)-u'(\mu)v'(-\lambda)]^2+\lambda[v'(\mu)u(-\lambda)-u'(\mu)v(-\lambda)]^2\}}. \tag{11}$$

Equation (11) taken together with (9), (10) and (1) fully solves the problem. The functions $v(t)$ and $u(t)$ (which are real for real values of the variable t) and their derivatives $v'(t)$ and $u'(t)$ are tabulated in [3].

Let us find the limiting expressions for the probability of penetration of the barrier in the quasi-classical case.

As we know, quasi-classical motion implies that the wavelength of the particle

$$\lambda\!\!\!^{-}=\frac{\hbar}{\sqrt{2m[E-U(x)]}}$$

does not change much over distances $\Delta x\sim\lambda\!\!\!^{-}$.

In the regions $x < -a$ and $x > a$, the motion is free and therefore quasi-classical $\left(\lambda = \frac{1}{k_0} = \text{const, and thus } \frac{d\lambda}{dx} = 0\right)$. According to (1), (5), and (6), we have for the regions $-a \leqslant x \leqslant 0$ and $0 \leqslant x \leqslant a$ respectively

$$\lambda = \left(\frac{a}{\varkappa_0^2}\right)^{1/3} \frac{1}{i\sqrt{\zeta}}, \qquad \frac{d\lambda}{dx} = \frac{d\lambda}{d\zeta}\frac{d\zeta}{dx} = -\frac{1}{2i\zeta^{3/2}}$$

and

$$\lambda = \left(\frac{a}{\varkappa_0^2}\right)^{1/3} \frac{1}{i\sqrt{\eta}}, \qquad \frac{d\lambda}{dx} = \frac{d\lambda}{d\eta}\frac{d\eta}{dx} = \frac{1}{2i\eta^{3/2}}.$$

Thus, the quasi-classical condition $\left|\frac{d\lambda}{dx}\right| \ll 1$ leads to the requirements

$$|\zeta| \gg 1 \text{ and } |\eta| \gg 1. \tag{12}$$

Let us consider the region of energy $E < U_0$ (i.e., $k_0 < \varkappa_0$, $\mu > 0$).

We denote the width of the barrier at the energy E by $2l$; Then, we obviously have

$$l = a\frac{U_0 - E}{U_0} = a\left(1 - \frac{k_0^2}{\varkappa_0^2}\right), \qquad a - l = a\frac{k_0^2}{\varkappa_0^2}. \tag{13}$$

We know beforehand that the quasi-classical conditions (12) are violated near the classical return points $x = \pm\, l$ (where $\zeta = 0$, $\eta = 0$). However, it is possible to formulate the conditions for an "integral" quasi-classical system (a system which is quasi-classical throughout essentially all of the region) which ensures a "quasi-classical" probability of penetration of the barrier. For this, it is obviously necessary to require that the regions Δx which are not quasi-classical (those regions corresponding to the regions $\Delta\zeta \sim 1$ and $\Delta\eta \sim 1$) be small relative to the distances l and $(a - l)$.

We have:

$$(\Delta x)_{\text{non-q.c.}} = \frac{(\Delta\zeta)_{\text{non-q.c.}}}{\left|\frac{d\zeta}{dx}\right|} \sim \left(\frac{a}{\varkappa_0^2}\right)^{1/3}$$

According to (13), (9) and (10), the condition $(\Delta x)_{\text{non-q.c.}} \ll l$ leads to the requirement $\mu \gg 1$, and the condition $(\Delta x)_{\text{non-q.c.}} \ll (a - l)$ to the requirement $\lambda \gg 1$.

We note that for the inequality $\lambda \gg 1$ to be satisfied, it is in any event necessary that $k_0 a \equiv \frac{a}{\lambda_0} \gg 1$. This is evident from the definition of λ (9) written in the form $\lambda = (k_0 a)^{2/3}\left(\frac{k_0}{\varkappa_0}\right)^{4/3}$. In exactly the same way, we see that for an energy $E > U_0$ (i.e., $k_0 > \varkappa_0$, $\mu < 0$) the condition for a quasi-classical system is the inequality $|\mu| \gg 1$, which automatically ensures the inequality $\lambda \gg 1$. As we can see from (10), for $k_0 \gtrsim \varkappa_0$, the inequality $|\mu| \gg 1$ requires in any event that the above-noted "trivial" quasi-classical condition $k_0 a \equiv \frac{a}{\lambdabar_0} \gg 1$ be satisfied.

Thus, for both $E > U_0$ and $E < U_0$, the quasi-classical transmission coefficient γ can be obtained from (11) when $|\mu| \gg 1$ and $\lambda \gg 1$, i.e., by using asymptotic expansions for the functions $u(t)$ and $v(t)$.

According to [3], these expansions have the following form (we retain everywhere only the main terms; $t > 0$ and $t \gg 1$, $x \equiv \frac{2}{3} t^{3/2}$):

$$\left.\begin{aligned} &u(t) \approx t^{-1/4} e^{x}, && u'(t) \approx t^{1/4} e^{x}; \\ &v(t) \approx \frac{1}{2} t^{-1/4} e^{-x}, && v'(t) \approx -\frac{1}{2} t^{1/4} e^{-x}; \end{aligned}\right\} \tag{14}$$

$$\left.\begin{aligned} &u(-t) \approx t^{-1/4} \cos\left(x + \frac{\pi}{4}\right), \\ &u'(-t) \approx t^{1/4} \sin\left(x + \frac{\pi}{4}\right); \\ &v(-t) \approx t^{-1/4} \sin\left(x + \frac{\pi}{4}\right), \\ &v'(-t) \approx -t^{1/4} \cos\left(x + \frac{\pi}{4}\right). \end{aligned}\right\} \tag{15}$$

Let us compute the quasi-classical probability of penetration of the barrier for two cases:

I. $E > U_0$ $\mu \gg 1$, $\lambda \gg 1$.
II. $E > U_0$ $|\mu| \gg 1$ (and consequently $\lambda \gg 1$).

In case I, we use equations (14) to substitute for $u(\mu)$, etc., and equations (15) to substitute for $u(-\lambda)$, etc. In the sums, we drop the exponentially small terms $\sim e^{-x}$* and easily find

$$\gamma \approx e^{-\frac{8}{3}\mu^{3/2}} = e^{-\frac{8}{3}\frac{a\sqrt{2m}}{\hbar U_0}(U_0 - E)^{3/2}} \tag{16}$$

As it should be in the quasi-classical case, $\gamma \ll 1$ (and $\gamma \to 0$ as $\hbar \to 0$).

*We note that there is absolutely no sense in considering these terms, since we have neglected even the exponentially large terms $\sim \frac{1}{x} e^{x}$, etc., relative to terms $\sim e^{x}$.

Exactly the same result (16) is obtained of course from the well-known quasi-classical formula

$$\gamma = e^{-2\int_{-l}^{l}\sqrt{\frac{2m}{\hbar^2}[U(x)-E]}\,dx}$$

In case II, we substitute $u(\mu) = u(-|\mu|)$, etc., and use equations (15) to substitute for $u(-\lambda)$, etc. Then, in this approximation, we arrive at the obvious result $\gamma \approx 1$.

In conclusion, we note two fairly trivial limiting cases.

If for fixed a and E, $U_0 \to 0$, then $\lambda \to \infty$ and $\mu \to -\infty$. Thus, according to Case II, $\gamma \to 1$.

If, on the other hand, $E \to 0$ for fixed a and U_0, then $\lambda \to 0$. Thus, for any $\mu \to (\varkappa_0 a)^{2/3}$, $\gamma \to 0$ [see (11)], as in the case of a barrier of any other shape.

CHAPTER III

Computation of Probabilities and Average Values. Transformation to Other State Spaces

1. The wave function of a freely moving particle has the form

$$\psi(\boldsymbol{r}) = Ae^{\frac{i\boldsymbol{pr}}{\hbar}}, \tag{1}$$

where $\boldsymbol{p}$ is the momentum of the particle and A is a constant.

The probability current density is equal to

$$\boldsymbol{j} = -\frac{i\hbar}{2m}(\psi^* \operatorname{grad}\psi - \psi \operatorname{grad}\psi^*) \tag{2}$$

(m is the mass of the particle).

Substituting (1) into (2), and remembering that

$$\operatorname{grad}\left(e^{\pm\frac{i\boldsymbol{pr}}{\hbar}}\right) = e^{\pm\frac{i\boldsymbol{pr}}{\hbar}} \operatorname{grad}\left(\pm\frac{i\boldsymbol{pr}}{\hbar}\right) = \pm e^{\pm\frac{i\boldsymbol{pr}}{\hbar}} \frac{i\boldsymbol{p}}{\hbar},$$

we arrive at the result

$$\boldsymbol{j} = \frac{\boldsymbol{p}}{m}|A|^2 = \frac{\boldsymbol{p}}{m}|\psi(\boldsymbol{r})|^2,$$

the meaning of which is obvious (compare with the equation from hydrodynamics $\boldsymbol{j} = \rho\boldsymbol{v}$).

2. Before computing the required probability, it is necessary to determine the probability density in the space of the three independent and commuting variables x, p_y, and z, and to integrate this density over p_y and z within the given limits, and over x from $-\infty$ to $+\infty$. The probability density is equal to the square of the modulus of the wave function in the corresponding state space, in the given case, the (x, p_y, z)-space. Under the assumption that the initial wave function $\Psi(x, y, z)$ is normalized to unity, the wave function in the above space is

$$F(x, p_y, z) = \frac{1}{\sqrt{2\pi\hbar}} \int_{-\infty}^{\infty} \Psi(x, y, z) e^{-\frac{ip_y y}{\hbar}} dy. \tag{1}$$

From the above discussion, the desired probability is

$$\int_{z_1}^{z_2}\int_{p_1}^{p_2}\int_{-\infty}^{\infty}|F(x, p_y, z)|^2\,dx\,dp_y\,dz. \tag{2}$$

We emphasize that this quantity — the probability that z and p_y lie simultaneously within the given intervals, irrespective of the value of x — is, in the general case, by no means equal to the product of the probability of finding z within the given interval (irrespective of the values of x and y)

$$\int_{z_1}^{z_2}\int_{-\infty}^{\infty}\int_{-\infty}^{\infty}|\Psi(x, y, z)|^2\,dx\,dy\,dz\;* \tag{3}$$

and the probability of finding p_y in the given interval (for any x and z)

$$\int_{-\infty}^{\infty}\int_{p_1}^{p_2}\int_{-\infty}^{\infty}|F(x, p_y, z)|^2\,dx\,dp_y\,dz. \tag{4}$$

In other words, the quantities z and p_y are not generally speaking statistically independent.

However, in the special case where the wave function Ψ is a product of variables in x, y, and z respectively

$$\Psi(x, y, z) = \psi_1(x)\,\psi_2(y)\,\psi_3(z),$$

from which, according to (1),

$$F(x, p_y, z) = \psi_1(x)\,f(p_y)\,\psi_3(z),$$

it is easily seen that probability (2) is equal to the product of probabilities (3) and (4); i.e., in this case, z and p_y are statistically independent.

3. The possible values of the angular momentum M_z are determined from the nonzero terms of the expansion of the given wave function into a series of eigenfunctions of the operator M_z

$$\psi_m = \frac{1}{\sqrt{2\pi}}\,e^{im\varphi} \qquad (M_z = m\hbar),$$

while the probability of these values is determined from the squares of the moduli of the corresponding Fourier coefficients.

---

*Or, which is the same, $\int_{z_1}^{z_2}\int_{-\infty}^{\infty}\int_{-\infty}^{\infty}|F(x, p_y, z)|^2\,dx\,dp_y\,dz$

We have

$$\Psi = A\cos^2\varphi = A\,\frac{1+\cos 2\varphi}{2} = A\left(\frac{1}{2}+\frac{1}{4}e^{2i\varphi}+\frac{1}{4}e^{-2i\varphi}\right).$$

Thus, the possible values of the angular momentum are 0, $+2\hbar$, $-2\hbar$, while their respective normalized probabilities are

$$w(0)=\frac{2}{3}, \quad w(+2\hbar)=\frac{1}{6}, \quad w(-2\hbar)=\frac{1}{6}.$$

The average value of the angular momentum is

$$\overline{M}_z = \sum_{M_z} M_z w(M_z) = 0\cdot\frac{2}{3}+2\hbar\cdot\frac{1}{6}+(-2\hbar)\cdot\frac{1}{6}=0\,*;$$

The same result is of course obtained from the equation

$$\overline{M}_z = \frac{\int_0^{2\pi}\Psi^*\hat{M}_z\Psi\,d\varphi}{\int_0^{2\pi}\Psi^*\Psi\,d\varphi} \sim \int_0^{2\pi}\Psi^*\frac{d\Psi}{d\varphi}\,d\varphi = 0.$$

4. Obviously, three values of $m' \equiv \frac{M_{z'}}{\hbar}$ are possible: $+1$, 0, -1. The probabilities of these values of $M_{z'}$, normalized, are equal to the squares of the moduli of the coefficients in the expansion of the normalized wave function $\psi_{l=1,\,m=1}(\vartheta,\varphi)$ into normalized eigenfunctions of the operator $\hat{M}_{z'}$:

$$\psi_{l'=1,\,m'=1}(\vartheta',\varphi'), \quad \psi_{l'=1,\,m'=0}(\vartheta',\varphi'), \quad \psi_{l'=1,\,m'=-1}(\vartheta',\varphi').$$

This expansion has the form

$$\psi_{11}(\vartheta,\varphi) = c_1\psi_{11}(\vartheta',\varphi') + c_0\psi_{10}(\vartheta',\varphi') + c_{-1}\psi_{1,-1}(\vartheta',\varphi'). \tag{1}$$

To find the coefficients c_i most rapidly, it is convenient to represent the spherical harmonics in (1) in the form of homogeneous functions of Cartesian coordinates

---

*The equation $\overline{M}_z = 0$ could have been predicted from the fact that the Ψ-function for the state under consideration is real; i.e., the azimuthal component of the probability current density

$$i_\varphi = \frac{\hbar}{2im}\left(\Psi^*\frac{\partial\Psi}{\partial\varphi} - \Psi\,\frac{\partial\Psi^*}{\partial\varphi}\right)$$

is equal to zero.

$$\psi_{11}(\vartheta, \varphi) = -\sqrt{\frac{3}{8\pi}} \sin\vartheta e^{i\varphi} = -\sqrt{\frac{3}{8\pi}} \frac{x+iy}{r},$$

$$\psi_{11}(\vartheta', \varphi') = -\sqrt{\frac{3}{8\pi}} \sin\vartheta' e^{i\varphi'} = -\sqrt{\frac{3}{8\pi}} \frac{x'+iy'}{r'},$$

$$\psi_{1,-1}(\vartheta', \varphi') = \sqrt{\frac{3}{8\pi}} \sin\vartheta' e^{-i\varphi'} = \sqrt{\frac{3}{8\pi}} \frac{x'-iy'}{r'},$$

$$\psi_{10}(\vartheta', \varphi') = \sqrt{\frac{3}{4\pi}} \cos\vartheta' = \sqrt{\frac{3}{4\pi}} \cdot \frac{z'}{r'},$$

where

$$r = \sqrt{x^2 + y^2 + z^2}, \quad r' = \sqrt{x'^2 + y'^2 + z'^2}.$$

The coordinate system x', y', z' is found from the system x, y, z by rotating it through an angle α about an axis lying in the (x, y)-plane and passing through the origin of coordinates (for instance, it is convenient to direct the x-axis along this axis of rotation).

Then, we have

$$x = x', \quad y = y'\cos\alpha - z'\sin\alpha, \quad z = y'\sin\alpha + z'\cos\alpha, \quad r = r'. \tag{2}$$

Substituting the expressions for the ψ-function into (1) and replacing x, y, and z by x', y', and z' according to equations (2), we arrive at the equation

$$\begin{aligned} &x'(1 - c_1 + c_{-1}) + \\ &+ iy'(\cos\alpha - c_1 - c_{-1}) - iz'(\sin\alpha + i\sqrt{2}c_0) = 0. \end{aligned} \tag{1'}$$

This equation, as well as equation (1) from which it is obtained, must be identically equal to zero for all values of x', y', z'. For this, it is necessary that

$$1 - c_1 + c_{-1} = 0, \quad \cos\alpha - c_1 - c_{-1} = 0, \quad \sin\alpha + i\sqrt{2}c_0 = 0.$$

Solving this system of three equations with three unknowns, we find

$$c_0 = \frac{i}{\sqrt{2}}\sin\alpha, \quad c_1 = \cos^2\frac{\alpha}{2}, \quad c_{-1} = -\sin^2\frac{\alpha}{2}.$$

The corresponding probabilities are

$$W(0) = \frac{1}{2}\sin^2\alpha, \quad W(1) = \cos^4\frac{\alpha}{2}, \quad W(-1) = \sin^4\frac{\alpha}{2}.$$

As we could have expected on the basis of the normalization of the ψ-function,

$$W(0) + W(1) + W(-1) = 1.$$

Finally, the average value of the component of angular momentum along the z'-axis is (in units of $\hbar$)

$$\overline{m}' = 1 \cdot W(1) + 0 \cdot W(0) + (-1) \cdot W(-1) = \\ = \cos^4 \frac{\alpha}{2} - \sin^4 \frac{\alpha}{2} = \cos \alpha;$$

i.e., it is equal to its classical value.

5. The potential energy is of the form shown in the figure.* A well of "small depth" means that the depth U_0 is much smaller than a certain quantity with the dimensions of energy obtained from the remaining variables appearing in the problem: the mass of the particle m, the width of the well a, and Planck's constant $\hbar$.

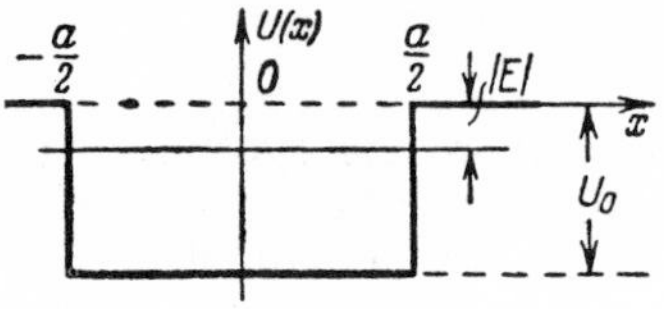

It is easily verified that there is only one such constant, namely $\frac{\hbar^2}{ma^2}$. Thus, the condition that the depth of the well is small has the form

$$U_0 \ll \frac{\hbar^2}{ma^2}. \tag{1}$$

We are looking for a stationary state with an energy $E < 0$. The Schrödinger equation inside the well has the form ($|E| = -E$ is the depth of the level)

$$\psi'' + \frac{2m}{\hbar^2}(U_0 - |E|)\psi = 0 \quad \left(-\frac{a}{2} \leqslant x \leqslant \frac{a}{2}\right), \tag{2}$$

while outside the well it has the form

$$\psi'' - \frac{2m}{\hbar^2}|E|\psi = 0 \quad \left(|x| \geqslant \frac{a}{2}\right). \tag{3}$$

Using the notation

$$\frac{2m}{\hbar^2}(U_0 - |E|) = k^2, \tag{4}$$

$$\frac{2m}{\hbar^2}|E| = \varkappa^2, \tag{4'}$$

we can write the solutions of equations (2) and (3) in the form**

$$\psi = A \sin kx + B \cos kx \qquad \left(-\frac{a}{2} \leqslant x \leqslant \frac{a}{2}\right), \tag{5}$$

---

*By selecting the origin of coordinates at the center of the well, we can use the symmetry of the problem most conveniently.

**Because of the symmetry of the problem, we can, for the present, confine ourselves to the consideration of one half of the region outside the well.

$$\psi = Ce^{\varkappa x} + De^{-\varkappa x} \qquad \left(x \geqslant \frac{a}{2}\right). \tag{6}$$

From the requirement that the solution be finite (as $x \to \infty$), it follows that it is necessary that $C = 0$. Moreover, because of the symmetry of the potential energy $U(x)$ relative to the point $x = 0$, the Hamiltonian $\hat{H} = -\frac{\hbar^2}{2m}\frac{d^2}{dx^2} + U(x)$ commutes with the parity operator relative to $x = 0$. Consequently, in view of the fact that the given energy level is nondegenerate ([1], pp. 76 and 78), the stationary state which we are looking for must be characterized by a definite parity. Thus, only one of the terms in (5) is left.

Since, in a sufficiently small well, the energy level we are looking for will be the only one (and will accordingly be equal to the ground-state energy), the ψ-function corresponding to it must not have any nodes. Therefore, the odd function $\sin kx$ is dropped. Thus, the ψ-function is even and has the form

$$\psi = B\cos kx \qquad \left(-\frac{a}{2} \leqslant x \leqslant \frac{a}{2}\right), \tag{5'}$$

$$\psi = De^{-\varkappa x} \qquad \left(x \geqslant \frac{a}{2}\right), \tag{6'}$$

$$\psi = De^{\varkappa x} \qquad \left(x \leqslant -\frac{a}{2}\right). \tag{6''}$$

From the continuity of the logarithmic derivatives $\frac{\psi'}{\psi}$ of solutions (5′) and (6′) at the edge of the well $x = \frac{a}{2}$, we obtain a transcendental equation for $|E|$:

$$\operatorname{tg}\frac{ka}{2} = \frac{\varkappa}{k}. \tag{7}$$

By comparing (4) and (1), it is seen that

$$\frac{ka}{2} = \sqrt{\frac{2m}{\hbar^2}(U_0 - |E|)}\,\frac{a}{2} < \sqrt{\frac{ma^2U_0}{2\hbar^2}} \ll 1. \tag{8}$$

Accordingly, in equation (7) we substitute $\operatorname{tg}\frac{ka}{2} \approx \frac{ka}{2}$ and, using (4) and (4′), we reduce it to the form

$$\frac{m}{\hbar^2}(U_0 - |E|) = \frac{1}{a}\sqrt{\frac{2m|E|}{\hbar^2}}. \tag{9}$$

Equation (9) amounts to a quadratic expression. However, it is not necessary to solve this quadratic expression, since, according to (7) and (8),

$$\frac{\varkappa}{k} \ll 1, \quad \text{i.e.,} \quad |E| \ll U_0 - |E|$$

and thus, all the more so, $|E| \ll U_0$. Therefore, in the left member of (9), it is possible to neglect $|E|$ relative to U_0, after which we find directly

$$|E| = \frac{ma^2}{2\hbar^2} U_0^2. \tag{10}$$

The ratio of the depth of the level to the depth of the well is [cf. (1)]

$$\frac{|E|}{U_0} = \frac{ma^2 U_0}{2\hbar^2} \ll 1.$$

According to (4) and (4′), the value of $|E|$ which we have found determines the parameters of the ψ-function k and $\varkappa$.

Let us now determine the coefficients B and D. We note first of all that, since

$$\frac{\varkappa a}{2} \ll \frac{ka}{2} \ll 1 \qquad \left(\text{i.e., } \cos\frac{ka}{2} \approx e^{-\frac{\varkappa a}{2}} \approx 1\right),$$

the ψ-function (5′) inside the well is practically constant ($\approx B$). Moreover, the condition of the continuity of ψ at $x = \frac{a}{2}$ gives in the approximation of (1) simply $B = D$.

The requirement of normalization of unity yields

$$1 = \int_{-\infty}^{\infty} |\psi(x)|^2 dx = 2\int_0^{\infty} |\psi(x)|^2 dx \approx$$

$$\approx 2\int_0^{a/2} B^2 dx + 2\int_{a/2}^{\infty} B^2 e^{-2\varkappa x} dx = \frac{B^2}{\varkappa}(\varkappa a + e^{-\varkappa a}) \approx \frac{B^2}{\varkappa}.$$

Whence,

$$B \approx \sqrt{\varkappa} = \left(\frac{2m|E|}{\hbar^2}\right)^{1/4} = \frac{\sqrt{maU_0}}{\hbar}. \tag{11}$$

Thus, in the approximation of (1), the wave function of the given stationary state has the form

$$\left.\begin{aligned} &\psi \approx \sqrt{\varkappa} = \text{const} && \left(-\frac{a}{2} \leqslant x \leqslant \frac{a}{2}\right), \\ &\psi = \sqrt{\varkappa}e^{-\varkappa x} && \left(x \geqslant \frac{a}{2}\right), \\ &\psi = \sqrt{\varkappa}e^{\varkappa x} && \left(x \leqslant -\frac{a}{2}\right). \end{aligned}\right\} \tag{12}$$

The probability distribution in the position space is given by the quantity $[\psi(x)]^2 dx$.

To find the momentum distribution function $p_x \equiv p$ it is necessary to write the wave function for the given state in the p-space

$$G(p) = \frac{1}{\sqrt{2\pi\hbar}} \int_{-\infty}^{\infty} \psi(x) e^{-\frac{ipx}{\hbar}} dx. \tag{13}$$

Substituting $\psi(x)$ from (12), we obtain, after performing a simple computation in the approximation of (1),*

$$G(p) \approx \sqrt{\frac{2}{\pi}} (\hbar\varkappa)^{3/2} \frac{\cos\frac{pa}{2\hbar} + \frac{\hbar\varkappa}{p}\sin\frac{pa}{2\hbar}}{\hbar^2\varkappa^2 + p^2}.$$

The probability that the particle will have a momentum with the range from p to $p + dp$ is

$$W(p)\,dp = [G(p)]^2\,dp = \frac{2}{\pi}(\hbar\varkappa)^3 \left(\frac{\cos\frac{pa}{2\hbar} + \frac{\hbar\varkappa}{p}\sin\frac{pa}{2\hbar}}{\hbar^2\varkappa^2 + p^2}\right)^2 dp. \tag{14}$$

Because of (13) and the normalization of $\psi(x)$, the normalization $\int_{-\infty}^{\infty} W(p)\,dp = 1$ automatically follows.

$W(p) = W(-p)$, as it should.

For $|p| \ll \hbar\varkappa$ (and, all the more so, for $|p| \ll \frac{\hbar}{a}$) we have, according to (14),

$$W(p) \approx \frac{2}{\pi\hbar\varkappa} = \text{const}, \tag{14'}$$

while, for $|p| \gg \hbar\varkappa$,

$$W(p) \approx \frac{2}{\pi}(\hbar\varkappa)^3 \frac{\cos^2\frac{pa}{2\hbar}}{p^4}. \tag{14''}$$

Thus, the probability decreases rapidly as $|p|$ increases.

6. The error of the argument consists in identifying the accuracy of the spatial localization of the particle Δx with the dimensions of the potential well a (in terms of orders of magnitude). In reality, the accuracy of the spatial localization of the particle is determined by the "spread" of the probability distribution in position

---

*We note that the wave function is real [in any space, compare $\psi(x)$ and $G(p)$], as it should be in one-dimensional finite motion.

space $|\psi(x)|^2$ [correspondingly, the uncertainty in the momentum is given by the width of the probability distribution of the momentum space $|G(p)|^2$, and so on]. As can be seen from the normalization integral $\int |\psi|^2 dx$ in the previous problem, the probabilities of finding the particle inside and outside the well are respectively equal to $\varkappa a$ and $(1-\varkappa a)$, where $\varkappa a = \frac{ma^2U_0}{\hbar^2} \ll 1$.

Making use of a rough classical analogy, we can say that the particle spends far more time outside the well than inside.*

Accordingly, as shown by equation (12) of the preceding problem, the order of magnitude of the effective spread of the position distribution function is

$$(\Delta x)_{\text{eff}} \sim \frac{1}{\varkappa} \gg a. \tag{1}$$

On the other hand, the effective spread of the momentum distribution function is, as follows from a comparison of (14′) and (14″) in Problem No. 5,

$$(\Delta p)_{\text{eff}} \sim \hbar\varkappa. \tag{2}$$

Multiplying (1) and (2), we obtain the uncertainty principle

$$(\Delta p)_{\text{eff}} (\Delta x)_{\text{eff}} \sim \hbar, \tag{3}$$

as we would expect.

Let us now determine the numerical coefficient in (3). For this purpose, we compute the product of the standard deviations of the momentum and the position:

$$\Delta p \equiv \sqrt{\overline{(p-\bar{p})^2}} \quad \text{and} \quad \Delta x \equiv \sqrt{\overline{(x-\bar{x})^2}}. \tag{4}$$

As we know,

$$\overline{(p-\bar{p})^2} = \overline{p^2} - (\bar{p})^2, \tag{5′}$$

$$\overline{(x-\bar{x})^2} = \overline{x^2} - (\bar{x})^2. \tag{5″}$$

---

*This is a typically quantum-mechanical phenomenon, since the region outside the well is forbidden classically. In the three-dimensional case, a qualitative illustration is provided by the deuteron, the radius of which is considerably greater than the radius of the interaction forces between the proton and the neutron, as a result of which the particle spends a considerable amount of time outside the potential well.

From equations (12) and (14) of the preceding problem, it is immediately seen that

$$\left.\begin{aligned}\bar{x} &= \int\limits_{-\infty}^{\infty} x\,[\psi(x)]^2\,dx = 0,\\ \bar{p} &= \int\limits_{-\infty}^{\infty} p\,[G(p)]^2\,dp = 0.\end{aligned}\right\} \qquad (6)$$

Furthermore, using (12), we find, in the approximation we have adopted, $a^2 \ll \frac{\hbar^2}{mU_0}$:

$$\overline{x^2} = \int\limits_{-\infty}^{\infty} x^2\,[\psi(x)]^2\,dx \approx \frac{1}{2\varkappa^2}. \qquad (7)$$

Likewise, it is more convenient to compute the quantity

$$\overline{p^2} = \int\limits_{-\infty}^{\infty} p^2\,[G(p)]^2\,dp$$

in the position space, i.e., from the equation

$$\overline{p^2} = \int\limits_{-\infty}^{\infty} \psi(x)\,\hat{p}^2\psi(x)\,dx = \int\limits_{-\infty}^{\infty} \psi(x)\left(\frac{\hbar}{i}\frac{\partial}{\partial x}\right)^2\psi(x)\,dx =$$

$$= -\hbar^2 \int\limits_{-\infty}^{\infty} \psi(x)\frac{d^2\psi}{dx^2}\,dx.$$

Simplifying this expression somewhat by integrating by parts

$$\overline{p^2} = \hbar^2 \int\limits_{-\infty}^{\infty} \left(\frac{d\psi}{dx}\right)^2 dx$$

and substituting $\psi(x)$ from equation (12) in Problem No. 5, we obtain (in the same approximation)

$$\overline{p^2} \approx \hbar^2\varkappa^2. \qquad (8)$$

We note that the value of $\overline{p^2}$ which we have found does not correspond at all to the kinetic energy in the classically permitted region (i.e., inside the well)

$$U_0 - |E| \approx U_0,$$

but to a much smaller quantity $|E|$. This result could have been predicted qualitatively, since the particle spends the greater part of the time in the classically forbidden region (where its "kinetic energy" is negative), making a large negative contribution to the average kinetic energy $(\overline{E-U}) = \frac{1}{2m}\overline{p^2}$.

Using (4) and (8), we finally obtain

$$\Delta p = \hbar\varkappa, \qquad \Delta x = \frac{1}{\sqrt{2}\varkappa}.$$

Hence,

$$\Delta p\,\Delta x = \frac{\hbar}{\sqrt{2}}.^{*}$$

7. If the normalized ψ-function for the ground state

$$\psi(r) = \frac{1}{\sqrt{\pi a^3}} e^{-\frac{r}{a}} \qquad \left(a \equiv \frac{\hbar^2}{me^2}\right) \tag{1}$$

is used, the average value for the n-th power of r will be expressed by

$$\overline{r^n} = \int r^n [\psi(r)]^2\, dV. \tag{2}$$

Substituting (1) into this equation, integrating over the angles, and performing the substitution of variables $\frac{2r}{a} = t$, we obtain

$$\overline{r^n} = \frac{1}{\pi a^3}\cdot 4\pi\left(\frac{a}{2}\right)^{n+3}\int\limits_0^\infty t^{n+2}e^{-t}\,dt.$$

The resulting integral is $\Gamma(n+3)$. Finally, we find

$$\overline{r^n} = \frac{\Gamma(n+3)}{2^{n+1}} a^n. \tag{3}$$

As can be seen from (3) or (2), the quantity $\overline{r^n}$ has a meaning only for $n > -3$. In particular, for $n = 1$ and $n = 2$, we have

$$\overline{r} = \frac{3}{2} a, \qquad \overline{r^2} = 3a^2.$$

---

*We recall that the smallest possible value of $\Delta p\,\Delta x$ is equal to $\hbar/2$ (this value being obtained for a "Gaussian wave packet" $\psi \sim e^{-bx^2}$).

Therefore, the standard deviation of the radius is

$$\sqrt{\overline{(r-\bar{r})^2}}=\sqrt{\overline{r^2}-(\bar{r})^2}=\frac{\sqrt{3}}{2}a.$$

8. Since the protons (which capture the negative mesons) are distributed approximately uniformly throughout the volume of the nucleus, the probability that a meson will be captured from the K-orbit is obviously proportional to

$$\frac{\int\limits_{V_n}|\psi(r)|^2dV}{\int|\psi(r)|^2dV}, \tag{1}$$

where ψ is the wave function of a meson in the K-orbit.

The integral in the denominator is taken over all space, while the integral in the numerator is taken over the volume of the nucleus V_n, which, it is known, is approximately equal to Z.*

Regarding the radius of the nucleus R as small relative to the radius of the K-orbit of the meson $a=\frac{\hbar^2}{Z\mu e^2}$ (where μ is the mass of the meson), and considering that the ψ-function of the meson changes significantly only over distances of the order of a, we obtain in the numerator $\approx|\psi(0)|^2\cdot V_n$, where $\psi(0)$ is the wave function of the meson at the origin of coordinates (i.e., in the region of the nucleus).

If a normalized ψ-function

$$\psi(r)=\frac{1}{\sqrt{\pi a^3}}e^{-\frac{r}{a}}$$

is used [making the denominator in (1) equal to unity], it is immediately seen (since $a\sim\frac{1}{Z}$) that ratio (1) and, consequently, the probability of capture are proportional to

$$Z^3\cdot Z=Z^4.$$

We note that the approximation $a\gg R$ which we have used is not legitimate for heavy nuclei.

---

* $$V_n=\frac{4}{3}\pi R^3=\frac{4\pi}{3}(r_0A^{1/3})^3=\frac{4\pi}{3}r_0^3A\approx\frac{4\pi}{3}r_0^3\cdot 2Z,$$

where

$$r_0=\text{const}\approx 1.2\cdot 10^{-13}\text{ cm}.$$

Indeed, in veiw of the fact that $R \approx r_0 A^{1/3} \approx r_0 (2Z)^{1/3}$, where $r_0 \approx \frac{1}{2}\left(\frac{1}{137}\right)^2$ atomic units and $\mu \approx 200$ atomic units, the above inequality is equivalent to

$$Z \ll 45$$

(see Problem No. 13, Chapter II).

9. The normalized position wave function for the ground state of hydrogen is

$$\psi(r) = \frac{1}{\sqrt{\pi a_0^3}} e^{-\frac{r}{a_0}},$$

where

$$a_0 = \frac{\hbar^2}{me^2}.$$

The normalized momentum wave function for the same state is

$$G(p) = \frac{1}{(2\pi\hbar)^{3/2}} \int \psi(r) e^{-\frac{ipr}{\hbar}} dr.$$

This integral is computed by transforming to spherical coordinates with the polar axis directed along p:

$$2\pi \int_0^\infty \int_{-1}^{1} \exp\left(-\frac{r}{a_0} - i\frac{pr\cos\theta}{\hbar}\right) r^2 \, dr \, d\cos\theta =$$

$$= 2\pi \frac{\hbar}{ip} \int_0^\infty \left[e^{-\left(\frac{1}{a_0} - \frac{ip}{\hbar}\right) r} - e^{-\left(\frac{1}{a_0} + \frac{ip}{\hbar}\right) r}\right] r \, dr = \frac{8\pi a_0^3 \hbar^4}{(\hbar^2 + a_0^2 p^2)^2}.$$

The probability density in p-space is

$$[G(p)]^2 = \frac{8 a_0^3 \hbar^5}{\pi^2 (\hbar^2 + a_0^2 p^2)^4}. \tag{1}$$

As we would expect on the basis of the lack of a preferred direction, this probability depends only on the magnitude of p. The probability of finding the momentum within the range of absolute values from p to $p + dp$ is obtained by multiplying $[G(p)]^2$ by the volume element in momentum space $4\pi p^2 \, dp$:

$$w(p)\, dp = \frac{32}{\pi} \left(\frac{\hbar}{a_0}\right)^5 \frac{p^2 \, dp}{\left(\frac{\hbar^2}{a_0^2} + p^2\right)^4}. \tag{2}$$

We can easily verify that the normalization requirement $\int_0^\infty w(p)\,dp = 1$ is satisfied by using the formula $\int_0^\infty \frac{x^2\,dx}{(1+x^2)^4} = \frac{\pi}{32}$. The function $w(p)$ has a maximum at $p = p_m = \frac{1}{\sqrt{3}}\frac{\hbar}{a_0}$ (p_m is the "most probable momentum"). For $p \ll \frac{\hbar}{a_0}$

$$[G(p)]^2 \approx \text{const}, \quad w(p) \sim p^2,$$

while for $p \gg \frac{\hbar}{a_0}$

$$[G(p)]^2 \sim \frac{1}{p^8}, \quad w(p) \sim \frac{1}{p^6}.$$

Thus, the probability decreases rapidly with increasing p.

Therefore, the distribution function of the momentum is appreciably different from zero only in the range $(\Delta p)_{\text{eff}} \sim \frac{\hbar}{a_0}$.

Since the effective range of the position is $(\Delta r)_{\text{eff}} \sim a_0$, we obtain by necessity the uncertainty relationship

$$(\Delta p)_{\text{eff}}\,(\Delta r)_{\text{eff}} \sim \hbar.$$

10. The potential φ which we must determine is equal to the sum of the potential $\varphi_p = \frac{e}{r}$ produced by the proton and the potential produced by the electron $\bar{\varphi}_e$ (which is averaged out over the wave function for the ground state of hydrogen $\psi = \frac{1}{\sqrt{\pi a^3}} e^{-\frac{r}{a}}$, where $a = \frac{\hbar^2}{me^2}$):

$$\varphi(\mathbf{r}) = \varphi_p(\mathbf{r}) + \bar{\varphi}_e(\mathbf{r}) = \frac{e}{r} - e\int \frac{\psi_0^2(\mathbf{r}')}{|\mathbf{r}-\mathbf{r}'|}\,dV'. \tag{1}$$

The potential $\bar{\varphi}_e$ is, of course, the same as the potential of the static electron "cloud" with density $\rho(\mathbf{r}') = -e\psi_0^2(\mathbf{r}')$. Therefore, $\bar{\varphi}_e$ can be found simply as a spherically symmetric solution of Poisson's equation

$$\frac{1}{r}\frac{d^2(r\bar{\varphi}_e)}{dr^2} = -4\pi\rho(r) = 4\pi e\frac{1}{\pi a^3} e^{-\frac{2r}{a}}.$$

From this $\bar{\varphi}_e$ is easily obtained by twice integrating from r to ∞.

The integral in (1) is computed most easily by using the fact that $\frac{1}{|\mathbf{r}-\mathbf{r}'|}$ is a generating function of Legendre polynomials:

$$\text{for } r' < r \qquad \frac{1}{|\mathbf{r}-\mathbf{r}'|} = \frac{1}{r}\sum_{l=0}^{\infty} P_l(\cos\theta')\left(\frac{r'}{r}\right)^l,$$

$$\text{for } r' > r \qquad \frac{1}{|\mathbf{r}-\mathbf{r}'|} = \frac{1}{r'}\sum_{l=0}^{\infty} P_l(\cos\theta')\left(\frac{r}{r'}\right)^l,$$

where θ' is the angle between $\mathbf{r}'$ and $\mathbf{r}$.

After breaking up the region of integration over r' into two parts ($r' \leqslant r$ and $r' \geqslant r$), we see that, in integrating over the angle θ', only zero terms are left in the sums $\sum\limits_{l=0}^{\infty}$ in each of the parts (a consequence of the orthogonality of the Legendre polynomials). This yields

$$\varphi(r) = \frac{e}{r} - \frac{4e}{a^3}\left(\frac{1}{r}\int_0^r e^{-\frac{2r'}{a}} r'^2\,dr' + \int_r^{\infty} e^{-\frac{2r'}{a}} r'\,dr'\right)$$

As we could have predicted, the potential $\overline{\varphi_e}$ (and consequently φ) is spherically symmetric. Integrating, we finally find

$$\varphi(r) = e\left(\frac{1}{r} + \frac{1}{a}\right)e^{-\frac{2r}{a}}.$$

For the limiting cases of $r \ll a$ and $r \gg a$, we obtain the obvious results $\varphi \approx \frac{e}{r}$ (Coulomb field of the proton) and $\varphi \approx \frac{e}{a}e^{-\frac{2r}{a}}$ (practically totally screening of the proton by the electron).

11. To avoid computational difficulties, we shall first consider a symmetric well of very large, but finite depth U_0 (see figure), and then take the limit $U_0 \to \infty$.

For instance, let us compute the average force $\bar{f}$ exerted by the particle on the right wall of the well.

The operator for the force exerted on a particle by an external field (the wall of the well) is $\left[-\frac{dU(x)}{dx}\right]$, where $U(x)$ is the potential-energy operator of the particle. From Newton's third law, the force with which the particle acts on the wall is equal in magnitude and opposite in sign to the above force, i.e.,

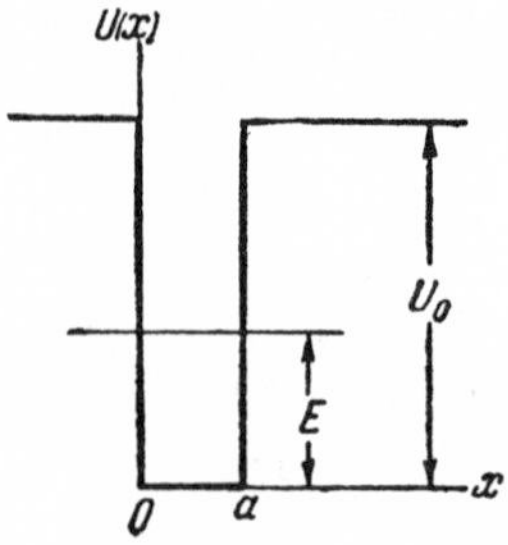

$$f(x) = \frac{dU(x)}{dx}. \tag{1}$$

Its average value is

$$\bar{f} = \int_{-\infty}^{\infty} f(x)\,[\psi(x)]^2\,dx, \tag{2}$$

where $\psi(x)$ is the wave function (real), and $f(x)$ is taken for the wall under consideration (the right wall).

$U(x)$ is everywhere constant, except at the point $x = a$, where $U(x)$ jumps to U_0. Therefore, (1) can be written in the form

$$f(x) = U_0 \delta(x - a), \tag{3}$$

where δ is a delta function.* Substituting (3) into (2), we obtain

$$\bar{f} = U_0 [\psi(a)]^2. \tag{4}$$

To find $\psi(a)$, we turn to the well-known solution of a rectangular well of finite depth ([1], pp. 81-83).

The ψ-function has the following form (we are interested only in the case $U_1 = U_2 \equiv U_0$, and m and E are the mass and energy of the particle):

$$\left.\begin{aligned} &\psi(x) = c_1 e^{\varkappa x} \qquad (x \leqslant 0), \\ &\text{where} \\ &\varkappa = \sqrt{\frac{2m}{\hbar^2}(U_0 - E)}, \end{aligned}\right\} \tag{5}$$

$$\left.\begin{aligned} &\psi(x) = c \sin(kx + \delta) \qquad (0 \leqslant x \leqslant a), \\ &\text{where} \\ &k = \sqrt{\frac{2mE}{\hbar^2}}, \\ &\sin(ka + \delta) = -\sin\delta = -\frac{\hbar k}{\sqrt{2mU_0}}, \end{aligned}\right\} \tag{6}$$

$$\psi(x) = c_2 e^{-\varkappa x} \qquad (x \geqslant a). \tag{5'}$$

According to (6), the value of $\psi(a)$, with which we are concerned, is

$$\psi(a) = c \sin(ka + \delta) = -c \frac{\hbar k}{\sqrt{2mU_0}}. \tag{7}$$

Equation (2) implies that the ψ-function must be normalized. From this requirement, it is immediately possible to determine the coefficient c, if it is considered that in the normalization integral $\int_{-\infty}^{\infty} [\psi(x)]^2 dx = 1$ only the region $0 \leqslant x \leqslant a$ is important.

Indeed, outside this region, in accordance with (5) and (5') the ψ-function decreases exponentially to a negligible value over a

---

*Indeed, from (1) we have $(\varepsilon \to 0)$;

$$\int_{a-\varepsilon}^{a+\varepsilon} f(x)\, dx = U(a + \varepsilon) - U(a - \varepsilon) = U_0.$$

The same obviously follows from (3).

very small distance of the order of $\frac{1}{\varkappa} \approx \frac{\hbar}{\sqrt{2mU_0}}$ (we remember that we are going to take the limit $U_0 \to \infty$ and thus we can neglect the finite E relative to U_0). Therefore, the contribution of the regions $x \leqslant 0$ and $x \geqslant a$ to the total probability $\int_{-\infty}^{\infty} \psi^2 \, dx$ is neglibibly small.

Thus

$$1 = \int_{-\infty}^{\infty} [\psi(x)]^2 \, dx \approx \int_0^a [\psi(x)]^2 \, dx = c^2 \int_0^a \sin^2(kx + \delta) \, dx =$$

$$= c^2 \left[\frac{a}{2} - \frac{1}{2k} \sin ka \cdot \cos(ka + 2\delta)\right]. \tag{8}$$

Let us now take the limit $U_0 \to \infty$.

According to (6), as $U_0 \to \infty$ we have: $\delta \to n\pi$, $(ka + \delta) \to n_1\pi$, and consequently $ka \to (n_1 - n)\pi$ (where n and n_1 are integers). Thus, the last term in (8) tends toward zero.

Indeed,

$$\frac{1}{2k} \sin ka \cos(ka + 2\pi n) = \frac{1}{4k} \sin 2ka \to \frac{1}{4k} \sin[2\pi(n_1 - n)] = 0.$$

Consequently, as we would expect for a well with $U_0 = \infty$, we obtain

$$c = \sqrt{\frac{2}{a}}. \tag{9}$$

Using (9), (7), (6), and (4), we finally find

$$\bar{f} = \frac{2E}{a}. \tag{10}$$

U_0 has dropped from the result, showing the legitimacy of taking the limit $U_0 \to \infty$.

Of course, the force $\bar{f}$ has been obtained with the correct sign (for the right wall of the well, $\bar{f} > 0$).*

We note that equation (10), which does not contain $\hbar$ explicitly, remains exactly the same in classical mechanics. Indeed, in

---

*The average force acting on both walls is obviously equal to zero. Indeed, the operator for this total force is

$$U_0 \{\delta(x - a) - \delta(x)\}.$$

Hence, in consideration of the symmetry of the problem,

$$\bar{f} = U_0 \{[\psi(a)]^2 - [\psi(0)]^2\} = 0.$$

This result is correct for finite motion with any type of potential energy.

classical mechanics, $\bar{f}_{cl}$ (the force averaged over time!) is equal to the product of the impulse imparted to the wall by the particle in a single impact ($2mv$) and the number of impacts per unit time $\frac{v}{2a}$ (v is the velocity of the particle):

$$\bar{f}_{cl} = 2mv \cdot \frac{v}{2a} = \frac{2E}{a}.$$

12. To find the probability distribution, we expand the ψ-function of the given nonstationary state into a series of wave functions ψ_n of the stationary states in the well

$$\psi(x) = \sum_{n=1}^{\infty} c_n \psi_n(x), \qquad (1)$$

where

$$\psi_n(x) = \sqrt{\frac{2}{a}} \sin \frac{\pi n}{a} x \qquad (n = 1,\ 2,\ 3,\ \ldots). \qquad (2)$$

The probability of finding the particle in the n-th level is

$$w_n = |c_n|^2 = \left| \int_0^a \psi(x) \psi_n^*(x)\, dx \right|^2. \qquad (3)$$

At the same time,

$$\sum_{n=1}^{\infty} w_n = \int_0^a |\psi(x)|^2 dx.$$

To obtain normalized probabilities w_n, we normalize the initial ψ-function. This is done by taking $A^2 = \left[\int_0^a x^2 (a - x)^2 dx \right]^{-1} = 30a^{-5}$.

Substituting ψ and ψ_n into (3), we have

$$w_n = \frac{30}{a^5} \cdot \frac{2}{a} \left[\int_0^a x(a - x) \sin \frac{\pi n x}{a} dx \right]^2.$$

Computing the integral, we finally find

$$w_n = \frac{240}{(\pi n)^6} [1 - (-1)^n]^2. \qquad (4)$$

These probabilities $w_n = c_n^2$ are different from zero only for $n = 1, 3, 5, \ldots$. According to (2), these values of n correspond to even functions $\psi_n(x)$ (relative to the center of the well $x=\frac{a}{2}$). Thus, the superposition (1) contains only even states (as is required because of the symmetry of the initial ψ-function relative to $x=\frac{a}{2}$).

Let us verify that the probabilities w_n are normalized.

Using the equation ([13], pp. 21, 444)

$$\sum_{k=1}^{\infty}\frac{1}{(2k-1)^{2m}}=\frac{(2^{2m}-1)\,\pi^{2m}}{2\cdot(2m)!}\,|B_{2m}|, \tag{5}$$

where B_{2m} are the so-called Bernoulli numbers, we have (for the case under consideration, $2m=6$, $B_{2m}=B_6=\frac{1}{42}$):

$$\sum_{n=1}^{\infty}w_n=\frac{240}{\pi^6}\cdot 2^2\sum_{n=1,3,5,\ldots}^{\infty}\frac{1}{n^6}=\frac{960}{\pi^6}\sum_{k=1}^{\infty}\frac{1}{(2k-1)^6}=$$

$$=\frac{960}{\pi^6}\cdot\frac{(2^6-1)\,\pi^6}{2\cdot 6!}\cdot\frac{1}{42}=1,$$

which is what was required.

According to (4), the probability of finding the particle in an even level corresponding to the quantum number n decreases rapidly as n increases. The probability of finding it in the ground state ($n=1$) is

$$w_1=\frac{240}{\pi^6}\cdot 2^2\approx 0.999,$$

so that the total probability of finding it in all the excited levels ($n=3, 5, \ldots$) is only 0.001. This is connected with the fact that the initial ψ-function is extremely close to the ψ-function for the ground state of the particle in the well

$$\psi_1=\sqrt{\frac{2}{a}}\sin\frac{\pi x}{a}.$$

Thus, we can say that the state we are considering is "almost stationary."*

The energy levels of the particle in this well are given by the expression

$$E_n=\frac{\pi^2\hbar^2}{2\mu a^2}n^2 \qquad (n=1,\ 2,\ 3,\ \ldots). \tag{6}$$

---

*We introduce this term for this problem alone. It should not be confused with the generally accepted term "quasi-stationary state," the meaning of which is entirely different ([6], Sections 66, 97).

According to (4) and (6), the average energy of the particle in the nonstationary state we are considering is

$$\overline{E}=\sum_{n=1}^{\infty}E_n w_n=\frac{\pi^2\hbar^2}{2\mu a^2}\cdot\frac{240\cdot 2^2}{\pi^6}\sum_{n=1,3,5,\ldots}^{\infty}\frac{1}{n^4}.$$

Using (5), we find $\left(2m=4,\ B_4=-\frac{1}{30}\right)$: $\sum\limits_{n=1,3,5,\ldots}^{\infty}\frac{1}{n^4}=\frac{\pi^4}{96}$; therefore,

$$\overline{E}=\frac{\pi^2\hbar^2}{2\mu a^2}\cdot\frac{10}{\pi^2}\approx 1{,}014E_1, \tag{7}$$

where E_1 is the energy of the ground state.

The same equation (7) is naturally obtained by averaging the Hamiltonian $\hat{H}=\hat{T}+U$ over the normalized ψ-function

$$\overline{E}=\int\psi^*\hat{H}\psi\,dx=-\frac{\hbar^2}{2\mu}\int_0^a\psi\frac{d^2\psi}{dx^2}dx=\frac{\hbar^2a^3}{6\mu}A^2=\frac{5\hbar^2}{\mu a^2}. \tag{7'}$$

In the given state, the mean square energy of the particle is

$$\overline{E^2}=\sum_{n=1}^{\infty}E_n^2w_n=\left(\frac{\pi^2\hbar^2}{2\mu a^2}\right)^2\cdot\frac{960}{\pi^6}\sum_{n=1,3,5,\ldots}^{\infty}\frac{1}{n^2}=30\left(\frac{\hbar^2}{\mu a^2}\right)^2. \tag{8}$$

From (7′) and (8), the standard deviation of the energy is

$$\Delta E=\sqrt{\overline{(E-\overline{E})^2}}=\sqrt{\overline{E^2}-(\overline{E})^2}=\sqrt{5}\frac{\hbar^2}{\mu a^2}, \tag{9}$$

which represents a quantity comparable with $\overline{E}\approx E_1$.

This relatively large standard deviation is obviously a consequence of the appreciable contribution of the excited levels to the magnitude of $\overline{E^2}$ (as a consequence of the fact that $E_n^2\sim n^4$).

13. 1. The probability which we have to determine is equal to the sum over M_z of the squared modulus of the wave function of the given state (free motion with a momentum $\boldsymbol{p}=\hbar\boldsymbol{k}$) written in the $(r,\ M^2,\ M_z)$-space. This wave function is the corresponding coefficient in the expansion of the plane wave $A\cdot e^{ikr}$ (i.e., the ψ-function in the position or $\boldsymbol{r}$-space) into those functions in the $\boldsymbol{r}$-space which are simultaneously eigenfunctions of the three operators $\hat{r}$, $\hat{M}^2$, and $\hat{M}_z$.

We know that this expansion exists. Indeed, all three of these operators are independent and commute with one another. This is seen most easily by writing them in spherical coordinates:

$$\hat{r}=r,\ \hat{M}^2=-\hbar^2\left[\frac{1}{\sin\theta}\frac{\partial}{\partial\theta}\left(\sin\theta\frac{\partial}{\partial\theta}\right)+\frac{1}{\sin^2\theta}\frac{\partial^2}{\partial\varphi^2}\right],$$

$$\hat{M}_z=\frac{\hbar}{i}\frac{\partial}{\partial\varphi};$$

Therefore, these operators correspond to a complete system of simultaneous eigenfunctions.

It is easily seen that the required eigenfunction of $\hat{r}$, $\hat{M}^2$, $\hat{M}_z$ corresponding to the eigenvalues $r=r_0$, $M^2=\hbar^2 l(l+1)$, $M_z=\hbar m$ is in the (r, θ, φ)-space

$$\psi_{r_0, l, m}(r, \theta, \varphi)=\frac{1}{r_0}\delta(r-r_0)\,Y_{lm}(\theta, \varphi), \tag{1}$$

where $Y_{lm}(\theta, \varphi)$ is a spherical harmonic normalized to unity with respect to $d\Omega$.

Indeed, a solution of the equations

$$rR_{r_0}(r)=r_0R_{r_0}(r) \quad\text{and}\quad (r-r_0)R_{r_0}(r)=0$$

is $R_{r_0}(r)=\text{const}\cdot\delta(r-r_0)$. The constant is taken equal to $\frac{1}{r_0}$ from the normalization requirement

$$\int_0^\infty R_{r_0}(r)R_{r_0'}(r)r^2\,dr=\delta(r_0'-r_0).$$

The functions (1) satisfy the orthogonality and normalization requirements

$$\int_0^{2\pi}\int_0^{\pi}\int_0^{\infty}\psi^*_{r_0, l, m}\psi_{r_0', l', m'}r^2\,dr\sin\theta\,d\theta\,d\varphi=\delta(r_0-r_0')\,\delta_{ll'}\delta_{mm'}. \tag{2}$$

Directing the polar axis of our coordinate system (r, θ, φ) along $\boldsymbol{k}$, we can write the initial ψ-function as a superposition of functions of the type of (1)

$$Ae^{ikr}=Ae^{ikr\cos\theta}=\int_0^\infty\sum_{l=0}^{\infty}\sum_{m=-l}^{l}c_{r', l, m}\psi_{r', l, m}(r, \theta, \varphi)\,dr'. \tag{3}$$

The set of coefficients $c_{r, l, m}\equiv c_{l, m}(r)$ for all possible r, l, and m is the ψ-function of a state with definite $\boldsymbol{p}$ in the (r, M^2, M_z)-space.

The probability which we were to determine is, in accordance with the selection of the constant A (see below):

$$W_l(r)\,dr=\sum_{m=-l}^{l}|c_{l, m}(r)|^2\,dr=|c_{l, 0}(r)|^2\,dr.$$

In this equation, we have used the fact that, in our superposition, $c_{l, m}(r)\neq 0$ only for $m=0$.

Indeed, since the left member of (3) does not depend on the azimuth φ, the right member too can contain only functions which are independent of φ, i.e., functions with $m=0$.*

Substituting the explicit form of the functions into (3) from (1), integrating over dr', and considering that $Y_{l0}(\theta)=\sqrt{\frac{2l+1}{4\pi}}P_l(\cos\theta)$, where P_l is a Legendre polynomial, we have

$$Ae^{ikr\cos\theta}=\frac{1}{r}\sum_{l=0}^{\infty}\sqrt{\frac{2l+1}{4\pi}}\,c_{l,0}(r)\,P_l(\cos\theta). \tag{4}$$

Comparing (4) with the well-known formula for the expansion of a plane wave into Legendre polynomials [10] ([6], p. 318)

$$e^{ikr\cos\theta}=\sum_{l=0}^{\infty}(2l+1)\,i^l\sqrt{\frac{\pi}{2kr}}\,J_{l+\frac{1}{2}}(kr)\,P_l(\cos\theta), \tag{5}$$

where $J_{l+\frac{1}{2}}(kr)$ is a Bessel function of the first kind of the order $\left(l+\frac{1}{2}\right)$, we find

$$c_{l,0}(r)=A\cdot i^l\sqrt{(2l+1)\frac{2\pi^2 r}{k}}\,J_{l+\frac{1}{2}}(kr), \tag{6}$$

Hence, we obtain the probability of finding the particle at a distance r (within the interval dr) from the origin of coordinates, with a square of the total angular momentum $M^2=\hbar^2 l(l+1)$ relative to this origin:

$$W_l(r)\,dr=|c_{l,0}(r)|^2\,dr=|A|^2\frac{(2l+1)\,2\pi^2}{k}\left[J_{l+\frac{1}{2}}(kr)\right]^2 r\,dr.$$

In particular, in normalizing the plane wave Ae^{ikr} to $\delta(\boldsymbol{k}'-\boldsymbol{k})$, when $A=\frac{1}{(2\pi)^{3/2}}$,

$$W_l(r)\,dr=\frac{2l+1}{4\pi k}\left[J_{l+\frac{1}{2}}(kr)\right]^2 r\,dr. \tag{7}$$

---

*This corresponds to the fact that the plane wave $e^{ikr}=e^{ikr\cos\theta}$ is the eigenfunction of $\hat{M}_z=\frac{\hbar}{i}\frac{\partial}{\partial\varphi}$, corresponding to the eigenvalue $\frac{M_z}{\hbar}=m=0$.

As we know, for $kr \ll 1$,

$$J_{l+\frac{1}{2}}(kr) \approx \sqrt{\frac{2}{\pi}} \frac{(kr)^{l+\frac{1}{2}}}{1\cdot 3\cdot 5 \dots (2l+1)},$$

while for $kr \gg 1$ (and $kr \gg l$)

$$J_{l+\frac{1}{2}}(kr) \approx \sqrt{\frac{2}{\pi kr}} \sin\left(kr - \frac{l\pi}{2}\right).$$

In accordance with this, for a given l, the probability (7) behaves as $(kr)^{2l} r^2$ for small r (the effect of centrifugal repulsion). As we would expect, as $r \to 0$, $W_l(r)$ is smaller, the smaller is k. For large r, the probability (7) behaves as $\sin^2\left(kr - \frac{l\pi}{2}\right)$, and therefore $\int_0^\infty W_l(r)\,dr = \infty$ for any l.

2. Let us verify that the normalization is preserved in changing from the $\boldsymbol{r}$-space [the $(2\pi)^{-3/2} e^{i\boldsymbol{kr}}$ wave function] to the (r, l, m)-space [the wave function $c_{l,m}(r)$].

Since $\frac{1}{(2\pi)^3} \int e^{-i\boldsymbol{kr}} e^{i\boldsymbol{k'r}} d\boldsymbol{r} = \delta(\boldsymbol{k}' - \boldsymbol{k})$, the following condition must also be satisfied:

$$\sum_{l=0}^{\infty} \sum_{m=-l}^{l} \int_0^\infty c^*_{l,m}(r)\, c'_{l,m}(r)\, dr = \delta(\boldsymbol{k}' - \boldsymbol{k}). \tag{8}$$

Here, $c'_{l,m}(r)$ denotes the wave function in the (r, l, m)-space corresponding to the function $(2\pi)^{-3/2} e^{i\boldsymbol{k'r}}$ in the $\boldsymbol{r}$-space [cf. (3)]

$$\frac{1}{(2\pi)^{3/2}} e^{i\boldsymbol{k'r}} = \frac{1}{(2\pi)^{3/2}} e^{ik'r\cos\theta'} =$$

$$= \int_0^\infty \sum_{l=0}^{\infty} \sum_{m=-l}^{l} c'_{l,m}(r')\, \psi_{r',l,m}(r, \theta, \varphi)\, dr'. \tag{9}$$

Here, on the right, are the functions (1) of the previous coordinates (r, θ, φ), whose polar axis is the $\boldsymbol{k}$-direction [according to the definition of the (r, l, m)-space we have selected, in which, in particular, M^2 and M_z are independent variables relative to the fixed coordinate system with a polar axis $\boldsymbol{k}$]. On the left is the angle θ' between the radius vector $\boldsymbol{r}$ and $\boldsymbol{k}'$.

We have the identity

$$\cos\theta' = \cos\theta\cos\alpha + \sin\theta\sin\alpha\cos\chi,$$

where α is the angle between $\boldsymbol{k}'$ and $\boldsymbol{k}$, and χ is the angle between the planes $(\boldsymbol{r}, \boldsymbol{k})$ and $(\boldsymbol{k}', \boldsymbol{k})$, In addition (see [1], p. 555)

$$P_l(\cos\theta') = P_l(\cos\theta)P_l(\cos\alpha) + \\ + 2\sum_{m=1}^{l}\frac{(l-m)!}{(l+m)!}P_l^{(m)}(\cos\theta)P_l^{(m)}(\cos\alpha)\cos m\chi. \tag{10}$$

Since $c_{l,m} = 0$ for $m \neq 0$, the left member of (8) reduces to

$$\sum_{l=0}^{\infty}\int_0^{\infty} c_{l,0}^*(r)\,c'_{l,0}(r)\,dr,$$

Thus, it is only necessary to find $c'_{l,0}(r)$. Multiplying both sides of equation (9) by $\psi^*_{r'',l,0}\ (r, \theta, \varphi)\ r^2 dr \sin\ \theta\, d\theta\, d\varphi$ and integrating throughout $\boldsymbol{r}$-space, we obtain, using (2):

$$c'_{l,0}(r'') = \frac{1}{(2\pi)^{3/2}}\int_0^{2\pi}\int_0^{\pi}\int_0^{\infty} e^{ik'r\cos\theta'}\psi^*_{r'',l,0}(r, \theta, \varphi)\,r^2\sin\theta\,dr\,d\theta\,d\varphi.$$

This integral is easily evaluated, if we substitute

$$\psi^* = \frac{1}{r''}\delta(r-r'')Y_{l0}(\theta, \varphi) = \frac{1}{r''}\delta(r-r'')\sqrt{\frac{2l+1}{4\pi}}P_l(\cos\theta),$$

replace $e^{ik'r\cos\theta'}$ by its expansion (5) into the polynomials $P_l(\cos\theta')$, and use the addition theorem (10).

If we select the $(\boldsymbol{k}', \boldsymbol{k})$-plane as the initial plane of the azimuth φ, we have $\chi = \varphi$. Then, in all the sums (10) (for each l), after integration over φ, only the first terms are left, while all the other terms (with $m \neq 0$) disappear, since $\int_0^{2\pi}\cos m\varphi\,d\varphi = 0$.

Then, using the orthogonality and normalization requirement

$$\int_0^{\pi} P_l(\cos\theta)P_{l'}(\cos\theta)\sin\theta\,d\theta = \frac{2}{2l+1}\delta_{ll'},$$

we obtain:

$$c'_{l,0}(r) = \sqrt{\frac{r}{4\pi k'}}\sqrt{2l+1}\,i^l J_{l+\frac{1}{2}}(k'r)P_l(\cos\alpha). \tag{11}$$

As we expect, for $\boldsymbol{k}' = \boldsymbol{k}$ (i.e., for $k' = k$ and $\alpha = 0$), this expression becomes $c_{l,0}(r)$ [cf. (6), $A = \frac{1}{(2\pi)^{3/2}}$].

In computing the normalization sum

$$\sum_{l=0}^{\infty}\int_0^{\infty} c^*_{l,0}(r)\, c'_{l,0}(r)\, dr =$$

$$= \sum_{l=0}^{\infty}(2l+1)\frac{P_l(\cos\alpha)}{4\pi\sqrt{kk'}}\int_0^{\infty} J_{l+\frac{1}{2}}(kr)\, J_{l+\frac{1}{2}}(k'r)\, r\, dr$$

we note that the integral in it is proportional to $\delta(k'-k)$.

Indeed, for $k'=k$, it diverges, while for $k'\neq k$, it is equal to zero, since the radial functions of free motion, having the same total angular momentum l but different energies, are mutually orthogonal:

$$\int_0^{\infty} R_{k'l}R_{kl}r^2\, dr = 0\,^* \qquad (k'\neq k).$$

To compute the coefficient of the δ-function, we shall use, in the entire region of integration over r, the asymptotic expression

$$J_{l+\frac{1}{2}}(kr)\approx\sqrt{\frac{2}{\pi kr}}\sin\left(kr-\frac{l\pi}{2}\right)$$

[and likewise for $J_{l+\frac{1}{2}}(k'r)$]. This is legitimate, since it means neglecting a finite quantity relative to an infinitely large quantity (in view of the fact that, as $k'\to k$ the integral diverges at the upper limit).

Thus, if we drop (for the same reason) the nondivergent integral $\int_0^{\infty}\cos[(k+k')r-l\pi]\, dr$ and use the equation

$$\delta(\beta)=\frac{1}{2\pi}\int_{-\infty}^{\infty} e^{i\beta x}\, dx=\frac{1}{\pi}\int_0^{\infty}\cos\beta x\, dx,$$

---

*Indeed, the function $R_{kl}(r)$ satisfies the equation $R''_{kl}+\frac{2}{r}R'_{kl}+\left[k^2-\frac{l(l+1)}{r^2}\right]R_{kl}=0$, and consequently it is connected with $J_{l+\frac{1}{2}}(kr)$ by the relationship $R_{kl}(r)=\frac{\text{const}}{\sqrt{r}}J_{l+\frac{1}{2}}(kr)$ (as is easily verified).

we obtain (cf. [12]):

$$\int_0^\infty J_{l+\frac{1}{2}}(kr)\, J_{l+\frac{1}{2}}(k'r)\, r\, dr = \frac{2}{\pi\sqrt{kk'}}\int_0^\infty \sin\left(kr - \frac{l\pi}{2}\right)\times$$

$$\times \sin\left(k'r - \frac{l\pi}{2}\right) dr = \frac{1}{\pi\sqrt{kk'}}\int_0^\infty \cos\left[(k'-k)\, r\right] dr = \frac{1}{\sqrt{kk'}}\delta(k'-k).$$

Finally, using the easily verifiable equation*

$$\sum_{l=0}^{\infty}(2l+1)\, P_l(\cos\alpha) = 4\delta(1-\cos\alpha)$$

we find

$$\sum_{l=0}^{\infty}\int_0^\infty c^*_{l,0}(r)\, c'_{l,0}(r)\, dr = \frac{1}{\pi kk'}\delta(k'-k)\,\delta(1-\cos\alpha).$$

This is what was required, since the right member is equal to $\delta(\boldsymbol{k}'-\boldsymbol{k})$, since we obtain unity as a result of multiplying this member by $d\boldsymbol{k}' = k'^2 dk' \cdot 2\pi \sin\alpha\, d\alpha$ and integrating it throughout the entire $\boldsymbol{k}'$-space.

14. In the position space, the wave function for the given state of the particle is

$$\psi_{nlm}(\boldsymbol{r}) = R_{nl}(r)\, Y_{lm}(\theta, \varphi), \tag{1}$$

where $R_{nl}(r)$ is the radial function, the form of which is determined by the form of the potential energy of the particle $U(r)$; and $Y_{lm}(\theta, \varphi)$ is a spherical harmonic of the angles θ and φ of the radius vector $\boldsymbol{r}$ of the particle in a fixed coordinate system K, whose origin $(r \equiv 0)$ is selected at the center force, and whose polar axis (z) is taken along the "quantization axis" of the M_z-component of angular momentum.

The angular function $Y_{lm}(\theta, \varphi)$ is, like the complete ψ-function (1), an eigenfunction of the operators $\hat{M}^2$ and $\hat{M}_z$, simultaneously corresponding to the eigenvalues $l(l+1)\hbar^2$ and $m\hbar$ respectively:

$$\left.\begin{aligned} \hat{M}^2_{(r)}\, Y_{lm}(\theta, \varphi) &= l(l+1)\,\hbar^2 Y_{lm}(\theta, \varphi), \\ \hat{M}_{z\,(r)} Y_{lm}(\theta, \varphi) &= m\hbar Y_{lm}(\theta, \varphi), \end{aligned}\right\} \tag{2}$$

where the index $(\boldsymbol{r})$ on the operators indicates the space.

---

*See, for instance, [1], p. 456. However, in the equation given there, the coefficient should be 4, rather than 2. This is connected with the fact that this δ-function becomes ∞ at the region of integration, so that its integral is equal to 1/2.

Let us make the assumption (confirmed by computation) that the wave function $G_{nlm}(\boldsymbol{p})$ in the momentum space has a structure analogous to that of (1):

$$G_{nlm}(\boldsymbol{p}) = F_{nl}(p)\, S_{lm}(\theta', \varphi'), \tag{3}$$

where p is the absolute magnitude, and θ' and φ' are the spherical angles of the vector $\boldsymbol{p}$ in the same coordinate system K.

The quantum members n, l, m in (1) and (3) are naturally the same, since they represent a complete set of the quantities (E, M^2 and M_z) which characterize the given physical state of the particle and which are in no way connected with the choice of space (i.e., with the group of independent variables of the ψ-function selected).

The angular function S_{lm} must simultaneously be an eigenfunction of the operators $\hat{M}^2$ and $\hat{M}_z$ taken in the $\boldsymbol{p}$-space; i.e., it must satisfy the equations

$$\left.\begin{aligned} \hat{M}^2_{(\boldsymbol{p})} S_{lm}(\theta', \varphi') &= l(l+1)\,\hbar^2 S_{lm}(\theta', \varphi'), \\ \hat{M}_{z\,(\boldsymbol{p})} S_{lm}(\theta', \varphi') &= m\hbar S_{lm}(\theta', \varphi'). \end{aligned}\right\} \tag{4}$$

Thus, to determine the form of the function $S_{lm}(\theta', \varphi')$,* it is necessary to establish the form of the angular-momentum operators in the $\boldsymbol{p}$-space. For this, we shall use, first of all, the fact that the operators $\hat{\boldsymbol{r}}$ and $\hat{\boldsymbol{p}}$ appear symmetrically (with the exception of the sign) in the expression for the operator $\hat{\boldsymbol{M}}$:

$$\hat{\boldsymbol{M}} = \hat{\boldsymbol{r}} \times \hat{\boldsymbol{p}}, \tag{5}$$

and, second, the fact that they have a "mirror" form (also with the exception of the sign) in canonically conjugate spaces

$$\hat{\boldsymbol{p}}_{(\boldsymbol{r})} = -i\hbar \frac{\partial}{\partial \boldsymbol{r}}, \qquad \hat{\boldsymbol{r}}_{(\boldsymbol{p})} = i\hbar \frac{\partial}{\partial \boldsymbol{p}}. \tag{6}$$

According to (5) and (6), we have*

$$\hat{\boldsymbol{M}}_{(\boldsymbol{r})} = -i\hbar\, \boldsymbol{r} \times \frac{\partial}{\partial \boldsymbol{r}}, \qquad \hat{\boldsymbol{M}}_{(\boldsymbol{p})} = -i\hbar\, \boldsymbol{p} \times \frac{\partial}{\partial \boldsymbol{p}}; \tag{7}$$

i.e., the angular-momentum operators in the $\boldsymbol{d}$-space are expressed in terms of $\boldsymbol{p}$ and $\frac{\partial}{\partial \boldsymbol{p}}$ in exactly the same way as they are expressed

---

*To obtain the second of formulas (7), the equation $\frac{\partial}{\partial \boldsymbol{p}} \times \boldsymbol{p} = -\boldsymbol{p} \times \frac{\partial}{\partial \boldsymbol{p}}$ was used, based on the fact that $\left(\frac{\partial}{\partial \boldsymbol{p}} \times \boldsymbol{p}\right)_x \equiv \frac{\partial}{\partial p_y} p_z - \frac{\partial}{\partial p_z} p_y$, etc.

in terms of $\boldsymbol{r}$ and $\frac{\partial}{\partial \boldsymbol{r}}$ in the $\boldsymbol{r}$-space. In particular, the operators $\hat{M}^2_{(p)}$ and $\hat{M}_{z\,(p)}$, written in the form of the spherical coordinates (θ', φ'), have the usual form

$$\hat{M}^2_{(p)} = -\hbar^2\left[\frac{1}{\sin^2\theta'}\frac{\partial^2}{\partial\varphi'^2} + \frac{1}{\sin\theta'}\frac{\partial}{\partial\theta'}\left(\sin\theta'\frac{\partial}{\partial\theta'}\right)\right], \quad \hat{M}_{z\,(p)} = \frac{\hbar}{i}\frac{\partial}{\partial\varphi'}.$$

Consequently, equations (2) and (4) for the eigenfunctions of the angular momentum in the $\boldsymbol{r}$- and $\boldsymbol{p}$-spaces have the same form, and therefore their solutions coincide:

$$S_{lm}(\theta', \varphi') = Y_{lm}(\theta', \varphi'); \tag{8}$$

i.e., the angular dependence of the ψ-function (3) in the $\boldsymbol{p}$-space is exactly the same as that of the ψ-function (1) in the $\boldsymbol{r}$-space (we remember that the two pairs of spherical angles θ', φ' and θ, φ are taken relative to the same axes).

To determine the form of the function $F_{nl}(p)$, we shall use the relationship between wave functions (1) and (3)

$$G_{nlm}(\boldsymbol{p}) = \frac{1}{(2\pi\hbar)^{3/2}}\int \psi_{nlm}(\boldsymbol{r})\, e^{-\frac{i\boldsymbol{pr}}{\hbar}}\, d\boldsymbol{r}. \tag{9}$$

We denote the angle between $\boldsymbol{r}$ and $\boldsymbol{p}$ by γ. For it, we have the known identity

$$\cos\gamma = \cos\theta\cos\theta' + \sin\theta\sin\theta'\cos(\varphi - \varphi').$$

Substituting (1) into (9) and using the notation $\frac{\boldsymbol{p}}{\hbar} = \boldsymbol{k}$, we have

$$G_{nlm}(\boldsymbol{p}) = \frac{1}{(2\pi\hbar)^{3/2}}\int_0^{2\pi}\int_0^{\pi}\int_0^{\infty} R_{nl}(r)\, Y_{lm}(\theta, \varphi)\times$$

$$\times\, e^{-ikr\cos\gamma}\, r^2 \sin\theta\, dr\, d\theta\, d\varphi. \tag{9'}$$

Taking the complex conjugate of the well-known expansion of a plane wave into Legendre polynomials, we obtain

$$e^{-ikr\cos\gamma} = \sum_{l'=0}^{\infty}(2l'+1)(-i)^{l'}\sqrt{\frac{\pi}{2kr}}\, J_{l'+\frac{1}{2}}(kr)\, P_{l'}(\cos\gamma). \tag{10}$$

We shall use, moreover, the addition theorem ([1], p. 555)

$$P_{l'}(\cos\gamma) = P_{l'}(\cos\theta)\, P_{l'}(\cos\theta') +$$

$$+ 2\sum_{m'=1}^{l'}\frac{(l'-m')!}{(l'+m')!}\, P_{l'}^{m'}(\cos\theta)\, P_{l'}^{m'}(\cos\theta')\cos m'(\varphi - \varphi').$$

We can easily see that this equation can be transformed to a more convenient form

$$P_{l'}(\cos\gamma)=\frac{4\pi}{2l'+1}\sum_{m'=-l'}^{l'} Y^*_{l'm'}(\theta,\ \varphi)\,Y_{l'm'}(\theta',\ \varphi'), \tag{11}$$

where

$$Y_{lm}(\theta,\ \varphi)=\sqrt{\frac{(l-|m|)!\,(2l+1)}{(l+|m|)!\,4\pi}}\,P_l^{|m|}(\cos\theta)\,e^{im\varphi} \tag{12}$$

is a spherical harmonic satisfying the orthonormal condition

$$\int_0^{2\pi}\int_0^{\pi} Y^*_{l'm'}(\theta,\ \varphi)\,Y_{lm}(\theta,\ \varphi)\sin\theta\,d\theta\,d\varphi=\delta_{l'l}\delta_{m'm}. \tag{13}$$

If we substitute (10) and (11) into (9′), change the order of integration and summation, and consider (13), we find

$$G_{nlm}(p)=\frac{4\pi}{(2\pi\hbar)^{3/2}}\int_0^{\infty} dr R_{nl}(r)\,r^2\sqrt{\frac{\pi}{2kr}}\sum_{l'=0}^{\infty}\sum_{m'=-l'}^{l'}(-i)^{l'}J_{l'+\frac{1}{2}}(kr)\times$$

$$\times Y_{l'm'}(\theta',\ \varphi')\int_0^{2\pi}\int_0^{\pi} Y^*_{l'm'}(\theta,\ \varphi)\cdot Y_{lm}(\theta,\ \varphi)\sin\theta\,d\theta\,d\varphi=$$

$$=\frac{4\pi}{(2\pi\hbar)^{3/2}}\int_0^{\infty} dr\,R_{nl}(r)\,r^2\sqrt{\frac{\pi}{2kr}}\sum_{l'=0}^{\infty}\sum_{m'=-l'}^{l'}(-i)^{l'}J_{l'+\frac{1}{2}}(kr)\times$$

$$\times\,Y_{l'm'}(\theta',\ \varphi')\,\delta_{l'l}\delta_{m'm}=$$

$$=\frac{4\pi}{(2\pi\hbar)^{3/2}}\int_0^{\infty} dr\,R_{nl}(r)\,r^2\sqrt{\frac{\pi}{2kr}}(-i)^l J_{l+\frac{1}{2}}(kr)\,Y_{lm}(\theta',\ \varphi'). \tag{14}$$

Thus, we have confirmed the correctness of equations (3) and (8) by direct computation from equation (9). It is now obvious that

$$F_{nl}(p)=\frac{4\pi(-i)^l}{(2\pi\hbar)^{3/2}}\int_0^{\infty}\sqrt{\frac{\pi}{2kr}}\,J_{l+\frac{1}{2}}(kr)\,R_{nl}(r)\,r^2\,dr. \tag{15}$$

Simplifying the numerical coefficient in (15) and transforming again to $p=\hbar k$, we finally have

$$G_{nlm}(p)=F_{nl}(p)\,Y_{lm}(\theta',\ \varphi')=$$

$$=\left\{\frac{(-i)^l}{\hbar\sqrt{p}}\int_0^{\infty} J_{l+\frac{1}{2}}\left(\frac{pr}{\hbar}\right)R_{nl}(r)\,r^{3/2}\,dr\right\}\cdot Y_{lm}(\theta',\ \varphi'). \tag{16}$$

The probability distribution function of the different values of the momentum $\boldsymbol{p}$ in this stationary state is given by the expression

$$w(\boldsymbol{p})\,d\boldsymbol{p} = |G_{nlm}(\boldsymbol{p})|^2\,d\boldsymbol{p}. \tag{17}$$

At the same time, as can easily be verified with equation (9) and the equation $\frac{1}{(2\pi\hbar)^3}\int e^{\frac{i\boldsymbol{p}(\boldsymbol{r}-\boldsymbol{r}')}{\hbar}}\,d\boldsymbol{p} = \delta(\boldsymbol{r}-\boldsymbol{r}')$, the normalization of the function $G(\boldsymbol{p})$ coincides with the normalization of the function $\psi(\boldsymbol{r})$:

$$\int |G_{nlm}(\boldsymbol{p})|^2\,d\boldsymbol{p} = \int |\psi_{nlm}(\boldsymbol{r})|^2\,d\boldsymbol{r}.$$

Thus, according to (1), (16) and (13),

$$\int_0^\infty |F_{nl}(p)|^2 p^2\,dp = \int_0^\infty |R_{nl}(r)|^2 r^2\,dr. \tag{18}$$

15. The probability distribution function which we are looking for is given by equations (16) and (17) of the preceding problem, where, according to the results of problem No. 7 of Chapter II, $R_{nl}(r)$ must be replaced by the function

$$R_{nl}(r) = \left\{\begin{array}{ll} B_{nl}\frac{1}{\sqrt{r}}J_{l+\frac{1}{2}}\left(\lambda_{ln}\frac{r}{a}\right) & (r \leqslant a), \\ 0 & (r \geqslant a). \end{array}\right\} \tag{1}$$

Here, a is the radius of the potential box, λ_{ln} is the n-th root of the Bessel function $J_{l+\frac{1}{2}}$, and B_{nl} is the normalization constant (of no importance for our purposes).

Performing the substitution indicated above, we have

$$w(\boldsymbol{p})\,d\boldsymbol{p} = \frac{B_{nl}^2}{\hbar^2 p}\left\{\int_0^a J_{l+\frac{1}{2}}\left(\frac{pr}{\hbar}\right)J_{l+\frac{1}{2}}\left(\lambda_{ln}\frac{r}{a}\right)r\,dr\right\}^2 \times$$
$$\times |Y_{lm}(\theta', \varphi')|^2 p^2\,dp \sin\theta'\,d\theta'\,d\varphi'. \tag{2}$$

Computing the resulting integral by means of the formula [4, 13]

$$\int x J_p(\alpha x) J_p(\beta x)\,dx = \frac{\beta x J_p(\alpha x) J_{p-1}(\beta x) - \alpha x J_{p-1}(\alpha x) J_p(\beta x)}{\alpha^2 - \beta^2},$$

and introducing, for convenience, the notation

$$\frac{p}{\hbar} = k, \qquad \frac{\lambda_{ln}}{a} = k_{ln}, \tag{3}$$

we have

$$\int_0^a J_{l+\frac{1}{2}}(kr)\,J_{l+\frac{1}{2}}(k_{ln}r)\,r\,dr = \frac{\lambda_{ln}J_{l-\frac{1}{2}}(\lambda_{ln})\,J_{l+\frac{1}{2}}(ka)}{k^2-k_{ln}^2}. \tag{4}$$

Hence, finally,

$$w(\boldsymbol{p})\,d\boldsymbol{p} = w(\boldsymbol{k})\,d\boldsymbol{k} =$$

$$= G_{nl}\left[\frac{J_{l+\frac{1}{2}}(ka)}{k^2-k_{ln}^2}\right]^2 k\,dk\cdot|Y_{lm}(\theta',\ \varphi')|^2\sin\theta'\,d\theta'\,d\varphi', \tag{5}$$

where

$$G_{nl} = [B_{nl}\lambda_{ln}J_{l-\frac{1}{2}}(\lambda_{ln})]^2. \tag{6}$$

The distribution of the directions of the vector $\boldsymbol{p}=\hbar\boldsymbol{k}$ is given by the factor $|Y_{lm}|^2$. This distribution obviously does not depend on the angle φ'; i.e., it is axially symmetric (relative to the quantization axis z), as it should be.

Let us investigate the distribution function $f(k)$ of the absolute values of $k=\frac{p}{\hbar}$.

For $ka \ll 1$, we have

$$J_{l+\frac{1}{2}}(ka)\approx\frac{1}{\Gamma\left(l+\frac{3}{2}\right)}\left(\frac{ka}{2}\right)^{l+\frac{1}{2}},$$

and likewise for $k^2 \ll k_{ln}^2$ (since $k_{ln}a=\lambda_{ln}>1$; see any table of the zeros of the Bessel functions). Accordingly, we obtain from (5)

$$f(k)\,dk \sim k^{2l+2}\,dk \quad (ka \ll 1). \tag{7}$$

In the opposite limiting case, for $ka \gg \lambda_{ln} > 1$ (i.e., $k^2 \gg k_{ln}^2$), we have

$$J_{l+\frac{1}{2}}(ka)\approx\sqrt{\frac{2}{\pi ka}}\sin\left(ka-\frac{l\pi}{2}\right),$$

and therefore

$$f(k)\,dk \sim \frac{\sin^2\left(ka-\frac{l\pi}{2}\right)}{k^4}\,dk \qquad (ka \gg \lambda_{ln}). \tag{8}$$

For values of ka equal to the roots of the function $J_{l+\frac{1}{2}}$ (except the n-th root λ_{ln}), the distribution function $f(k)$ becomes zero according to (5). For $ka=\lambda_{ln}$ (i.e., $k=k_{ln}$), the distribution function $f(k)$ has its greatest maximum ("resonance").* This means that, in measuring the kinetic energy $E=\frac{p^2}{2\mu}$ of a particle in a spherical well, the value $E=\frac{\hbar^2\lambda_{ln}^2}{2\mu a^2}$ will be obtained with greatest probability, this energy being exactly equal to the particle's energy measured from the bottom of the well in the stationary state under consideration (see problem No. 7, Chapter II).

16. From the conditions specified in the problem, the system forms a spherical isotropic oscillator with a frequency

$$\omega=\sqrt{\frac{k}{\mu}},$$

where k is the elastic constant, and $\mu=\frac{m_1m_2}{m_1+m_2}$ is the reduced mass of particles 1 and 2.

The wave function of the moving system is obviously the product of the wave function of the free motion of the system's center of mass**

$$\text{const}\cdot e^{\frac{i}{\hbar}(m_1+m_2)\,\boldsymbol{V}_0\boldsymbol{R}} \tag{1}$$

and the wave function of the ground state of the oscillator in the center-of-mass system (see problem No. 11, Chapter II)

$$\text{const}\cdot e^{-\frac{\mu\omega}{2\hbar}r^2}, \tag{2}$$

where $\boldsymbol{R}$ and $\boldsymbol{r}$ represent the coordinates of the center of mass and the relative coordinates, respectively connected with the coordinates of the particles in the local laboratory system $\boldsymbol{r}_1$ and $\boldsymbol{r}_2$ by the equations

$$\boldsymbol{r}=\boldsymbol{r}_1-\boldsymbol{r}_2,\qquad \boldsymbol{R}=\frac{m_1\boldsymbol{r}_1+m_2\boldsymbol{r}_2}{m_1+m_2}, \tag{3}$$

$$\boldsymbol{r}_1=\boldsymbol{R}+\frac{m_2}{m_1+m_2}\boldsymbol{r},\quad \boldsymbol{r}_2=\boldsymbol{R}-\frac{m_1}{m_1+m_2}\boldsymbol{r}. \tag{3'}$$

---

*We find the value of $f(k)$ at this maximum by using the well-known relation $\frac{dJ_p}{dx}=-\frac{p}{x}J_p+J_{p-1}$, whence, $J'_{l+\frac{1}{2}}(\lambda_{ln})=J_{l-\frac{1}{2}}(\lambda_{ln})$. Consequently, $\lim\limits_{k\to k_{ln}}\frac{J_{l+\frac{1}{2}}(ka)}{k^2-k_{ln}^2}=\frac{aJ_{l-\frac{1}{2}}(\lambda_{ln})}{2k_{ln}}$, and so on.

**From now on, we shall not write out the normalization constants, and introduce instead the normalization directly into the final result.

To find the probability distribution function, it is necessary to transform the wave function of the moving oscillator, which we have written in the $(\boldsymbol{R}, \boldsymbol{r})$-space, to the $(\boldsymbol{p}_1, \boldsymbol{p}_2)$-space, where $\boldsymbol{p}_1$ and $\boldsymbol{p}_2$ are the momenta of the particles in the local laboratory system. According to the general rules of quantum mechanics, the wave function in the $(\boldsymbol{p}_1, \boldsymbol{p}_2)$-space is given by the expression

$$c(\boldsymbol{p}_1, \boldsymbol{p}_2) = \text{const} \int\int \psi(\boldsymbol{r}_1, \boldsymbol{r}_2)\, e^{-\frac{i}{\hbar}(\boldsymbol{p}_1\boldsymbol{r}_1 + \boldsymbol{p}_2\boldsymbol{r}_2)}\, d\boldsymbol{r}_1\, d\boldsymbol{r}_2, \tag{4}$$

where $\psi(\boldsymbol{r}_1, \boldsymbol{r}_2)$ is the product of functions (1) and (2) after they have been transformed to the variables $\boldsymbol{r}_1$ and $\boldsymbol{r}_2$ by means of (3). The integration is taken throughout the entire $(\boldsymbol{r}_1, \boldsymbol{r}_2)$-space.

In integral (4), we transform to the variables $(\boldsymbol{R}, \boldsymbol{r})$* by means of (3′), obtaining

$$c(\boldsymbol{p}_1, \boldsymbol{p}_2) = \text{const} \int e^{\frac{i}{\hbar}\boldsymbol{P}_0\boldsymbol{R} - \frac{i}{\hbar}(\boldsymbol{p}_1 + \boldsymbol{p}_2)\boldsymbol{R}}\, d\boldsymbol{R} \cdot \int e^{-\alpha r^2 - i\boldsymbol{\beta}\boldsymbol{r}}\, d\boldsymbol{r}, \tag{5}$$

where we have used the following notation:

$$\boldsymbol{P}_0 \equiv (m_1 + m_2)\, \boldsymbol{V}_0, \tag{6}$$

$$\alpha \equiv \frac{\mu\omega}{2\hbar}, \tag{6′}$$

$$\boldsymbol{\beta} \equiv \frac{1}{\hbar} \frac{m_2\boldsymbol{p}_1 - m_1\boldsymbol{p}_2}{m_1 + m_2}. \tag{6″}$$

The integral in terms of $d\boldsymbol{R}$ in (5) is obviously equal to

$$(2\pi)^3\, \delta\left(\frac{\boldsymbol{p}_1 + \boldsymbol{p}_2 - \boldsymbol{P}_0}{\hbar}\right) = \hbar\, (2\pi)^3\, \delta(\boldsymbol{p}_1 + \boldsymbol{p}_2 - \boldsymbol{P}_0),$$

while the integral in terms of $d\boldsymbol{r}$ reduces, after transformation to Cartesian coordinates, to the product of three like integrals of the form $\int_{-\infty}^{\infty} e^{-\alpha x^2 - i\beta_x x}\, dx$ (and likewise for y and z). Computing these integrals by means of the well-known formula**

$$\int_{-\infty}^{\infty} e^{-\alpha x^2 \pm i\beta x}\, dx = \sqrt{\frac{\pi}{\alpha}}\, e^{-\frac{\beta^2}{4\alpha}}$$

---

*The Jacobian of the transformation $\left|\frac{\partial(\boldsymbol{r}_1, \boldsymbol{r}_2)}{\partial(\boldsymbol{R}, \boldsymbol{r})}\right|$ is equal to unity, as can be easily verified.

**This formula can be obtained by making the exponent a perfect square, and then using Poisson's integral $\int_{-\infty}^{\infty} e^{-\alpha x^2}\, dx = \sqrt{\frac{\pi}{\alpha}}$.

and considering (6′) and (6″), we finally obtain an expression for (5):

$$c(p_1, p_2) = \text{const} \cdot \delta(p_1 + p_2 - P_0)\, e^{-\frac{1}{2\hbar\mu\omega}\left(\frac{m_2 p_1 - m_1 p_2}{m_1 + m_2}\right)^2}$$

The probability distribution function which we are looking for is determined from the squared modulus of this wave function

$$W(p_1, p_2)\, dp_1\, dp_2 = |c(p_1, p_2)|^2\, dp_1\, dp_2 =$$

$$= \text{const} \cdot \delta^2 (p_1 + p_2 - P_0)\, e^{-\frac{1}{\hbar\mu\omega}\left(\frac{m_2 p_1 - m_1 p_2}{m_1 + m_2}\right)^2} dp_1\, dp_2, \qquad (7)$$

where δ^2 is the square of the δ-function.

The first factor in the probability distribution function (7) obviously expresses the law of conservation of the total momentum of the system, and consequently implies a single-valued relationship between p_1 and p_2:

$$p_1 + p_2 = P_0 \equiv (m_1 + m_2)\, V_0.$$

The second factor gives, as it should, the probability distribution function of the momentum p of the relation motion* for the isotropic oscillator: $e^{-\frac{p^2}{\omega\mu\hbar}}$.

To find the probability distribution function $W_1(p_1)\, dp_1$, of the different values of p_1 independently of p_2, it is necessary to integrate (7) over all p_2. Because of the δ-function, this integration obviously reduces to the substitution of $p_2 = P_0 - p_1$ in the expression

$$\text{const} \cdot \delta(p_1 + p_2 - P_0)\, e^{-\frac{1}{\mu\hbar\omega}\left(\frac{m_2 p_1 - m_1 p_2}{m_1 + m_2}\right)^2} dp_1,$$

This yields

$$W_1(p_1)\, dp_1 = \text{const} \cdot \delta(0)\, e^{-\frac{1}{\mu\hbar\omega}\left(p_1 - \frac{m_1}{m_1 + m_2} P_0\right)^2} dp_1. \qquad (8)$$

The delta function $\delta(0)$ obtained here necessarily had to arise, since the state under consideration lies in a continuous spectrum [cf. (1)], and thus the normalization integral

$$\int\int W(p_1, p_2)\, dp_1\, dp_2 = \int W_1(p_1)\, dp_1 \qquad (9)$$

must diverge. From (8), it is seen that this condition is fulfilled only if $W_1(p_1)$ has an infinite constant factor.

---

*Indeed, $p = \mu(v_1 - v_2) = \frac{m_1 m_2}{m_1 + m_2}(v_1 - v_2) = \frac{m_2 p_1 - m_1 p_2}{m_1 + m_2}$.

To obtain a finite expression for the probability, we form the ratio

$$\frac{W_1(\boldsymbol{p}_1)\,d\boldsymbol{p}_1}{\int W_1(\boldsymbol{p}_1)\,d\boldsymbol{p}_1}$$

(where the integration is taken over all $\boldsymbol{p}_1$), in which the factor $\delta(0)=\infty$ disappears. Using (8) and (6), we find

$$\frac{W_1(\boldsymbol{p}_1)\,d\boldsymbol{p}_1}{\int W_1(\boldsymbol{p}_1)\,d\boldsymbol{p}_1}=\frac{1}{(\pi\mu\hbar\omega)^{3/2}}\,e^{-\frac{1}{\mu\hbar\omega}(\boldsymbol{p}_1-m_1\boldsymbol{V}_0)^2}\,d\boldsymbol{p}_1. \tag{10}$$

In exactly the same way, we obtain the distribution function of the momentum $\boldsymbol{p}_2$:

$$\frac{W_2(\boldsymbol{p}_2)\,d\boldsymbol{p}_2}{\int W_2(\boldsymbol{p}_2)\,d\boldsymbol{p}_2}=\frac{1}{(\pi\mu\hbar\omega)^{3/2}}\,e^{-\frac{1}{\mu\hbar\omega}(\boldsymbol{p}_2-m_2\boldsymbol{V}_0)^2}\,d\boldsymbol{p}_2. \tag{11}$$

Here, obviously, $\int W_2(\boldsymbol{p}_2)\,d\boldsymbol{p}_2=\int W_1(\boldsymbol{p}_1)\,d\boldsymbol{p}_1$ [cf. (9)].

Distribution functions (10) and (11), which are both normalized, have maximums at $\boldsymbol{p}_1=m_1\boldsymbol{V}_0$ and $\boldsymbol{p}_2=m_2\boldsymbol{V}_0$ respectively, as expected.

We also emphasize that, of course,

$$W(\boldsymbol{p}_1,\ \boldsymbol{p}_2)\,d\boldsymbol{p}_1\,d\boldsymbol{p}_2\neq W_1(\boldsymbol{p}_1)\,d\boldsymbol{p}_1\cdot W_2(\boldsymbol{p}_2)\,d\boldsymbol{p}_2$$

[cf. (7), (10), and (11)].

The above inequality expresses the fact that the different values of $\boldsymbol{p}_1$ and $\boldsymbol{p}_2$ are not independent, since, when one of the momenta is given, the equation $\boldsymbol{p}_1+\boldsymbol{p}_2=\boldsymbol{P}_0$ determines uniquely the other.

17. The wave function of the given state has the form (see problem No. 5, Chapter II)

$$\psi_{n_1n_2n_3}(x,\ y,\ z)=\psi_{n_1}(x)\,\psi_{n_2}(y)\,\psi_{n_3}(z), \tag{1}$$

where ([1], p. 86)

$$\psi_{n_1}(x)=\left(\frac{\alpha}{\pi}\right)^{1/4}\frac{1}{\sqrt{2^{n_1}n_1!}}\,e^{-\frac{\alpha x^2}{2}}H_{n_1}(x\sqrt{\alpha})\quad\left(\alpha\equiv\frac{\mu\omega}{\hbar}\right); \tag{2}$$

The expressions for $\psi_{n_2}(y)$ and $\psi_{n_3}(z)$ are analogous.

Function (2) and, consequently, the complete ψ-function are normalized. We substitute into (1) and (2) the specified quantum numbers n_1, n_2, n_3, expand the Hermite polynomials $H_n(x)$ ($H_1=2x$, $H_2=4x^2-2$), and write $r^2=x^2+y^2+z^2$, obtaining

$$\psi_{n_1n_2n_3}(x,\ y,\ z)=\frac{\alpha}{\sqrt{2}}\left(\frac{\alpha}{\pi}\right)^{3/4}e^{-\frac{\alpha r^2}{2}}(4\alpha x^2-2)\,yz. \tag{3}$$

To find the probability distribution function of the possible values of l and m, it is necessary to write the ψ-function (3) in the form of a superposition of functions which are simultaneously eigenfunctions of the operators $\hat{H}$, $\hat{M}^2$ and $\hat{M}_z$. These eigenfunctions, which were found in problem No. 11, Chapter II, have the form

$$\psi_{plm}(r, \theta, \varphi) = R_{pl}(r) Y_{lm}(\theta, \varphi), \tag{4}$$

where Y_{lm} is a spherical harmonic, and R_{pl} is the radial function, which we write out below for specific quantum numbers ($p = 0$, 1, 2, ... is the radial quantum number, determining the number of nodes of the function R_{pl} for finite values of r).

This superposition has the form

$$\psi_{n_1n_2n_3}(x, y, z) = \sum_p \sum_l \sum_m c_{plm}\psi_{plm}(r, \theta, \varphi), \tag{5}$$

where the c_{plm} are constants which must be determined.

The set of coefficients c_{plm} forms the wave function of the given state of the oscillator in the (M^2, M_z)-space. The quantities $|c_{plm}|^2$ give the probabilities of the corresponding values of l and m, i.e., of M^2 and M_z (the value of p is uniquely related to l when the energy is given; see below).

These coefficients c_{plm} can be computed by using the Fourier transform method for expansion (5):

$$c_{plm} = \int \psi_{n_1n_2n_3}(x, y, z)\, \psi^*_{plm}(r, \theta, \varphi)\, dV. \tag{6}$$

However, in the given case of small quantum numbers, it is more convenient to proceed directly from the actual expansion (5), which we shall now simplify.

The energy of the oscillator in the given state is

$$E = \hbar\omega\left(n_1 + n_2 + n_3 + \frac{3}{2}\right) = \hbar\omega\left(4 + \frac{3}{2}\right). \tag{7}$$

On the other hand, in quantizing in spherical coordinates, we had

$$E = \hbar\omega\left(l + 2p + \frac{3}{2}\right). \tag{7'}$$

Since the ψ-function (3) corresponds to a definite value of the energy, its expansion (5) can include only those functions (4) which correspond to this same value of the energy.

Comparing (7) and (7'), we conclude that the suitable functions are the ψ_{plm} with $l + 2p = 4$, i.e., the functions belonging to the following combinations of the quantum numbers: ($p = 2$, $l = 0$), ($p = 1$, $l = 2$), and ($p = 0$, $l = 4$). At the same time, the possible values of m are contained (for a given l) within the range $-l \leqslant m \leqslant l$.

Therefore, in accordance with (4), the expansion (5) becomes

$$\psi_{n_1n_2n_3}(x, y, z) = c_{200}R_{20}(r)Y_{00}(\theta, \varphi) + $$
$$+ R_{12}(r)\sum_{m=-2}^{2} c_{12m}Y_{2m}(\theta, \varphi) + R_{04}(r)\sum_{m=-4}^{4} c_{04m}Y_{4m}(\theta, \varphi). \qquad (8)$$

Since the degree of degeneracy of a level with $n = 4$ ($n \equiv n_1 + n_2 + n_3$) is $\frac{5 \cdot 6}{2} = 15$ (see problem No. 5, Chapter II), the superposition (8) consists of 15 terms.

It is easily seen that, in the specific case which we are considering, where the state of the oscillator is described by the ψ-function (3), the number of nonzero terms in (8) is only six.

Indeed, let us consider the dependence of the ψ-function (3) on the azimuth φ. If we consider that $x = r\sin\theta\cos\varphi$, $y = r\sin\theta\sin\varphi$, $z = r\cos\theta$, and consequently $x^2 \sim \cos^2\varphi = \frac{1}{2} + \frac{1}{4}(e^{2i\varphi} + e^{-2i\varphi})$, $y \sim \sin\varphi = \frac{1}{2i}(e^{i\varphi} - e^{-i\varphi})$ we see that function (3) can be represented by a sum of terms depending on the azimuth, such as $e^{i\varphi}$, $e^{-i\varphi}$, $e^{3i\varphi}$, $e^{-3i\varphi}$. Since, on the other hand, $Y_{lm}(\theta, \varphi) \sim e^{im\varphi}$, we conclude that (8) can contain only terms with $m = \pm 1$ и $m = \pm 3$. Thus,

$$\psi_{n_1n_2n_3}(x, y, z) = R_{12}(r)\left[c_{121}Y_{21}(\theta, \varphi) + c_{12,-1}Y_{2,-1}(\theta, \varphi)\right] + $$
$$+ R_{04}(r)\left[c_{043}Y_{43}(\theta, \varphi) + c_{04,-3}Y_{4,-3}(\theta, \varphi) + \right.$$
$$\left. + c_{041}Y_{41}(\theta, \varphi) + c_{04,-1}Y_{4,-1}(\theta, \varphi)\right]. \qquad (9)$$

Let us write out the functions R_{pl} and Y_{lm} (normalized) which appear in this expansion. From problem No. 11, Chapter II, we have

$$\left.\begin{aligned} R_{12} &= \sqrt{2}\alpha^{7/4}\sqrt{\frac{\frac{7}{2}}{\Gamma\left(\frac{7}{2}\right)}}e^{-\frac{\alpha r^2}{2}}r^2F\left(-1, \frac{7}{2}, \alpha r^2\right) = \\ &= \sqrt{\frac{56}{15\sqrt{\pi}}}\alpha^{7/4}e^{-\frac{\alpha r^2}{2}}r^2\left(1 - \frac{2}{7}\alpha r^2\right), \\ R_{04} &= \alpha^{11/4}\sqrt{\frac{2}{\Gamma\left(\frac{11}{2}\right)}}e^{-\frac{\alpha r^2}{2}}r^4, \end{aligned}\right\} \qquad (10)$$

where

$$\Gamma\left(\frac{11}{2}\right) = \frac{9}{2}\cdot\frac{7}{2}\cdot\frac{5}{2}\cdot\frac{3}{2}\cdot\frac{1}{2}\sqrt{\pi} = \frac{945}{32}\sqrt{\pi}.$$

According to the well-known relations from the theory of spherical harmonics, which we have used repeatedly in previous problems (see also [14]),

$$\left.\begin{aligned} Y_{21} &= Y^*_{2,\,-1} = \sqrt{\frac{15}{8\pi}}\sin\theta\cos\theta e^{i\varphi}, \\ Y_{43} &= Y^*_{4,\,-3} = \frac{3}{4}\sqrt{\frac{35}{4\pi}}\sin^3\theta\cos\theta e^{3i\varphi}, \\ Y_{41} &= Y^*_{4,\,-1} = \frac{3}{4}\sqrt{\frac{5}{4\pi}}(7\cos^3\theta - 3\cos\theta)\sin\theta e^{i\varphi}. \end{aligned}\right\} \quad (11)$$

Transforming the ψ-function (3) into spherical coordinates r, θ, φ, we have

$$\begin{aligned} \psi_{n_1n_2n_3}(x, y, z) &= \\ &= \frac{1}{2\sqrt{2}\pi^{3/4}i}\alpha^{11/4}e^{-\frac{\alpha r^2}{2}}r^4\sin^3\theta\cos\theta\,(e^{i\varphi} - e^{-i\varphi} + e^{3i\varphi} - e^{-3i\varphi}) - \\ &\quad - \frac{1}{\sqrt{2}\pi^{3/4}i}\alpha^{7/4}e^{-\frac{\alpha r^2}{2}}r^2\sin\theta\cos\theta\,(e^{i\varphi} - e^{-i\varphi}). \end{aligned} \quad (12)$$

Expressing the combinations of $\left(\alpha^{11/4}e^{-\frac{\alpha r^2}{2}}r^4\right)$ and $\left(\alpha^{7/4}e^{-\frac{\alpha r^2}{2}}r^2\right)$ appearing here in terms of R_{12} and R_{04}, using (10); collecting terms in the proper way; and substituting for the resulting combinations of angular functions according to equations (11), we obtain, in complete agreement with (9),

$$\begin{aligned} \psi_{n_1n_2n_3}(x, y, z) &= \\ &= i\sqrt{\frac{1}{14}}R_{12}(Y_{21} - Y_{2,\,-1}) - i\sqrt{\frac{3}{8}}R_{04}(Y_{43} - Y_{4,\,-3}) + \\ &\quad + i\sqrt{\frac{3}{56}}R_{04}(Y_{41} - Y_{4,\,-1}). \end{aligned} \quad (13)$$

This equation is the solution of the problem. The squared moduli of the coefficients of expansion (13) give the desired probabilities w_{lm} of the different possible pairs of l and m:

$$\left.\begin{aligned} w_{21} = w_{2,\,-1} = \frac{1}{14}, \qquad w_{43} = w_{4,\,-3} = \frac{3}{8}, \\ w_{4,\,1} = w_{4,\,-1} = \frac{3}{56}. \end{aligned}\right\} \quad (14)$$

Since both members of equation (13) contain only normalized functions, the probability distribution (14) automatically satisfies the normalization condition

$$\sum_l\sum_m w_{lm} = 1.$$

Summing over m for a given l, we find from (14) the probability $w(l)$ of the two possible values of the total angular momentum l:

$$w(2) = \frac{1}{7}, \qquad w(4) = \frac{6}{7}.$$

Thus, in the state under consideration, the average value of the angular momentum $M^2 = l(l+1)\hbar^2$ is

$$\overline{M^2} = \hbar^2 \sum_l l(l+1) w(l) = 18\hbar^2.$$

The average value of the component of angular momentum $M_z = m\hbar$ is obviously equal to zero:

$$\overline{M}_z = \hbar \sum_l \sum_m m w_{lm} = 0.$$

This we would expect on the basis of the fact that the initial ψ-function (3) is real, since this makes the azimuthal component of the probability density equal to zero:

$$j_\varphi = \frac{\hbar}{2mi}\left(\psi^* \frac{\partial \psi}{\partial \varphi} - \psi \frac{\partial \psi^*}{\partial \varphi}\right) = 0.$$

18. The quantization of the hydrogen atom in parabolic coordinates is presented in [1] and [11].

In parabolic coordinates

$$\xi = r + z, \qquad \eta = r - z, \qquad \varphi = \operatorname{arctg} \frac{y}{x} \tag{1}$$

the normalized wave functions of the stationary states in the discrete spectrum have the form [1]*

$$\psi_{n_1 n_2 m}(\xi, \eta, \varphi) = \frac{\sqrt{2}}{n^2} f_{n_1 m}\left(\frac{\xi}{n}\right) f_{n_2 m}\left(\frac{\eta}{n}\right) \frac{e^{im\varphi}}{\sqrt{2\pi}}, \tag{2}$$

where

$$f_{pm}(x) = \frac{1}{|m|!} \sqrt{\frac{(p+|m|)!}{p!}}\, e^{-\frac{x}{2}} x^{\frac{|m|}{2}} F(-p, |m|+1, x), \tag{3}$$

and $n = n_1 + n_2 + |m| + 1$ is the total quantum number.

In these formulas and subsequent ones, we shall use the atomic units: $\mu = 1$, $e = 1$, $\hbar = 1$.

We substitute into (2) and (3) the values of the quantum numbers n_1, n_2 and m, where $n = 1 + m + n_2 + n_1 = 1 + 0 + 0 + 1 = 2$, obtaining for the ψ-function of the given state

$$\psi_{100}(\xi, \eta, \varphi) = \frac{1}{\sqrt{2\pi}} \cdot \frac{1}{2^{3/2}} e^{-\frac{1}{4}(\xi+\eta)} \left(1 - \frac{1}{2}\xi\right). \tag{4}$$

---

*In [1], formula (37.16), there is a misprint — the exponential and power coefficients in front of the confluent hypergeometric function are omitted.

The energy of this state is

$$E = -\frac{1}{2n^2} = -\frac{1}{8}\ \text{A. U.} = -\frac{1}{8}\frac{\mu e^4}{\hbar^2}.$$

1. To find the probability distribution function for z, it is necessary to integrate the squared modulus of the ψ-function (4) over the plane normal to the z-axis (for fixed z). For this, using (1), we first transform (4) to spherical coordinates, and then to cylindrical coordinates ρ, φ, z. This gives

$$|\psi_{100}|^2 = \frac{1}{16\pi} e^{-r}\left(1 - \frac{r+z}{2}\right)^2 = \frac{1}{16\pi} e^{-\sqrt{\rho^2+z^2}}\left(1 - \frac{\sqrt{\rho^2+z^2}+z}{2}\right)^2. \tag{5}$$

According to what we have said above, the distribution along z is

$$w(z)\,dz = dz\int_0^{2\pi}\int_0^{\infty}|\psi_{100}(\rho,\ \varphi,\ z)|^2\rho\,d\rho\,d\varphi.$$

Substituting (5) into this equation and carrying out the elementary integration, we find

$$w(z)\,dz = \frac{1}{8}e^{-|z|}\left\{\left[\left(\frac{|z|+z}{2}\right)^2+\frac{1}{2}\right](|z|+1) - |z|\frac{|z|+z}{2}\right\}dz. \tag{6}$$

In particular, for $z \geqslant 0$ (i.e., for $z = |z|$), we have

$$w_+(z)\,dz = \frac{1}{16}e^{-|z|}(2|z|^3+|z|+1)\,dz, \tag{6'}$$

while for $z \leqslant 0$ (i.e., for $z = -|z|$):

$$w_-(z)\,dz = \frac{1}{16}e^{-|z|}(|z|+1)\,dz. \tag{6''}$$

Comparing (6′) and (6″), we see that, in complete agreement with the general property of quantization in parabolic coordinates [1], the probability distribution function (6) is not symmetric about the plane $z = 0$. Namely, the probability of finding the electron in the half space $z \geqslant 0$ is greater than that of finding it in the half space $z \leqslant 0$ (as it should be for $n_1 > n_2$).

The total probabilities of finding the electron in the half spaces $z \geqslant 0$ and $z \leqslant 0$ respectively are

$$\int_0^{\infty} w_+(z)\,dz = \frac{7}{8}, \qquad \int_{-\infty}^{0} w_-(z)\,dz = \frac{1}{8}.$$

Thus, $\int_{-\infty}^{\infty} w(z)\,dz = 1$, as should follow from the normalization of the ψ-function (2) and (3). The average value of z is

$$\bar{z} = \int_{-\infty}^{\infty} z w(z)\,dz = +3 \text{ A. U.} = +3\frac{\hbar^2}{\mu e^2}.$$

Considering that the charge of the electron is equal to - 1 atomic unit, we can conclude that, in the given state, the atom has a mean dipole moment equal to

$$\bar{d} = \bar{d}_z = -\bar{z} = -3 \text{ A. U.}$$

2. To find the probability distribution of l, we expand the ψ-function (4) of the given state into eigenfunctions of the angular momentum.

Since, in the given state, the energy (E) and the component of angular momentum along the axis of quantization (M_z) have definite values, the above mentioned expansion can contain only eigenfunctions of the angular momentum which belong to the same values of E and M_z. The functions which satisfy this requirement are obviously those eigenfunctions from the "spherical" quantization of a hydrogen atom

$$\psi_{nlm}(r, \theta, \varphi) = R_{nl}(r)\,Y_{lm}(\theta, \varphi) \tag{7}$$

which correspond to the given values of the quantum numbers n and m, namely $n = 2$, $m = 0$ (we recall that both of these quantum numbers appear, both in the quantization in spherical coordinates and in the quantization in parabolic coordinates, and that, in both cases, $E = \frac{1}{2n^2}$ A. U. and $M_z = m$ A. U.). Since, moreover, in the spherical quantization, $l \leqslant n-1$, the expansion of function (4) contains only functions (7) with $l = 1$ and $l = 0$.

Therefore, we have

$$\psi_{100}(\xi, \eta, \varphi) = c_1 R_{21}(r)\,Y_{10}(\theta, \varphi) + c_0 R_{20}(r)\,Y_{00}(\theta, \varphi). \tag{8}$$

Into this equation we substitute function (14) after it has been transformed to spherical coordinates by means of (1)

$$\psi_{100} = \frac{1}{\sqrt{2\pi}} \cdot \frac{1}{2^{3/2}} e^{-\frac{r}{2}} \left[1 - \frac{r}{2}(1 + \cos\theta)\right],$$

as well as the normalized functions ([1], p. 149)

$$R_{21} = \frac{1}{2\sqrt{6}} e^{-\frac{r}{2}} r, \qquad R_{20} = \frac{1}{\sqrt{2}} e^{-\frac{r}{2}}\left(1 - \frac{r}{2}\right),$$

$$Y_{10} = \sqrt{\frac{3}{4\pi}} \cos\theta, \qquad Y_{00} = \frac{1}{\sqrt{4\pi}}.$$

Thus, we obtain the equation

$$1-\frac{r}{2}-\frac{r}{2}\cos\theta=c_0\sqrt{2}-c_0\frac{r}{\sqrt{2}}+c_1\frac{r}{\sqrt{2}}\cos\theta.$$

Since the two sides of this equation, which is obtained from (8), must be satisfied identically (i.e., equal for all r and θ), it is necessary that $c_0\sqrt{2}=1, \frac{c_0}{\sqrt{2}}=\frac{1}{2}, \frac{c_1}{\sqrt{2}}=-\frac{1}{2}$. Whence, $c_0=\frac{1}{\sqrt{2}}$, $c_1=-\frac{1}{\sqrt{2}}$.

According to (8), the squares of these coefficients give the probability $w(l)$ of the possible values of l (0 and 1), namely

$$w(0)=|c_0|^2=\frac{1}{2}, \qquad w(1)=|c_1|^2=\frac{1}{2}. \tag{9}$$

Since we have used normalized wave functions, we have obtained probabilities which are automatically normalized. The mean value of the square of the angular momentum is, according to (9),

$$\overline{M^2}=\sum_{l=0,1} l(l+1)\,w(l)=1 \text{ A. U. } =\hbar^2.$$

19. Introducing the operators $\hat{L}_1$ and $\hat{M}_1$,

$$\hat{L}_1=\hat{L}-\overline{L}, \qquad \hat{M}_1=\hat{M}-\overline{M}, \tag{1}$$

we have

$$(\Delta L)^2=\overline{L_1^2}, \qquad (\Delta M)^2=\overline{M_1^2}. \tag{2}$$

Let us consider the integral

$$J=\int|(\alpha\hat{L}_1-i\hat{M}_1)\psi|^2\,d\tau, \tag{3}$$

which depends on an arbitrary real parameter α (ψ is a wave function, and the integration is taken over all configuration space).

Because the function inside the integral is nonnegative, we have for all α:

$$J(\alpha)\geqslant 0. \tag{4}$$

Rewriting (3) in the form

$$J=\int(\alpha\hat{L}_1-i\hat{M}_1)\psi\cdot(\alpha\hat{L}_1^*+i\hat{M}_1^*)\psi^*\,d\tau,$$

and using self-conjugate property of the operators $\hat{L}_1^*$ and $\hat{M}_1^*$, and also the definition of the average value, we have

$$J = \int \psi^* (\alpha \hat{L}_1 + i\hat{M}_1)(\alpha \hat{L}_1 - i\hat{M}_1)\psi \, d\tau =$$
$$= \int \psi^* (\alpha^2 \hat{L}_1^2 - i\alpha [\hat{L}_1, \hat{M}_1] + \hat{M}_1^2)\psi \, d\tau =$$
$$= \alpha^2 \overline{L_1^2} - i\alpha \overline{[\hat{L}_1, \hat{M}_1]} + \overline{M_1^2}.$$

It is easily seen that $[\hat{L}_1, \hat{M}_1] = [\hat{L}, \hat{M}] \equiv i\hat{K}$. Moreover, considering (2), we obtain

$$J = \alpha^2 (\Delta L)^2 + \alpha \overline{K} + (\Delta M)^2.$$

The condition (4) that this trinomial, which is quadratic in α, be nonnegative, is the inequality

$$4 (\Delta L)^2 (\Delta M)^2 \geqslant (\overline{K})^2,$$

or

$$\Delta L \, \Delta M \geqslant \frac{1}{2} |\overline{K}|,$$

Q.E.D.

20. For simplicity, we shall consider a single particle. Its wave functions in the $\boldsymbol{r}$- and $\boldsymbol{p}$-spaces are connected by the relation

$$\psi(\boldsymbol{r}) = \frac{1}{(2\pi\hbar)^{3/2}} \int g(\boldsymbol{p}) e^{\frac{i\boldsymbol{pr}}{\hbar}} d\boldsymbol{p}. \quad (1)$$

If the ψ-function is even, i.e., $\psi(-\boldsymbol{r}) = \psi(\boldsymbol{r})$, then, according to (1), we have

$$\int g(\boldsymbol{p}) e^{\frac{i\boldsymbol{pr}}{\hbar}} d\boldsymbol{p} = \int g(\boldsymbol{p}) e^{-\frac{i\boldsymbol{pr}}{\hbar}} d\boldsymbol{p}$$

or

$$\int g(\boldsymbol{p}) \sin\left(\frac{\boldsymbol{pr}}{\hbar}\right) d\boldsymbol{p} = 0. \quad (2)$$

Since the two sides of this equation must be satisfied identically (i.e., for all $\boldsymbol{r}$), and since the sine is an odd function, we conclude that the wave function $g(\boldsymbol{p})$ must be even (like ψ):

$$g(-\boldsymbol{p}) = g(\boldsymbol{p}).$$

If the ψ-function is odd, i.e., $\psi(-\boldsymbol{r}) = -\psi(\boldsymbol{r})$, then

$$\int g(\boldsymbol{p}) \cos\left(\frac{\boldsymbol{pr}}{\hbar}\right) d\boldsymbol{p} = 0.$$

Hence, it follows that the function $g(\boldsymbol{p})$ must be odd (like ψ):

$$g(-\boldsymbol{p}) = -g(\boldsymbol{p}).$$

This result clearly characterizes the parity of a state as a physical quantity which is not connected with the choice of space.

An illustration of this statement is provided by problems No. 5, No. 9, and No. 14 of this Chapter (this is easily seen by comparing the parity of the ψ- and g-functions in each of these problems). We note that in the first two of these problems the parity I is equal to $+1$, while in the third problem the parity is $I=(-1)^l$.

21. 1. The wave function of a particle at rest is the eigenfunction of the momentum operator $\hat{p}$ corresponding to the eigenvalue $p=0$.

In the r-space, the eigenfunction of $\hat{p}$ corresponding to the eigenvalue p and normalized to a δ-function has the form

$$\psi_p(r)=\frac{1}{(2\pi\hbar)^{3/2}}e^{\frac{ipr}{\hbar}}. \tag{1}$$

Setting $p=0$ in this expression, we obtain the desired ψ-function

$$\psi_{p=0}(r)=\frac{1}{(2\pi\hbar)^{3/2}}=\text{const}. \tag{1'}$$

This function is completely independent of the coordinates. This corresponds to the fact that, for $p=0$, the deBroglie wavelength of a particle is $\lambdabar=\frac{\hbar}{p}=\infty$.

In the p-space, the equation for an eigenfunction of the operator $\hat{p}=p$ corresponding to the eigenvalue p_0 has the form

$$pg_{p_0}(p)=p_0g_{p_0}(p) \quad \text{or} \quad (p-p_0)\,g_{p_0}(p)=0.$$

Hence, it is seen that, for all $p\neq p_0$, it is necessary that $g_{p_0}(p)=0$.

Considering also the normalization requirement

$$\int g^*_{p_0}(p)\,g_{p'_0}(p)\,dp=\delta(p_0-p'_0),$$

we conclude that

$$g_{p_0}(p)=\delta(p-p_0). \tag{2}$$

Setting $p_0=0$ in this expression, we obtain the wave function for a particle at rest*

$$g_{p_0=0}(p)=\delta(p). \tag{2'}$$

2. In the $\hat{r}$-space, the ψ-function of a localized particle, i.e., the eigenfunction of the radius-vector operator r_0 corresponding to the eigenvalue r, has the form ([1], p. 32)

---

*Wave functions (1′) and (2′), and also (3′) and (4′)(see below), are related by equation (1), p. 124, as they should be.

$$\psi_{r_0}(r) = \delta(r - r_0) \tag{3}$$

This equation has the same form and is derived in the same way as equation (2).

In the p-space, the operator $\hat{r}$ is $i\hbar\frac{\partial}{\partial p}$. Therefore, the equation for the eigenfunction $g_{r_0}(p)$, which we must determine, has the form

$$i\hbar\frac{\partial}{\partial p}g_{r_0}(p) = r_0 g_{r_0}(p).$$

Obviously, the solution of this equation, normalized to a δ-function, is [cf. (1)]

$$g_{r_0}(p) = \frac{1}{(2\pi\hbar)^{3/2}}e^{-\frac{ir_0 p}{\hbar}} \tag{4}$$

In particular, if the particle is localized at the origin of coordinates, then, setting $r_0 = 0$ in formulas (3) and (4), we have [cf. (1') and (2')]

$$\psi_{r_0=0}(r) = \delta(r), \tag{3'}$$

$$g_{r_0=0}(p) = \frac{1}{(2\pi\hbar)^{3/2}} = \text{const.} \tag{4'}$$

22. The eigenvalues of the operators $\hat{M}^2$ and $\hat{M}_z$ are equal to $l(l+1)\hbar^2$ and $m\hbar$ respectively, where $l = 0, 1, 2, \ldots,$ and $-l \leqslant m \leqslant l$.

In any space, the equations for the corresponding eigenfunctions ψ_{lm} have the form

$$\left.\begin{aligned}\hat{M}^2\psi_{lm} &= l(l+1)\hbar^2\psi_{lm},\\ \hat{M}_z\psi_{lm} &= m\hbar\psi_{lm}.\end{aligned}\right\} \tag{1}$$

In the (M^2, M_z)-space, the operation by $\hat{M}^2$ and $\hat{M}_z$ reduces simply to mutiplication by M^2 and M_z. Thus, equations (1) become

$$\left.\begin{aligned}[M^2 - l(l+1)\hbar^2]\,\psi_{lm}(M^2, M_z) &= 0,\\ (M_z - m\hbar)\,\psi_{lm}(M^2, M_z) &= 0,\end{aligned}\right\} \tag{2}$$

where M^2 and M_z are the variables of the selected space.

These equations are easily solved. Thus, from the first equation, it follows that $\psi_{lm} = 0$ for all M^2 not equal to $l(l+1)\hbar^2$. From the second equation, it follows that $\psi_{lm} = 0$ for all M_z not equal to $m\hbar$. Because equations (2) are linear, nonzero values of the function ψ_{lm} [corresponding to the values of the variables $M^2 = l(l+1)\hbar^2$ and $M_z = m\hbar$] can be normalized arbitrarily, say to unity.

Accordingly, introducing the Kronecker delta, we obtain the following expression for the eigenfunctions:

$$\psi_{lm}(M^2, M_z) = \delta_{M^2,\, l(l+1)\hbar^2}\,\delta_{M_z,\, m\hbar}. \tag{3}$$

These functions obviously satisfy the orthonormal condition

$$\sum_{M^2}\sum_{M_z} \psi^*_{lm}(M^2, M_z)\,\psi_{l'm'}(M^2, M_z) = \delta_{ll'}\delta_{mm'},$$

where the summation is taken over all the possible values of the variables M^2 and M_z — in other words, throughout the discrete (M^2, M_z)-space.

23. Let us consider the general case where the system has both a discrete and a continuous spectrum of energy eigenvalues.

We denote the eigenvalues of the energy in the discrete spectrum by $E_1, E_2, \ldots, E_n, \ldots,$ and in the continuous spectrum by ε. We shall use E to denote the energy as the variable of the space.

Repeating the same simple arguments of problems No. 21 and No. 22, we easily find expressions for the eigenfunctions of the Hamiltonian in the E-space corresponding to the eigenvalues E_n and ε respectively:

1) in the discrete spectrum

$$\psi_{E_n}(E) = \delta_{E,\,E_n},$$

these eigenfunctions being orthonormal,

$$\sum_E \psi_{E_n}(E)\,\psi_{E_k}(E) = \delta_{E_n,\,E_k} \equiv \delta_{nk};$$

2) in the continuous spectrum,

$$\psi_\varepsilon(E) = \delta(E - \varepsilon),$$

for which the orthonormal condition is

$$\int \psi_\varepsilon(E)\,\psi_{\varepsilon'}(E)\,dE = \delta(\varepsilon - \varepsilon').$$

24. The eigenfunctions of the operator $\hat{A}$ in the B-space are quantities which are complex conjugates of the eigenfunctions of the operator $\hat{B}$ in the A-space ([11], p. 47 and [1], p. 30).

Let us show the correctness of this "reciprocal relation."

Since it has somewhat different forms for operators with a discrete spectrum of eigenvalues and those with a continuous spectrum, we shall consider both of these cases below.

We shall denote the eigenfunctions of the operator $\hat{A}$ in any representation by ψ, and the eigenfunctions of the operator $\hat{B}$ by φ. We shall denote the eigenvalues of the operators $\hat{A}$ and $\hat{B}$ in the continuous spectrum by a and b, and their eigenvalues in the discrete spectrum by a_i and b_k. We shall write these eigenvalues as indices on the corresponding eigenfunctions. Finally, as usual, we shall write the variable of the space as the argument of the corresponding function.

For the initial space of the wave functions, let us select some arbitrary space. We shall call it the q-space,* and we specify that the variable q has a continuous spectrum of eigenvalues.

Then, following what we have said above, the wave functions used below have the following meanings (we consider first the case where both operators have a continuous spectrum of eigenvalues):

$\psi_a(q)$ — the eigenfunction of the operator $\hat{A}$ corresponding to the eigenvalue a in the q-space,

$\psi_a(b)$ — the same eigenfunction in the B-space;

$\varphi_b(q)$ — the eigenfunction of the operator $\hat{B}$ corresponding to the eigenvalue b in the q-space;

$\varphi_b(a)$ — the same eigenfunction in the A-space.

As we know, the function $\psi_a(b)$ represents a coefficient in the expansion of the function $\psi_a(q)$ into a generalized Fourier integral over the functions $\varphi_b(q)$:

$$\psi_a(q) = \int \psi_a(b)\,\varphi_b(q)\,db. \tag{1}$$

The Fourier transform of this equation is

$$\psi_a(b) = \int \psi_a(q)\,\overset{*}{\varphi}_b(q)\,dq. \tag{2}$$

Conversely, the function $\varphi_b(a)$ represents a coefficient in the expansion of the function $\varphi_b(q)$ into a generalized Fourier integral over the functions $\psi_a(q)$:

$$\varphi_b(q) = \int \varphi_b(a)\,\psi_a(q)\,da, \tag{3}$$

whence,

$$\varphi_b(a) = \int \varphi_b(q)\,\overset{*}{\psi}_a(q)\,dq. \tag{4}$$

Comparing (2) and (4), we arrive at the required "reciprocal relation"

$$\psi_a(b) = \overset{*}{\varphi}_b(a). \tag{5}$$

Let us determine how formulas (1)-(5) change in the case where the two operators $\hat{A}$ and $\hat{B}$ each have a discrete spectrum of eigenvalues.

In this case, we shall be dealing with the functions $\psi_a(q)$ and $\varphi_b(q)$ in place of the functions $\psi_{a_i}(q)$ and $\varphi_{b_k}(q)$ respectively. Instead of (1), we have the expansion of the function $\psi_{a_i}(q)$ into a series of functions $\varphi_{b_k}(q)$:

---

*Of course, the variable q can coincide with one of the variables A or B.

$$\psi_{a_i}(q) = \sum_k C_{b_k}^{a_i} \varphi_{b_k}(q). \tag{1'}$$

The set of coefficients $C_{b_k}^{a_i}$ of this expansion (for all k) represents the eigenfunction of the operator $\hat{A}$ corresponding to the eigenvalue a_i, in the B-space. Symbolically, this can be written in the form of a column

$$\psi_{a_i}(b) \equiv \begin{Vmatrix} C_{b_1}^{a_i} \\ C_{b_2}^{a_i} \\ \vdots \\ C_{b_k}^{a_i} \\ \vdots \end{Vmatrix}.$$

Using the Fourier transform of the expansion (1′), we have

$$C_{b_k}^{a_i} = \int \psi_{a_i}(q) \varphi_{b_k}^*(q)\, dq. \tag{2'}$$

Likewise, the eigenfunction $\varphi_{b_k}(a)$ of the operator $\hat{B}$ corresponding to the eigenvalue b_k in the A-space is given by the set of coefficients $D_{a_i}^{b_k}$ (for all i) of the expansion of the function $\varphi_{b_k}(q)$ into a series of the functions $\psi_{a_i}(q)$:

$$\varphi_{b_k}(q) = \sum_i D_{a_i}^{b_k} \psi_{a_i}(q), \tag{3'}$$

whence,

$$D_{a_i}^{b_k} = \int \varphi_{b_k}(q) \psi_{a_i}^*(q)\, dq. \tag{4'}$$

Comparing (2′) with (4′), we obtain

$$C_{b_k}^{a_i} = \left(D_{a_i}^{b_k}\right)^*, \tag{5'}$$

This is the analogue of equation (5) for the case of a discrete spectrum.

The reciprocal relations (5) and (5′) which we have obtained are easily extended to the case where one of the operators $\hat{A}$ and $\hat{B}$ has a continuous spectrum of eigenvalues, and the other has a discrete spectrum. Furthermore, there is obviously no difficulty in extending these relations to the case where each of the symbols $\hat{A}$ and $\hat{B}$ stands for a complete set of commuting operators, rather than for a single operator.

Equations (5) and (5′) have a simple physical meaning. Indeed, in the case of a continuous spectrum, $|\psi_a(b)|^2\, db$ gives the probability of finding the variable b in the interval between b and $b + db$ when measuring it in the state ψ_a, while $|\varphi_b(a)|^2\, da$ gives the probability of finding the variable a in the interval from a to $a+da$ when measuring it in the state φ_b. Consequently, the equation

$$|\psi_a(b)|^2 = |\varphi_b(a)|^2, \tag{6}$$

which is obtained from (5) by taking the squared modulus, means that the corresponding probability densities are equal.

Similarly, in the case of a discrete spectrum, the quantity $\left|C^{a_i}_{b_k}\right|^2$ [see (1′)] gives the probability of obtaining the eigenvalue b_k in measuring the quantity B in the state ψ_{a_i}, while the quantity $\left|D^{b_k}_{a_i}\right|^2$ [see (3′)] gives the probability of obtaining the eigenvalue a_i in measuring the quantity A in the state φ_{b_k}. Thus, the equation

$$\left|C^{a_i}_{b_k}\right|^2 = \left|D^{b_k}_{a_i}\right|^2, \tag{6′}$$

obtained from (5′), means that the above-mentioned probabilities are equal to each other. We can say that the "probability of occurrence" ("share") of the eigenvalue b_k in a state with a definite value of A equal to a_i is equal to the "probability of occurence" ("share") of the eigenvalue a_i in a state with a definite value of B equal to b_k.

We note that equations (5) and (5′) or (6) and (6′) have a simple geometric analogue, namely that the scalar product of two vectors is commutative. This statement becomes clear if it is considered that expressions (2), (2′) and (4), (4′) represent scalar products of the vectors ψ_a and φ_b taken in one order or another in the (continuous) Hilbert space of the quantities q. This obviously becomes even more evident if the variable of the "auxiliary" space q is replaced by a quantity with a discrete spectrum of eigenvalues. Then, in place of the integrals over dq, we obtain sums over all of the eigenvalues, i.e., ordinary scalar products of the vectors ψ_a and φ_b in the Hilbert space of denumerable measurements.

25. Using the notation of the preceding problem, we obtain for the different cases:

1) In this example, the momentum operator $\hat{\boldsymbol{p}}$ plays the part of $\hat{A}$, and the radius vector $\hat{\boldsymbol{r}}$ plays the part of $\hat{B}$. For the eigenvalues a and b, we have $\boldsymbol{p}$ and $\boldsymbol{r}$ respectively. For the eigenfunction $\psi_a(b)$, we have the function $\psi_{\boldsymbol{p}}(\boldsymbol{r}) = (2\pi\hbar)^{-3/2} e^{\frac{i\boldsymbol{pr}}{\hbar}}$, while for $\varphi_b(a)$, we have the function $\varphi_{\boldsymbol{r}}(\boldsymbol{p}) = (2\pi\hbar)^{-3/2} e^{-\frac{i\boldsymbol{pr}}{\hbar}}$. Therefore, according to (5),

$$\psi_{\boldsymbol{p}}(\boldsymbol{r}) = \varphi^*_{\boldsymbol{r}}(\boldsymbol{p}).$$

2) The constants of motion of a freely moving particle consist of its momentum and angular momentum, in addition to the energy. However, the momentum and the angular momentum cannot have definite values simultaneously. In accordance with the conditions specified in the problem, we shall consider the following two

complete (and mutually exclusive) sets of quantities characterizing a stationary state of a freely moving particle*:

$\hat{A} \to$ the operator for the propagation vector $\hat{\boldsymbol{k}} = \frac{\hat{\boldsymbol{p}}}{\hbar}$;

$\hat{B} \to$ the operators for the energy $\hat{H}$ and the angular momentum $\hat{M}^2$, $\hat{M}_z$.

For the eigenvalues of these operators, we have: $a \to \boldsymbol{k}_0$, $b \to k_0$, l, m, where l and m are the quantum numbers of the angular momentum, and $k_0 = \frac{p_0}{\hbar} = \frac{\sqrt{2\mu E_0}}{\hbar}$ (we have placed a zero subscript on the eigenvalue of the propagation vector to distinguish it from $\boldsymbol{k}$, the space variable).

As usual, we take the $\boldsymbol{r}$-space as the q-space, obtaining

$$\psi_a(q) \to \psi_{\boldsymbol{k}_0}(\boldsymbol{r}) = (2\pi)^{-3/2} e^{i\boldsymbol{k}_0\boldsymbol{r}}, \tag{1}$$

$$\varphi_b(q) \to \varphi_{k_0 l m}(\boldsymbol{r}) = \sqrt{\frac{k_0}{r}}\, J_{l+\frac{1}{2}}(k_0 r)\, Y_{lm}(\theta, \varphi). \tag{2}$$

Functions (1) are normalized to $\delta(\boldsymbol{k}_0 - \boldsymbol{k}_0')$, and functions (2) to $\delta_{ll'}\delta_{mm'}\delta(k_0 - k_0')$.

As in problem No. 14, we select for the polar axis z the quantization axis of the angular momentum component (M_z), and denote by (θ, φ) and (θ', φ') the spherical angles of the vectors $\boldsymbol{r}$ and $\boldsymbol{k}$ respectively relative to this axis.

We can obtain the eigenfunction for the set of operators $\hat{H}$, $\hat{M}^2$, $\hat{M}_z$ in the $\boldsymbol{p}$- or $\boldsymbol{k}$-space [i.e., $\varphi_b(a)$] directly from the result of problem No. 14 by substituting the radial function of free motion $\sqrt{\frac{k_0}{r}}\, J_{l+\frac{1}{2}}(k_0 r)$ for R_{nl} in the general equation (16). We also replace p by $\hbar k$, drop the factor $\hbar^{-3/2}$ to transform from the $\boldsymbol{p}$- to the $\boldsymbol{k}$-space, and use the orthonormal condition (see problem No. 13)

$$\int_0^\infty J_{l+\frac{1}{2}}(kr)\, J_{l+\frac{1}{2}}(k_0 r)\, r\, dr = \frac{1}{\sqrt{k k_0}}\, \delta(k - k_0).$$

Thus, we obtain

$$\varphi_b(a) \to \varphi_{k_0 l m}(\boldsymbol{k}) = (-i)^l\, \frac{\delta(k - k_0)}{k}\, Y_{lm}(\theta', \varphi'). \tag{3}$$

---

*To be concise, we shall use here and elsewhere an arrow as a symbol indicating correspondence, etc.

To find the eigenfunction of the operator $\hat{k}$ in the (k, l, m)-space [i.e., $\psi_a(b)$], according to equation (2) of problem No. 24, it is necessary to evaluate the integral

$$\psi_a(b) \to \psi_{k_0}(k, l, m) = \int \psi_{k_0}(r)\, \varphi^*_{klm}(r)\, dr.$$

Substituting (1) and (2) into this [and remembering that k must be replaced by k_0 in function (2) !], and carrying out the computation in exactly the same way as in problem No. 14, we find

$$\psi_a(b) \to \psi_{k_0}(k, l, m) = i^l \frac{\delta(k-k_0)}{k_0} Y^*_{lm}(\theta', \varphi').$$

In complete agreement with equation (5) of problem No. 24, this function is the complex conjugate of function (3).

3) Above, we quantized this system in Cartesian and spherical coordinates. In the notation of problems No. 24 and No. 17, we have:

$$\left.\begin{array}{ll} \hat{A} \to \text{set} & \hat{H}_1, \hat{H}_2, \hat{H}_3 \\ \hat{B} \to \text{set} & \hat{H}, \hat{M}^2, \hat{M}_z \end{array}\right\}, \quad \text{where } \hat{H} = \hat{H}_1 + \hat{H}_2 + \hat{H}_3.$$

$$\left.\begin{array}{l} a \to (n_1, n_2, n_3) \\ b \to (n, l, m) \text{ or } (p, l, m) \end{array}\right\}, \text{ where } n = n_1 + n_2 + n_3, \quad p = \frac{1}{2}(n-l).$$

$$q \to r(x, y, z \text{ or } r, \theta, \varphi),$$

$$\psi_a(q) \to \psi_{n_1 n_2 n_3}(x, y, z),$$

$$\varphi_b(q) \to \psi_{plm}(r, \theta, \varphi).$$

$\psi_a(b)$ → the set of quantities c_{plm} for all p, l, m. According to equation (5′) of problem No. 24, we obtain: $\varphi_b(a)$ → the set of quantities c_{plm}.

Hence, for example, we obtain the following probabilities [cf. equations (6′) and (14) of problem No. 17]: in measuring in the "a-state" $n_1 = 2$, $n_2 = 1$, $n_3 = 1$, the probability of obtaining the pair of values $l = 2$, $m = 1$ is equal to $\frac{1}{14}$; conversely, in measuring in the "b-state" $n = 4$, $l = 2$, $m = 1$, the probability of obtaining the set of values $n_1 = 2$, $n_2 = 1$, $n_3 = 1$ is also equal to $\frac{1}{14}$. Analogous relations are obtained for the other combinations of quantum numbers.

4) We dealt with the quantization of this system in spherical and parabolic coordinates above. In the notation of problem No. 18, we have:

$$\left.\begin{array}{l} a \to (n_1, n_2, m) \\ b \to (n, l, m) \end{array}\right\}, \quad \text{where} \quad n = n_1 + n_2 + |m| + 1.$$

$$q \to r(\xi, \eta, \varphi \quad \text{or} \quad r, \theta, \varphi),$$

$$\psi_a(q) \to \psi_{n_1 n_2 m}(\xi, \eta, \varphi), \quad \varphi_b(q) \to \psi_{nlm}(r, \theta, \varphi).$$

The coefficients c_1 and c_0 in equation (8) of problem No. 18 represent nonzero values (components) of the wave function ψ (b). From (5′) of problem No. 24, it follows that the nonzero values (components) of the wave function $\varphi_b(a)$ are the quantities c_1^* and c_0^* (in our example, $c_1^* = c_1$, $c_0^* = c_0$).

In this same problem, we found that, in the a-state ($n_1 = 1$, $n_2 = 0$, $m = 0$), the "shares" of the b-state($n = 2$, $l = 1$, $m = 0$) and ($n = 2$, $l = 0$, $m = 0$) are each equal to $\frac{1}{2}$. Conversely, in each of these two b-states, according to equation (6′) of problem No. 24, the share of the a-state ($n_1 = 1$, $n_2 = 0$, $m = 0$) is also equal to $\frac{1}{2}$.*

26. We denote the given finite displacement in $\boldsymbol{p}$-space by $\hbar \boldsymbol{q}$, and the operator which we must determine by $\hat{L}_q$. By definition, this operator must transform the momentum wave function $G(\boldsymbol{p}_1, \boldsymbol{p}_2, \ldots, \boldsymbol{p}_N)$ of the system of particles to the same function G, but with the momenta shifted by the amount $\hbar \boldsymbol{q}$:

$$\hat{L}_q^{(p)} G(\boldsymbol{p}_1, \boldsymbol{p}_2, \ldots, \boldsymbol{p}_N) = G(\boldsymbol{p}_1 + \hbar \boldsymbol{q}, \boldsymbol{p}_2 + \hbar \boldsymbol{q}, \ldots, \boldsymbol{p}_N + \hbar \boldsymbol{q}). \tag{1}$$

(From now on, we use a superscript on the operator to denote the space of the operator.)

Expanding the right member of equation (1) into a Taylor series of powers of $\hbar \boldsymbol{q}$ and performing the same simple computations as in problem No. 10, Chapter I, we see that the operator has the form

$$\hat{L}_q^{(p)} = e^{\hbar q \sum_{i=1}^{N} \frac{\partial}{\partial p_i}} = e^{-iq \sum_{i=1}^{N} \hat{r}_i}, \tag{2}$$

where we have also made use of the fact that in the $\boldsymbol{p}$-space $\hat{\boldsymbol{r}}_i = i\hbar \frac{\partial}{\partial \boldsymbol{p}_i}$.

---

*It is easily seen that the other half of the total probability in each of these two b-states belongs to the a-state ($n_1 = 0$, $n_2 = 1$, $m = 0$). Thus, both b-states represent a superposition of the same (two) a-states, the coefficients of the two superpositions having the same modulus, but different phases (these coefficients are $-\frac{1}{\sqrt{2}}$, $\frac{1}{\sqrt{2}}$ and $\frac{1}{\sqrt{2}}$, $\frac{1}{\sqrt{2}}$ respectively).

Consequently, in the $\boldsymbol{r}$-space, the operator $\hat{L}_q$ has the form

$$\hat{L}_q^{(r)} = e^{-iq\sum_{i=1}^{N} r_i}, \tag{3}$$

where the $\boldsymbol{r}_i$ are the radius vectors of the particles of the system. Thus, the effect of the given operator on the wave function of the system Ψ in the $\boldsymbol{r}$-space reduces to a multiplication of this wave function by $e^{-iq\sum_i r_i}$:

$$\hat{L}_q^{(r)}\Psi(\boldsymbol{r}_1, \ldots, \boldsymbol{r}_N) = e^{-iq\sum_{i=1}^{N} r_i}\Psi(\boldsymbol{r}_1, \ldots, \boldsymbol{r}_N). \tag{4}$$

The exponential factor in the right member of this equation obviously represents the Ψ-function for free motion of the system with a velocity $\left(-\frac{\hbar q}{m}\right)$.* This is as it should be, since the transformation of independent variable $\boldsymbol{p}\to\boldsymbol{p}+\hbar\boldsymbol{q}$ is equivalent to a change in the eigenvalue $\boldsymbol{p}_0\to\boldsymbol{p}_0-\hbar\boldsymbol{q}$ (or, in other words, to a transformation to a system of coordinates which moves relative to the initial system with a velocity $+\frac{\hbar q}{m}$ and in which the eigenvalues of the momentum of the particles are obviously equal to $\boldsymbol{p}_{0i}-\hbar\boldsymbol{q}$).

Let us consider a very simple example — free motion of a particle with a momentum $\boldsymbol{p}_0$. Its wave functions in the $\boldsymbol{p}$- and $\boldsymbol{r}$-spaces have the form

$$G_{p_0}(\boldsymbol{p}) = \delta(\boldsymbol{p}-\boldsymbol{p}_0), \qquad \Psi_{p_0}(\boldsymbol{r}) = e^{\frac{i\boldsymbol{p}_0\boldsymbol{r}}{\hbar}}.$$

Operating on these functions with the operator $\hat{L}_q$, we have

$$\hat{L}_q G_{p_0}(\boldsymbol{p}) = G_{p_0}(\boldsymbol{p}+\hbar\boldsymbol{q}) = \delta(\boldsymbol{p}+\hbar\boldsymbol{q}-\boldsymbol{p}_0) = \\ = \delta[\boldsymbol{p}-(\boldsymbol{p}_0-\hbar\boldsymbol{q})] = G_{p_0-\hbar q}(\boldsymbol{p}), \tag{5}$$

$$\hat{L}_q\Psi_{p_0}(\boldsymbol{r}) = e^{-i\boldsymbol{q}\boldsymbol{r}}\Psi_{p_0}(\boldsymbol{r}) = e^{i\left(\frac{\boldsymbol{p}_0}{\hbar}-\boldsymbol{q}\right)\boldsymbol{r}} = \Psi_{p_0-\hbar q}(\boldsymbol{r}). \tag{6}$$

Equations (5) and (6) clearly illustrate what we said above concerning the displacements $(+\hbar\boldsymbol{q})$ and $(-\hbar\boldsymbol{q})$.

---

*Here, we have in mind the case of particles with the same mass m.

27. Denoting the first of the operators which we must determine by $\hat{M}_{(p)}$, we have

$$\text{in the } \boldsymbol{r}\text{-space} \qquad \left(\hat{\frac{1}{r}} = \frac{1}{r}\right): \quad \frac{1}{r}\psi(\boldsymbol{r}) = \varphi(\boldsymbol{r}), \tag{1}$$

$$\text{in the } \boldsymbol{p}\text{-space} \qquad \left(\hat{\frac{1}{r}} = \hat{M}_{(p)}\right): \quad \hat{M}_{(p)}g(\boldsymbol{p}) = f(\boldsymbol{p}), \tag{2}$$

where $g(\boldsymbol{p})$, and $f(\boldsymbol{p})$ are the Fourier transforms of the functions $\psi(\boldsymbol{r})$ and $\varphi(\mathrm{r})$ respectively (the wave functions in the $\boldsymbol{p}$-space), being related to them by the equations

$$g(\boldsymbol{p}) = \frac{1}{(2\pi\hbar)^{3/2}} \int \psi(\boldsymbol{r})\, e^{-\frac{i\boldsymbol{pr}}{\hbar}}\, d\boldsymbol{r}, \tag{3}$$

$$f(\boldsymbol{p}) = \frac{1}{(2\pi\hbar)^{3/2}} \int \varphi(\boldsymbol{r})\, e^{-\frac{i\boldsymbol{pr}}{\hbar}}\, d\boldsymbol{r}. \tag{4}$$

Both in this problem and in certain other problems, we shall need the expansion of $\frac{1}{r}$ into a Fourier integral. We give a simple derivation of this equation. We have:

$$\frac{1}{r} = \int a(\boldsymbol{k})\, e^{i\boldsymbol{kr}}\, d\boldsymbol{k}. \tag{5}$$

We apply the Laplace operator Δ to both sides of this equation. We have the obvious identity

$$\Delta(e^{i\boldsymbol{kr}}) = -k^2 e^{i\boldsymbol{kr}}, \tag{6}$$

and the identity

$$\Delta\left(\frac{1}{r}\right) = -4\pi\delta(\boldsymbol{r}), \tag{7}$$

where $\delta(\boldsymbol{r})$ is a δ-function.* Consequently, operating with the Laplacian on (5), we obtain

$$-4\pi\delta(\boldsymbol{r}) = -\int k^2 a(\boldsymbol{k})\, e^{i\boldsymbol{kr}}\, d\boldsymbol{k}.$$

Whence, from the Fourier theorem and the definition of the δ-function,

---

*Identity (7) can be easily verified by writing Δ in the form div grad and integrating both sides over all space by appling the Gauss-Ostrogradskiy theorem.

$$k^2 a(\mathbf{k}) = \frac{1}{(2\pi)^3} \int 4\pi\delta(\mathbf{r})\, e^{-i\mathbf{k}\mathbf{r}}\, d\mathbf{r} = \frac{1}{2\pi^2}.$$

Therefore,

$$a(\mathbf{k}) = a(k) = \frac{1}{2\pi^2 k^2}.$$

Finally,

$$\frac{1}{r} = \frac{1}{2\pi^2} \int \frac{e^{i\mathbf{k}\mathbf{r}}\, d\mathbf{k}}{k^2}. \tag{8}$$

To determine the form of $\hat{M}_{(\mathbf{p})}$ we substitute (1) into (4) and use equation (8), performing the substitution $\mathbf{k} = \frac{\mathbf{p}'}{\hbar}$. This yields

$$f(\mathbf{p}) = \frac{1}{(2\pi\hbar)^{3/2}} \int \frac{1}{r} \psi(\mathbf{r})\, e^{-\frac{i\mathbf{p}\mathbf{r}}{\hbar}}\, d\mathbf{r} =$$

$$= \frac{1}{(2\pi\hbar)^{3/2}} \cdot \frac{1}{2\pi^2\hbar} \int \int \frac{\psi(\mathbf{r})}{(p')^2}\, e^{-\frac{i}{\hbar}(\mathbf{p}-\mathbf{p}')\mathbf{r}}\, d\mathbf{p}'\, d\mathbf{r}.$$

Integrating over $\mathbf{r}$, we have, according to (3),

$$f(\mathbf{p}) = \frac{1}{2\pi^2\hbar} \int \frac{g(\mathbf{p}-\mathbf{p}')\, d\mathbf{p}'}{(p')^2}.$$

Taking $(\mathbf{p}-\mathbf{p}')$ as the new variable of integration and expressing according to equation (2), we obtain finally

$$\hat{M}_{(\mathbf{p})} g(\mathbf{p}) = \frac{1}{2\pi^2\hbar} \int \frac{g(\mathbf{p}')\, d\mathbf{p}'}{(\mathbf{p}-\mathbf{p}')^2}$$

(as obvious from the derivation, the integration is taken throughout $\mathbf{p}'$-space).

Thus, $\hat{\frac{1}{r}} \equiv \hat{M}_{(\mathbf{p})}$ is an integral operator with a kernel

$$G(\mathbf{p}, \mathbf{p}') = \frac{1}{2\pi^2\hbar\, (\mathbf{p}-\mathbf{p}')^2}.$$

Quite analogously, for the operator $\hat{\frac{1}{p}}$ in the $\mathbf{r}$-space, which we denote by $\hat{L}_{(\mathbf{r})}$, we obtain the equation

$$\hat{L}_{(\mathbf{r})} \psi(\mathbf{r}) = \frac{1}{2\pi^2\hbar} \int \frac{\psi(\mathbf{r}')\, d\mathbf{r}'}{(\mathbf{r}-\mathbf{r}')^2};$$

i.e., $\left(\hat{\frac{1}{p}}\right) \equiv \hat{L}_{(\mathbf{r})}$ is an integral operator with a kernel

$$G(\mathbf{r}, \mathbf{r}') = \frac{1}{2\pi^2\hbar\, (\mathbf{r}-\mathbf{r}')^2}.$$

28. Let $\psi(x)$ be a function operated on by the operator $\frac{\hat{1}}{p}$ (we omit here and elsewhere the superscript x on p). We denote by $\varphi(x)$ the function obtained as a result of this operation

$$\varphi = \frac{\hat{1}}{p}\psi. \tag{1}$$

Our problem consists in finding a way of determining the function $\varphi(x)$ from a given $\psi(x)$. For this, let us change to the momentum space. Denoting by $f(p)$ and $g(p)$ the Fourier transforms of the functions ψ and φ respectively, we write the equation corresponding to (1) in the momentum space in the form

$$g(p) = \frac{1}{p} f(p). \tag{1'}$$

Equation (1′) shows that, generally speaking, the function $g(p)$ has a pole at the point $p=0$; i.e., it does not satisfy the general requirements imposed on the ψ-function in quantum mechanics. To prevent these requirements from being violated, it is necessary that the function $f(p)$ become zero at $p = 0$:

$$f(0) = 0. \tag{2}$$

Since $f(p)$ represents the p-th component of the Fourier transform of $\psi(x)$, in the position space this condition is written in the form

$$\int_{-\infty}^{\infty} \psi(x)\, dx = 0. \tag{2'}$$

In the future, we shall assume that condition (2) is observed. Only in this case can the operator $\frac{\hat{1}}{p}$ be determined single-valuedly.

To solve the problem, it is necessary to transform equation (1′) to the position space. For this purpose, we multiply (1′) by $\frac{e^{i\frac{px}{\hbar}}}{\sqrt{2\pi\hbar}}$ and integrate over all values of p:

$$\varphi(x) = \frac{1}{\sqrt{2\pi\hbar}} \int_{-\infty}^{\infty} \frac{f(p)}{p} e^{\frac{ipx}{\hbar}} dp. \tag{3}$$

For our subsequent discussion, it is convenient to regard the integration in (3) as an integration along the real axis in the plane of the complex variable p. Since, on account of condition (2), the function under the integral does not have a pole at the point $p = 0$, it is possible, without changing the result, to move the path of integration downward in the neighborhood of this point (into the region $\mathrm{Im}\, p < 0$):

$$\varphi(x) = \frac{1}{\sqrt{2\pi\hbar}} \int_{\smile} \frac{f(p)}{p} e^{\frac{ipx}{\hbar}} dp. \tag{3'}$$

We substitute into this equation the expression for $f(p)$ in terms of $\psi(x)$:

$$f(p) = \frac{1}{\sqrt{2\pi\hbar}} \int_{-\infty}^{\infty} \psi(x') e^{-\frac{ipx'}{\hbar}} dx'. \tag{4}$$

Changing the order of integration over p and x', we obtain

$$\varphi(x) = \frac{1}{2\pi\hbar} \int_{-\infty}^{\infty} \psi(x') dx' \int_{\smile} \frac{e^{i\frac{p}{\hbar}(x-x')}}{p} dp. \tag{5}$$

Let us evaluate separately the integral over the momentum in (5)

$$\int_{\smile} \frac{e^{i\frac{p}{\hbar}(x-x')}}{p} dp. \tag{6}$$

The value of this integral will be different depending on the sign of the quantity $(x - x')$. For $x > x'$, we close the contour in (6) with a semicircle of infinite radius lying in the upper half plane. The integral over this semicircle is equal to zero. Therefore, integral (6) is equal to $2\pi i$ times the residue at the only pole $p = 0$ lying above the integration path. This residue is equal to unity, so that

$$\int_{\smile} \frac{e^{i\frac{p}{\hbar}(x-x')}}{p} dp = 2\pi i \qquad (x > x'). \tag{7}$$

For $x < x'$, it is possible to close the contour in (6) with an infinite semicircle lying in the lower half plane. Then, in view of the lack of poles beneath the integration path in (6), we evidently obtain

$$\int_{\smile} \frac{e^{i\frac{p}{\hbar}(x-x')}}{p} dp = 0 \qquad (x < x'). \tag{8}$$

Substituting (7) and (8) into (5), we find

$$\varphi(x) = \frac{i}{\hbar} \int_{-\infty}^{x} \psi(x')\,dx', \tag{9}$$

which gives the solution of the problem.

Thus, $\frac{\hat{1}}{p}$ is an integral operator of the form

$$\frac{\hat{1}}{p} = \frac{i}{\hbar} \int_{-\infty}^{x} dx'. \tag{10}$$

This result is natural, since we have been looking for an operator which is the inverse of the momentum operator $\hat{p} = \frac{\hbar}{i}\frac{\partial}{\partial x}$. Indeed, applying the operator $\hat{p}$ to equation (1), we have

$$\hat{p}\varphi(x) = \hat{p}\frac{\hat{1}}{p}\psi(x) = \psi(x). \tag{11}$$

Checking this result against equation (9), we likewise obtain

$$\hat{p}\varphi(x) = \frac{\hbar}{i}\frac{\partial}{\partial x}\left[\frac{i}{\hbar}\int_{-\infty}^{x}\psi(x')\,dx'\right] = \psi(x). \tag{11'}$$

Concerning the final expressions (9) and (10), it is necessary to note the following. We could have changed the contour in (3) in another way, as by shifting it to the upper half plane. Then, from the corresponding computations, we would have obtained, instead of equation (9), the equation

$$\varphi(x) = -\frac{i}{\hbar}\int_{x}^{\infty}\psi(x')\,dx'. \tag{9'}$$

Expression (9′) for $\varphi(x)$ differs from expression (9) by the quantity

$$\frac{i}{\hbar}\int_{-\infty}^{\infty}\psi(x')\,dx', \tag{12}$$

which is equal to zero for functions satisfying condition (2) [cf. (2′)]. Therefore, the definition (9) of the effect of the operator $\frac{\hat{1}}{p}$ coincides with (9′) and is generally single valued.

In the case where equation (2) does not hold, definitions (9) and (9′) differ from one another, indicating that the effect of the operator $\frac{\hat{1}}{p}$ is not single valued.

For the operator $\frac{\hat{1}}{x}$ in the p-space, it is fairly easy to obtain the following expression by means of analogous computations:

$$\frac{\hat{1}}{x} = -\frac{i}{\hbar} \int_{-\infty}^{p} dp'. \tag{13}$$

Thus, this operator is also an integral operator. The operator equation (13) is equivalent to the relation

$$\frac{\hat{1}}{x} f(p) = -\frac{i}{\hbar} \int_{-\infty}^{p} f(p')\, dp'.$$

CHAPTER IV

Matrices. Addition of Angular Momenta

1. If we select the origin of coordinates at the left edge of the well, the wave functions for the stationary states of a particle inside the well will have the form

$$\psi_n(x) = \sqrt{\frac{2}{a}} \sin \frac{\pi n x}{a} \qquad (n = 1, 2, 3, \ldots), \tag{1}$$

where a is the width of the well. Outside the well, $\psi \equiv 0$.

The matrix elements of the position x will be equal to

$$x_{mn} = \int_{-\infty}^{\infty} \psi_m^*(x)\, x \psi_n(x)\, dx = \int_0^a x \psi_m \psi_n\, dx. \tag{2}$$

Substituting (1) into (2) and performing an elementary calculation, we find

$$\begin{aligned} x_{mn} &= \frac{2}{a} \cdot \frac{1}{2} \int_0^a x \left[\cos \frac{\pi (m-n) x}{a} - \cos \frac{\pi (m+n) x}{a}\right] dx = \\ &= \frac{a}{\pi^2} \left\{ \frac{1 - \cos [\pi (m+n)]}{(m+n)^2} - \frac{1 - \cos [\pi (m-n)]}{(m-n)^2} \right\} = \\ &= \frac{4a}{\pi^2} \frac{[(-1)^{m-n} - 1]\, mn}{(m^2 - n^2)^2}. \end{aligned} \tag{3}$$

From equation (3), it is apparent that the only nondiagonal elements ($m \neq n$) which are not equal to zero are those which correspond to an odd difference ($m - n$), i.e., the elements for transitions between states with different parity.* The diagonal elements ($m = n$) are not equal to zero. They can be found for instance by taking the limit ($m - n$) $\to 0$ in the next-to-last expression of equation (3): $1 - \cos x \approx \frac{1}{2} x^2$, etc. This yields

---

*We recall that all the ψ-functions (1) have a definite parity (with respect to the center of the well $x = \frac{a}{2}$), the values $n = 1, 3, 5, \ldots$ corresponding to even functions, and the values $n = 2, 4, 6, \ldots$ to odd functions.

$$x_{mm} = \frac{a}{2}$$

(this result could have been predicted, since x_{mm} is the average value of x in the m-th state, and this average value is equal to $\frac{a}{2}$).

The selection rules we have obtained could have been predicted from the following simple considerations. The matrix of the position x is equal to the sum of the matrices of the quantities $\left(x - \frac{a}{2}\right)$ and $\frac{a}{2}$. Because $\left(x - \frac{a}{2}\right)$ is odd with respect to the center of the well, the elements of the first of these matrices are different from zero only for an odd product $\psi_m \psi_n$, i.e., only for odd $(m - n)$. The elements of the second matrix are obviously equal to $\frac{a}{2}\delta_{mn}$; i.e., it is a diagonal matrix. From this, the selection rules which we found above follow.

To find the momentum matrix $(p_x)_{mn} \equiv p_{mn}$, we shall use the well-known relation [1]

$$p_{mn} = \mu (\dot{x})_{mn} = \mu \frac{i}{\hbar} (E_m - E_n)\, x_{mn}, \tag{4}$$

where μ is the mass of the particle, and $E_n = \frac{\pi^2 \hbar^2}{2\mu a^2} n^2$ are the energy levels of the particle in the well.

Substituting x_{mn} from (3) into (4), we obtain

$$p_{mn} = \frac{2i\hbar}{a} \cdot \frac{[(-1)^{m-n} - 1]\, mn}{(m^2 - n^2)}. \tag{5}$$

It is easily verified that the diagonal elements of this matrix are equal to zero (as they should be, since these elements represent the average values of the momentum in the corresponding stationary states and are equal to zero because of the finiteness of the motion). Evidently the selection rules for the nondiagonal elements of the matrix p_{mn} are the same as for the matrix x_{mn}.

We note also that, according to (5), $p^*_{mn} = p_{nm}$; i.e., the momentum matrix is self-conjugate (Hermitian), as it should be. This is also true for x_{mn}.

2. The operator for the time derivative of the variable A, which does not depend explicitly on the time, has the form

$$\hat{\dot{A}} = \frac{i}{\hbar} [\hat{H}, \hat{A}] \equiv \frac{i}{\hbar} (\hat{H}\hat{A} - \hat{A}\hat{H}). \tag{1}$$

The average value of the variable $\dot{A}$ in a stationary state described by the function ψ_n is equal to the corresponding matrix element of operator (1):

$$\bar{\dot{A}} = \int \psi^*_n \hat{\dot{A}} \psi_n \, d\tau \equiv \dot{A}_{nn} = \frac{i}{\hbar} (HA - AH)_{nn}. \tag{2}$$

Because the Hamiltonian matrix in the energy space is diagonal and because the matrix elements of the variable A are finite in the case of a discrete spectrum, the right member of (2) is identically equal to zero. This proves the required equation $\dot{\bar{A}} = 0$.*

Specific examples of this equation are contained in problem No. 4 of this chapter and in problem No. 2 of Chapter X.

3. The virial theorem of classical mechanics [2, Section 14] states that if the potential energy of a dynamical system is a homogeneous function of its coordinates (Cartesian) and if the motion of the system is finite (takes place in a limited region of space), the time averages of the kinetic energy T and the potential energy U are connected by the equation

$$n\bar{U} = 2\bar{T}. \tag{1}$$

Here, the bar denotes the time average, and n indicates the degree of homogeneity of the function $U(x_1, x_2, \ldots, x_i, \ldots, x_{3N})$, where N is the number of point masses of the system. Therefore, from Euler's theorem on homogeneous functions,

$$nU = \sum_{i=1}^{3N} x_i \frac{\partial U}{\partial x_i}. \tag{2}$$

Theorem (1) continues to be true in quantum mechanics, if the average is taken to be the quantum-mechanical average (over the wave function). In this problem, we shall indicate this average by pointed brackets.

For the proof, it is convenient to use the matrix method.** We have

$$2\hat{T} - n\hat{U} = \sum_{i=1}^{3N} \left(\frac{\hat{p}_i^2}{\mu_i} - \hat{x}_i \frac{\partial \hat{U}}{\partial x_i} \right). \tag{3}$$

Using the operator equations

$$\hat{\dot{x}}_i = \frac{\hat{p}_i}{\mu_i}, \qquad \hat{\dot{p}}_i = -\frac{\partial \hat{U}}{\partial x_i}$$

we rewrite (3) in the form

$$2\hat{T} - n\hat{U} = \sum_{i=1}^{3N} (\hat{\dot{x}}_i \hat{p}_i + \hat{x}_i \hat{\dot{p}}_i). \tag{3'}$$

---

*The classical analogue of this property of the quantity $\dot{A}$ is the equality of its time average to zero for any finite value of A [2].

**We note that the proof with Schrödinger's equation in the position space is considerably more awkward. This is also true of the proof of the sum rule (see problem No. 6).

This operator equation is, of course, correct in any space.

Let us transform to the energy space, the base of which is the set of orthonormal eigenfunctions ψ_m of the Hamiltonian of the system $\hat{H}=\hat{T}+\hat{U}$.

Since, from the conditions of the problem, the motion is finite, these functions correspond to a discrete spectrum of energy levels, and therefore we are dealing with a matrix all of whose elements are finite. For this reason alone, the results we have obtained have a meaning.

Let us write the diagonal matrix element (m, m) of operator (3'). In other words, we shall average operator (3') over the wave function for a stationary state ψ_m.

From the multiplication and addition rules of matrices, we have

$$\langle 2T-nU\rangle_{\psi_m}\equiv(2T-nU)_{mm}= \\ =\sum_{i=1}^{3N}\sum_{l}[(\dot{x}_i)_{ml}(p_i)_{lm}+(x_i)_{ml}(\dot{p}_i)_{lm}]. \quad (4)$$

According to a well-known matrix relation [1, Section 11],

$$(\dot{x}_i)_{ml}=\frac{i}{\hbar}(E_m-E_l)(x_i)_{ml}, \qquad (\dot{p}_i)_{lm}=\frac{i}{\hbar}(E_l-E_m)(p_i)_{lm},$$

where E_m and E_l are energy levels of the system.

Thus, the expression under the double summation sign in (4) becomes zero, and we obtain the required quantum-mechanical generalization of equation (1)

$$n\langle U\rangle=2\langle T\rangle.$$

In particular, for $n=2$ (harmonic oscillations), we have $\langle U\rangle=\langle T\rangle$, while for $n=-1$ (Coulomb interaction), $\langle U\rangle=-2\langle T\rangle$.

4. The probability of a transition from a state characterized by the quantum numbers n_1, l_1, m_1 (the energy, angular momentum, and component of the angular momentum) to a state n_2, l_2, m_2 is proportional to the squared modulus of the corresponding matrix element of the operator ∇:

$$\nabla_{n_1l_1m_1,\, n_2l_2m_2}=\int\psi^*_{n_1l_1m_1}\nabla\psi_{n_2l_2m_2}\,d\tau, \quad (1)$$

where $d\tau=dx\,dy\,dz$. The set of matrix elements (1) forms the gradient operator (or, except for a constant factor, the momentum operator) in the representation of the quantities E, M^2, M_z.

According to the operator equation

$$\nabla = \frac{i}{\hbar}\hat{p} = \frac{i}{\hbar}\mu\hat{\dot{r}}$$

the matrix element (1) is proportional to the matrix element of the velocity operator $\hat{\dot{r}}$. However, from a well-known matrix relation (cf. problems No. 1 and No. 3),

$$(\dot{r})_{n_1 n_2} = i\frac{E_{n_1} - E_{n_2}}{\hbar}(r)_{n_1 n_2},$$

where E_{n_1} and E_{n_2} are energy levels. Therefore, the gradient matrix reduces to the matrix for the radius vector r:

$$\int \psi^*_{n_1 l_1 m_1} \nabla \psi_{n_2 l_2 m_2} d\tau = -\frac{(E_{n_1} - E_{n_2})\mu}{\hbar^2}\int \psi^*_{n_1 l_1 m_1} r \psi_{n_2 l_2 m_2} d\tau. \tag{2}$$

Hence, we see first of all that in the gradient matrix (or momentum matrix) the only nonzero elements are those which are not diagonal in n (i.e., elements which are not diagonal with respect to the energy). Consequently, the average value of the gradient or momentum of a particle in a stationary state in a discrete spectrum (a matrix element which is diagonal with respect to the energy) is equal to zero.*

According to (2), for $E_{n_1} \neq E_{n_2}$, the gradient matrix has the same selection rules for l and m as the matrix for r. Namely ([6, Section 88] or [1, Sections 27 and 29]), the only matrix elements which are not equal to zero are those corresponding to $l_1 - l_2 = \pm 1$, and also $m_1 - m_2 = 0$ (the selection rule for z and $\frac{\partial}{\partial z}$), $m_1 - m_2 = \pm 1$ (the selection rule for x, $\frac{\partial}{\partial x}$, y and $\frac{\partial}{\partial y}$).

5. The average value of the dipole moment of a system of N particles is equal to

$$\langle d \rangle = \int \ldots \int \psi^*(r_1, \ldots, r_N)\left(\sum_{i=1}^{N} e_i r_i\right)\psi(r_1, \ldots, r_N) d\tau_1 \ldots d\tau_N,$$

---

*This fact is obviously connected with the finiteness of the motion in the given case (if $p_{av} \neq 0$, the particle would travel to infinity). In the case of a continuous spectrum, when the motion is infinite (i.e., takes place in an unlimited region of space), the integral in (2) diverges, and our argument loses its strength. Thus, for a plane wave $\psi \sim e^{ipr/\hbar}$, the average value of the momentum is

$$p_{av} = p \neq 0.$$

where e_i is the charge of the i-th particle, $\sum_{i-1}^{N} e_i \boldsymbol{r}_i = \hat{\boldsymbol{d}}$ is the operator for the dipole moment of the system,* and the integration is taken over the configuration space of all the particles.

If the system is in a state with a definite parity, $\psi^*\psi$ will be a function which is even with respect to the coordinates of all the particles, whereas the dipole moment $\boldsymbol{d}$ will be odd in these coordinates. Consequently, the entire expression under the integral is odd. Since the integration over each of the coordinates takes place within infinite (i.e., symmetric) limits, it is obvious that $\langle \boldsymbol{d} \rangle = 0$.

This result can also be obtained by another, less rigorous method. Since the inversion operator commutes with the operators for the angular-momentum components and, in the quasi-classical case (i.e., for $M_i \gg \hbar$), the operators for the angular-momentum components commute with one another, it follows that, in a state with a definite parity, the value of the angular-momentum vector $\boldsymbol{J}$ of the system (in this particular case, its spin $\boldsymbol{I}$) has a definite value.

An angular momentum $\boldsymbol{J}$ which is not equal to zero distinguishes a definite direction in space which is the only direction along which the average dipole moment $\langle \boldsymbol{d} \rangle$ can be pointed:

$$\langle \boldsymbol{d} \rangle = \text{const} \cdot \boldsymbol{J}. \tag{1}$$

However, $\langle \boldsymbol{d} \rangle$ is a polar vector, whereas $\boldsymbol{J}$ is an axial vector. Consequently, to obtain the physically necessary invariance of equation (1) with respect to inversion, it is necessary that the constant in (1) be a pseudoscalar (which we obviously do not have available!).

Therefore, it is necessary that const = 0, i.e., $\langle \boldsymbol{d} \rangle = 0$.

6. The operator for the component of the dipole moment of a system of particles of mass μ and charge e along a certain axis (x) has the form $\hat{d}_x = e\sum_{i=1}^{N} x_i$, while its matrix element d_{mn} appearing in the sum rule is equal to

$$(d_x)_{mn} = \int \psi_m^*(\boldsymbol{r}_1, \ldots, \boldsymbol{r}_N)\, \hat{d}_x \psi_n(\boldsymbol{r}_1, \ldots, \boldsymbol{r}_N)\, d\boldsymbol{r}_1 \ldots d\boldsymbol{r}_N,$$

where the ψ_m, ψ_n, ... represent the complete orthonormal system of stationary wave functions of the system of particles (without the time-dependent factor).

---

*In the space we have selected (the position space), the effect of the operator for the dipole moment reduces simply to multiplication by $\boldsymbol{d} = \sum_i e_i \boldsymbol{r}_i$.

Introducing the operator for the time-derivative of the component of the dipole moment $\hat{\dot{d}}$ (from now on, we shall omit the subscript for the x-component everywhere) and using the equation

$$\dot{d}_{nm} = i\,\frac{E_n - E_m}{\hbar}\,d_{nm},$$

where the E_n are the energy levels of the system of particles, we easily obtain the following chain of equations:

$$\sum_n (E_n - E_m)\,|d_{mn}|^2 = \sum_n (E_n - E_m)\,d_{nm}d_{mn} =$$
$$= \frac{1}{2}\frac{\hbar}{i}\sum_n \dot{d}_{nm}d_{mn} - \frac{1}{2}\frac{\hbar}{i}\sum_n \dot{d}_{mn}d_{nm} = \frac{1}{2}\frac{\hbar}{i}(d\dot{d} - \dot{d}d)_{mm},$$

in which we have used the self-conjugate nature of the operator $\hat{d}$ ($d^*_{mn} = d_{nm}$) and the rule for multiplication of matrices.

If we take into account the definition of $\hat{d}$, the commutative property of the position operator $\hat{x}_i$ and the velocity operator $\hat{\dot{x}}_k = \frac{\hbar}{i\mu}\frac{\partial}{\partial x_k}$ for different particles ($i \neq k$), and the relation

$$\hat{x}_i\hat{\dot{x}}_i - \hat{\dot{x}}_i\hat{x}_i = \frac{i\hbar}{\mu},$$

we find

$$\sum_n (E_n - E_m)\,|d_{mn}|^2 = \frac{1}{2}\frac{\hbar}{i}e^2\sum_{i=1}^{N}(x_i\dot{x}_i - \dot{x}_i x_i)_{mm} = \frac{\hbar^2 e^2}{2\mu}N,$$

Q.E.D.

We emphasize that the computed sum does not contain m; i.e., it is identical for all "initial" states.

7. The eigenvalues of the matrix $\hat{c} \equiv c_{ij}$ (we denote them by λ) are determined from the equation

$$\left\| \begin{matrix} (c_{11} - \lambda) & c_{12} & c_{13} \dots \\ c_{21} & (c_{22} - \lambda) & c_{23} \dots \\ c_{31} & c_{32} & (c_{33} - \lambda) \dots \\ \dots & \dots & \dots \\ \dots & \dots & \dots \end{matrix} \right\| = 0,$$

where the symbol $\|\dots\|$ designates the determinant. In the case of second order matrices, this equation assumes the form

$$\lambda^2 - \lambda(c_{11} + c_{22}) + (c_{11}c_{22} - c_{12}c_{21}) = 0,$$

or

$$\lambda^2 - \lambda \cdot \mathrm{Sp}\,\hat{c} + \|c_{ij}\| = 0,$$

where $\mathrm{Sp}\,\hat{c}$ is the trace (the sum of the diagonal elements) of the matrix $\hat{c}$. Thus, the eigenvalues are expressed only in terms of the trace of the matrix and in terms of its determinant.

As is known, in computing the trace of a product of matrices, it is permissible to carry out cyclic permutation of the factors. Consequently,

$$\mathrm{Sp}\,(\hat{a}\hat{b}) = \mathrm{Sp}\,(\hat{b}\hat{a}).$$

Moreover, the determinant of a product of matrices is equal to the product of the determinants of the factors. Therefore,

$$\|\hat{a}\hat{b}\| = \|\hat{a}\| \cdot \|\hat{b}\| = \|\hat{b}\hat{a}\|.$$

Thus, both the traces and the determinants of the matrices $\hat{a}\hat{b}$ and $\hat{b}\hat{a}$ coincide, and consequently both matrices have the same eigenvalues.

8. The condition that a matrix $\hat{S}$ be unitary has the form

$$\hat{S}^{+} = \hat{S}^{-1}, \tag{1}$$

where $\hat{S}^{+}$ is the conjugate of the matrix, and $\hat{S}^{-1}$ is its inverse.

The condition that the matrix S be Hermitian (self-conjugate) has the form

$$\hat{S}^{+} = \hat{S}. \tag{2}$$

For both conditions (1) and (2) to hold simultaneously, it is evidently necessary that

$$\hat{S}^{-1} = \hat{S}, \quad \text{or} \quad \hat{S}^{2} = \hat{1}, \tag{3}$$

where $\hat{1}$ is an identity matrix.

Therefore, matrices which satisfy condition (3) are simultaneously unitary and Hermitian.

Examples of these matrices are doubled Pauli spin matrices

$$2\hat{s}_x = \begin{pmatrix} 0 & 1 \\ 1 & 0 \end{pmatrix}, \quad 2\hat{s}_y = \begin{pmatrix} 0 & -i \\ i & 0 \end{pmatrix}, \quad 2\hat{s}_z = \begin{pmatrix} 1 & 0 \\ 0 & -1 \end{pmatrix}.$$

9. Comparing the expression ([1], p. 108) for the nonzero matrix elements of the operators $(\hat{L}_x + i\hat{L}_y)$ and $(\hat{L}_x - i\hat{L}_y)$ *

$$(L_x + iL_y)_{M,\,M-1} = (L_x - iL_y)_{M-1,\,M} = \sqrt{(L+M)(L-M+1)}$$

with the definition of the matrix f_{mn} of some operator $\hat{f}$

$$\hat{f}\psi_n = \sum_m f_{mn}\psi_m,$$

we find immediately

---

*The subscript L in terms of which they are diagonal is omitted.

$$(\hat{L}_x + i\hat{L}_y)\psi_{LM} = (L_x + iL_y)_{M+1,\, M}\psi_{L,\, M+1} = \\ = \sqrt{(L+M+1)(L-M)}\,\psi_{L,\, M+1}, \tag{1}$$

$$(\hat{L}_x - i\hat{L}_y)\psi_{LM} = (L_x - iL_y)_{M-1,\, M}\psi_{L,\, M-1} = \\ = \sqrt{(L+M)(L-M+1)}\,\psi_{L,\, M-1}. \tag{2}$$

By adding and subtracting (1) and (2), we obtain

$$\hat{L}_x\psi_{LM} = \frac{1}{2}\sqrt{(L+M+1)(L-M)}\,\psi_{L,\, M+1} + \\ + \frac{1}{2}\sqrt{(L+M)(L-M+1)}\,\psi_{L,\, M-1}, \tag{3}$$

$$\hat{L}_y\psi_{LM} = -\frac{i}{2}\sqrt{(L+M+1)(L-M)}\,\psi_{L,\, M+1} + \\ + \frac{i}{2}\sqrt{(L+M)(L-M+1)}\,\psi_{L,\, M-1}. \tag{4}$$

Since all the above operators convert the function ψ_{LM} into a superposition of functions $\psi_{L,\, M\pm 1}$ which are orthogonal to it, the average values of the quantities corresponding to them in the state ψ_{LM} $\left(\overline{L_x + iL_y} = \int \psi^*_{LM}(\hat{L}_x + i\hat{L}_y)\psi_{LM}\, d\tau\right.$, etc.) are equal to zero:

$$\overline{L_x} = \overline{L_y} = \overline{L_x + iL_y} = \overline{L_x - iL_y} = 0.$$

This fact can easily be explained by using a graphic interpretation of the quantum-mechanical "vector" of angular momentum in the state ψ_{LM}, taking this "vector" to be the lateral surface of a circular cone with a height $L_z = M$ and with a length of the generatrix $\sqrt{L(L+1)}$. Obviously, the average values of the components L_x, L_y, etc., lying in the plane of the base of the cone will be equal to zero.

10. As is apparent from the definition of a complete set ([1], p. 15), we must prove that:

1) all the quantities of the new set can be determined simultaneously (i.e., operators commute with each other);

2) the quantities of the previous set which do not appear in the new set cannot be determined simultaneously with the quantities of the new set (i.e., their operators do not commute with at least some of the operators of the new set);

3) the total number of eigenstates is the same for the previous set of quantities and for the new set.

We shall prove these three properties in turn.

1) As we know, $[\hat{L}^2, \hat{L}_z] = 0$. Moreover, $[\hat{L}_1^2, \hat{L}_2^2] \equiv 0$, since the operators $\hat{L}_1^2$ and $\hat{L}_2^2$ operate on the variables of different subsystems.

Since $\hat{L}_z = \hat{L}_{1z} + \hat{L}_{2z}$, we have, using the results of problem No. 2, Chapter I,

$$[\hat{L}_1^2, \hat{L}_z] = [\hat{L}_1^2, \hat{L}_{1z}] + [\hat{L}_1^2, \hat{L}_{2z}] = 0 + 0 = 0.$$

Likewise, $[\hat{L}_2^2, \hat{L}_z] = 0$.

since $\hat{L}^2 = (\hat{\boldsymbol{L}}_1 + \hat{\boldsymbol{L}}_2)^2 = \hat{L}_1^2 + \hat{L}_2^2 + 2\hat{\boldsymbol{L}}_1\hat{\boldsymbol{L}}_2$, we have (compare
ns No. 1 and No. 2, Chapter I):

$$\hat{L}^2] = [\hat{L}_1^2, \hat{L}_1^2] + [\hat{L}_1^2, \hat{L}_2^2] + 2[\hat{L}_1^2, \hat{\boldsymbol{L}}_1\hat{\boldsymbol{L}}_2] =$$

$$= 0 + 0 + 2[\hat{L}_1^2, \sum_{k=1}^{3} \hat{L}_{1k}\hat{L}_{2k}] = 2\sum_{k=1}^{3} [\hat{L}_1^2, \hat{L}_{1k}\hat{L}_{2k}] =$$

$$= 2\sum_{k=1}^{3} \{[\hat{L}_1^2, \hat{L}_{1k}]\hat{L}_{2k} + \hat{L}_{1k}[\hat{L}_1^2, \hat{L}_{2k}]\} = 0,$$

since all the commutators inside the summation sign are equal to zero.

2) The operators $\hat{L}_{1z}$ and $\hat{L}_{2z}$ from the first set, which do not appear in the new set, obviously commute with $\hat{L}_1^2$, $\hat{L}_2^2$, and $\hat{L}_z$. However, they do not commute with $\hat{L}^2$. Indeed, using the commutation relations for the angular-momentum components, we have

$$[\hat{L}_{1z}, \hat{L}^2] = [\hat{L}_{1z}, \hat{L}_1^2] + [\hat{L}_{1z}, \hat{L}_2^2] + 2[\hat{L}_{1z}, \hat{L}_{1x}\hat{L}_{2x}] +$$

$$+ 2[\hat{L}_{1z}, \hat{L}_{1y}\hat{L}_{2y}] + 2[\hat{L}_{1z}, \hat{L}_{1z}\hat{L}_{2z}] =$$

$$= 0 + 0 + 2\{[\hat{L}_{1z}, \hat{L}_{1x}]\hat{L}_{2x} + \hat{L}_{1x}[\hat{L}_{1z}, \hat{L}_{2x}] +$$

$$+ [\hat{L}_{1z}, \hat{L}_{1y}]\hat{L}_{2y} + \hat{L}_{1y}[\hat{L}_{1z}, \hat{L}_{2y}] + [\hat{L}_{1z}, \hat{L}_{1z}]\hat{L}_{2z} +$$

$$+ \hat{L}_{1z}[\hat{L}_{1z}, \hat{L}_{2z}]\} = 2[i\hat{L}_{1y}\hat{L}_{2x} + 0 - i\hat{L}_{1x}\hat{L}_{2y} + 0 + 0 + 0] =$$

$$= 2i(\hat{L}_{1y}\hat{L}_{2x} - \hat{L}_{1x}\hat{L}_{2y}) \neq 0.$$

More concisely, using the unit axial tensor ε_{ikl}, we have in tensor form (the same subscript occurring twice implies summation):

$$[\hat{L}_{1k}, \hat{L}^2] = [\hat{L}_{1k}, 2\hat{L}_{1m}\hat{L}_{2m}] = 2[\hat{L}_{1k}, \hat{L}_{1m}]\hat{L}_{2m} =$$

$$= 2i\varepsilon_{kml}\hat{L}_{1l}\hat{L}_{2m} = -2i\varepsilon_{klm}\hat{L}_{1l}\hat{L}_{2m} = -2i(\hat{\boldsymbol{L}}_1 \times \hat{\boldsymbol{L}}_2)_k,$$

which is generally not equal to zero. [We have used the commutation relation $[\hat{L}_k, \hat{L}_m] = i\varepsilon_{kml}\hat{L}_l$ and the identities $\varepsilon_{ikl} = -\varepsilon_{ilk}$ and $(\boldsymbol{A} \times \boldsymbol{B})_i = \varepsilon_{ikl}A_kB_l$.]

3) Each state with definite values of the quantities in the first set is described by a simultaneous eigenfunction $\varphi_{L_1L_2M_1M_2}$ of the operators $\hat{L}_1^2$, $\hat{L}_2^2$, $\hat{L}_{1z}$, $\hat{L}_{2z}$ and is characterized by the four quantum numbers L_1, L_2, M_1, M_2, where M_1 and M_2 are the eigenvalues of $\hat{L}_{1z}$ and $\hat{L}_{2z}$, while $L_1(L_1+1)$ and $L_2(L_2+1)$ are the eigenvalues of $\hat{L}_1^2$ and $\hat{L}_2^2$.

Each eigenstate of the new set is described by the function $\psi_{L_1L_2LM}$ and is characterized by the four quantum numbers L_1, L_2, L, M, where the numbers L_1 and L_2 are common to the two sets, while M and $L(L+1)$ are eigenfunctions of $\hat{L}_z$ and $\hat{L}^2$ respectively.

For given L_1 and L_2, the total number of eigenstates of the set L_1^2, L_2^2, L_{1z}, L_{2z} is equal to the number of different possible pairs of the numbers M_1, and M_2, i.e., to $(2L_1+1)(2L_2+1)$. For given

L_1 and L_2, this must be the same as the total number of different eigenstates of the set L_1^2, L_2^2, L^2, L_z, i.e., the number of different possible pairs of the numbers L and M.

As we know, for given L and L_1, L_2 can assume the values

$$L_1+L_2, \quad L_1+L_2-1, \ldots, L_1+L_2-k, \ldots, |L_1-L_2|.$$

For each $L^{(k)} = L_1 + L_2 - k$ (for which, to be specific in this problem, we have taken $L_1 \geqslant L_2$ and, consequently, $k = 0, 1, 2, \ldots, 2L_2$), $2L^{(k)}+1$ different values of M are possible.

The required total number of different pairs (L, M) is obviously obtained by summing the quantities $(2L^{(k)}+1)$ over all possible k; i.e., it is equal to $\sum_{k=0}^{2L_2} [2(L_1+L_2-k)+1]$. Summing this arithmetic progression, we obtain

$$\sum_{k=0}^{2L_2} [2(L_1+L_2-k)+1] =$$

$$= \frac{2(L_1+L_2)+1+2(L_1-L_2)+1}{2}(2L_2+1) = (2L_1+1)(2L_2+1),$$

Q.E.D.

11. The wave function Ψ_{jm} of the state considered here is an eigenfunction of the operators $\hat{J}_1^2$, $\hat{J}_2^2$, $\hat{J}^2 = (\hat{J}_1+\hat{J}_2)^2$, $\hat{J}_z = \hat{J}_{1z}+\hat{J}_{2z}$.

To find the probability of the different values of m_1 and m_2 for given j_1 and j_2, it is necessary to write this ψ-function in the (j_1, j_2, m_1, m_2)-space, where j_1, m_1, etc., are quantum numbers giving the eigenvalues of the operators $\hat{J}_1^2$, $\hat{J}_{1z}$, etc. In other words, it is necessary to determine all the coefficients in the expansion of the function Ψ_{jm} into functions $\psi^{(1)}_{j_1m_1}\psi^{(2)}_{j_2m_2}$.

Considering that $m_1+m_2 = m$, we can write this expansion in the form

$$\Psi_{jm} = \sum_{m_1} c^{j}_{m_1,\, m-m_1}\psi^{(1)}_{j_1m_1}\psi^{(2)}_{j_2,\, m-m_1}. \tag{1}$$

The squares of the coefficients c give the probability of the different values of m_1 and $m_2 = m - m_1$.

In the case we are considering, the possible values of m_1 are equal to 1 and 0,* while the corresponding values of m_2 are $\left(-\frac{1}{2}\right)$ and $\frac{1}{2}$, respectively. Therefore, denoting the coefficients by c' and c'' for brevity, we have

---

*The value $m_1 = -1$ is obviously impossible, since it is necessary that $m_1+m_2 = \frac{1}{2}$, while $|m_2| = \frac{1}{2}$.

$$\Psi_{1/2,\ 1/2} = c'\psi^{(1)}_{1,1}\psi^{(2)}_{1/2,\ -1/2} + c''\psi^{(1)}_{1,0}\psi^{(2)}_{1/2,\ 1/2}. \tag{1'}$$

To find the coefficients c' and c'', we shall proceed in the following way. We apply to both sides of equation (1′) the operator

$$\hat{j}^2 = (\hat{\boldsymbol{J}}_1 + \hat{\boldsymbol{J}}_2)^2 = \hat{J}^2_1 + \hat{J}^2_2 + 2\hat{\boldsymbol{J}}_1\hat{\boldsymbol{J}}_2, \tag{2}$$

For computational purposes, it is convenient to write the last term of this expression in the form

$$2\hat{\boldsymbol{J}}_1\hat{\boldsymbol{J}}_2 = (\hat{J}_{1x} + i\hat{J}_{1y})(\hat{J}_{2x} - i\hat{J}_{2y}) + \\ + (\hat{J}_{1x} - i\hat{J}_{1y})(\hat{J}_{2x} + i\hat{J}_{2y}) + 2\hat{J}_{1z}\hat{J}_{2z}. \tag{3}$$

The left member of (1′) is an eigenfunction of $\hat{J}^2$, and the operation with $\hat{J}^2$ on it simply gives

$$\hat{j}^2\ [\text{left member of } (1')] = \frac{1}{2}\cdot\frac{3}{2}\cdot[\text{left member of } (1')] \tag{4}$$

(we have omitted here and shall continue to omit the factors $\hbar^2$ and $\hbar$).

Let us operate on the right member of (1′) with the operator $\hat{J}^2$ in the form of sum (2). Considering that the functions on the right are eigenfunctions of $\hat{J}^2_1$, $\hat{J}^2_2$, $\hat{J}_{1z}$, $\hat{J}_{2z}$ and that each of the operators acts only on the function of "its own" subsystem, we have

$$\left.\begin{aligned} \hat{J}^2_1\ [\text{right member of } (1')] &= 1\cdot 2\cdot[\text{right member of } (1')], \\ \hat{J}^2_2\ [\text{right member of } (1')] &= \frac{1}{2}\cdot\frac{3}{2}\,[\text{right member of } (1')], \\ 2\hat{J}_{1z}\hat{J}_{2z}\ [\text{right member of } (1')] &= -c'\psi^{(1)}_{1,1}\,\psi^{(2)}_{1/2,\ -1/2} + 0. \end{aligned}\right\} \tag{5}$$

The effect of the remaining part of the operator $\hat{J}^2$ [cf. (2) and (3)] is given by equations (1) and (2) of problem No. 9. From these, we have

$$(\hat{J}_{1x} + i\hat{J}_{1y})\,\psi^{(1)}_{1,1} \equiv 0, \qquad (\hat{J}_{2x} - i\hat{J}_{2y})\,\psi^{(2)}_{1/2,\ -1/2} \equiv 0,$$
$$(\hat{J}_{2x} + i\hat{J}_{2y})\,\psi^{(2)}_{1/2,\ 1/2} \equiv 0.$$

Therefore,

$$\left.\begin{aligned} &(\hat{J}_{1x} + i\hat{J}_{1y})(\hat{J}_{2x} - i\hat{J}_{2y})[\text{right member of } (1')] = \\ &\qquad = c''\sqrt{2\cdot 1}\,\psi^{(1)}_{1,1}\sqrt{1\cdot 1}\,\psi^{(2)}_{1/2,\ -1/2}, \\ &(\hat{J}_{1x} - i\hat{J}_{1y})(\hat{J}_{2x} + i\hat{J}_{2y})[\text{right member of } (1')] = \\ &\qquad = c'\sqrt{2\cdot 1}\,\psi^{(1)}_{1,0}\sqrt{1\cdot 1}\,\psi^{(2)}_{1/2,\ 1/2}. \end{aligned}\right\} \tag{6}$$

According to the meaning of the above computations, we can equate expression (4) to the sum of (5) and (6). Thus, collecting like terms, we obtain

$$(c' + \sqrt{2}c'')\,\psi_{1,1}^{(1)}\psi_{1/2,\,-1/2}^{(2)} + (2c'' + \sqrt{2}c')\,\psi_{1,0}^{(1)}\psi_{1/2,\,1/2}^{(2)} = 0.$$

For this equation to be satisfied identically, it is necessary that the coefficients of the two linearly independent functions equal zero separately:

$$c' + \sqrt{2}c'' = 0 \text{ and } 2c'' + \sqrt{2}c' = 0. \tag{7}$$

One of these equations follows from the other, and therefore they give only one relation between c' and c'' (as we would expect). A second relation is the normalization condition of the probabilities

$$|c'|^2 + |c''|^2 = 1. \tag{8}$$

Solving the system of equations (7) and (8), we find the required coefficients:

$$c' = +\sqrt{\frac{2}{3}}, \quad c'' = -\sqrt{\frac{1}{3}}.$$

The set of these two coefficients (i.e., the wave function) is determined, of course, only with an accuracy within an unimportant, common phase factor of the form $e^{i\alpha}$, where α is a real constant.*

Taking the squared moduli of c' and c'', we finally find:

$$\text{the probability of the values} \begin{cases} m_1 = 1, \quad m_2 = -\dfrac{1}{2} & \text{equals } \dfrac{2}{3}, \\ m_1 = 0, \quad m_2 = \dfrac{1}{2} & \text{equals } \dfrac{1}{3}. \end{cases}$$

In the state we are considering, the average value of m_1 is equal to

$$\overline{m}_1 = 1 \cdot \frac{2}{3} + 0 \cdot \frac{1}{3} = \frac{2}{3},$$

while the average value of m_2 is equal to

$$\overline{m}_2 = -\frac{1}{2} \cdot \frac{2}{3} + \frac{1}{2} \cdot \frac{1}{3} = -\frac{1}{6}.$$

As expected, $\overline{m}_1 + \overline{m}_2 = \overline{m} = m = \frac{1}{2}$.

---

*We have selected the phase of the wave function (c', c'') in the way usually done in the compilation of tables of the coefficients $c^{j}_{m_0\,m_*}$([1, Section 97] or [15, p. 81]).

12. As we know, the possible values of L are equal to

$$L_1+L_2,\ L_1+L_2-1,\ \ldots,\ |L_1-L_2|.$$

The component M of the total angular momentum of the system along the z-axis is determined uniquely when M_1 and M_2 are given and are equal to M_1+M_2. Moreover, we have

$$\hat{L}^2=(\hat{L}_1+\hat{L}_2)^2=\hat{L}_1^2+\hat{L}_2^2+2\hat{L}_1\hat{L}_2.$$

Let us average this operator equation over the ψ-function of the given state:

$$\overline{L^2}=\overline{L_1^2}+\overline{L_2^2}+2\,(\overline{L_{1x}L_{2x}}+\overline{L_{1y}L_{2y}}+\overline{L_{1z}L_{2z}}). \tag{1}$$

To find this average, we note that in the given state L_1^2 and L_2^2 have definite values, equal to $L_1(L_1+1)$ and $L_2(L_2+1)$ respectively. Moreover, because of the weakness of the interaction (i.e., the approximate independence of the two subsystems), we have $\overline{L_{1x}L_{2x}}=\overline{L}_{1x}\overline{L}_{2x}$, and so on.* At the same time, in the given state, L_{1z} and L_{2z} have definite values (equal to M_1 and M_2 respectively), while $\overline{L}_{1x}=\overline{L}_{2x}=\overline{L}_{1y}=\overline{L}_{2y}=0$ (see problem No. 9).

Thus,

$$\overline{L_1^2}=L_1(L_1+1),\qquad \overline{L_2^2}=L_2(L_2+1);$$

$$\overline{L_{1x}L_{2x}}=\overline{L_{1y}L_{2y}}=0,\qquad \overline{L_{1z}L_{2z}}=M_1M_2.$$

Substituting these values of the averages into (1), we find

$$\overline{L^2}=L_1(L_1+1)+L_2(L_2+1)+2M_1M_2. \tag{2}$$

13. Since $L_2=\frac{1}{2}$, M_2 can be equal either to $+\frac{1}{2}$, or to $-\frac{1}{2}$. Let us consider both cases simultaneously.

The value of M is single-valued and is equal to

$$M=M_1+M_2=M_1\pm\frac{1}{2}.$$

As regards L, the state of the aggregate system $(1+2)$ represents a superposition of two states with angular momenta $L_1+\frac{1}{2}$ and $L_1-\frac{1}{2}$:

$$\psi_{L_1M_1}\cdot\psi_{\frac{1}{2},\,\pm\frac{1}{2}}=c_{L_1+\frac{1}{2}}\Psi_{L_1+\frac{1}{2},\,M_1\pm\frac{1}{2}}+c_{L_1-\frac{1}{2}}\Psi_{L_1-\frac{1}{2},\,M_1\pm\frac{1}{2}}.$$

*In quantum mechanics, these relations hold because the ψ-function of the given state is separable into variables of the two subsystems, since each of the operators $\hat{L}_{1x}$, $\hat{L}_{2x}$, etc., acts only on the variables of its own subsystem.

The coefficients c of this superposition (whose squared moduli give the probabilities which we require) can be computed using problem No. 11 as a model.

However, here we shall present an even simpler method of solution, from which we can find the actual probabilities directly, without finding the probability amplitudes c.*

We denote the normalized probabilities of the values of the total angular momentum $L=L_1+\frac{1}{2}$ and $L=L_1-\frac{1}{2}$ by $w_{L_1+\frac{1}{2}}$ and $w_{L_1-\frac{1}{2}}$. Then, for the average value of L^2 in the given state, we have

$$\overline{L^2}=\left(L_1+\frac{1}{2}\right)\left(L_1+\frac{3}{2}\right)w_{L_1+\frac{1}{2}}+\left(L_1-\frac{1}{2}\right)\left(L_1+\frac{1}{2}\right)w_{L_1-\frac{1}{2}}. \tag{1}$$

On the other hand, from the result of the preceding problem, this same average value of L^2 (we substitute $L_2=\frac{1}{2}$, $M_2=\pm\frac{1}{2}$) is

$$\overline{L^2}=L_1(L_1+1)+\frac{1}{2}\cdot\frac{3}{2}\pm 2\cdot M_1\cdot\frac{1}{2}. \tag{2}$$

Equating (1) and (2), we obtain a relation between the probabilities $w_{L_1+\frac{1}{2}}$ and $w_{L_1-\frac{1}{2}}$:

$$\begin{aligned}\left(L_1+\frac{1}{2}\right)\left(L_1+\frac{3}{2}\right)w_{L_1+\frac{1}{2}}+\left(L_1-\frac{1}{2}\right)\left(L_1+\frac{1}{2}\right)w_{L_1-\frac{1}{2}}=&\\ =L_1(L_1+1)+\frac{3}{4}\pm M_1.&\end{aligned} \tag{3}$$

A second relation is the normalization condition

$$w_{L_1+\frac{1}{2}}+w_{L_1-\frac{1}{2}}=1. \tag{4}$$

Solving the system of equations (3) and (4), we obtain

$$\left.\begin{aligned}w_{L_1+\frac{1}{2}}&=\frac{L_1+1\pm M_1}{2L_1+1},\\ w_{L_1-\frac{1}{2}}&=\frac{L_1\mp M_1}{2L_1+1}.\end{aligned}\right\} \tag{5}$$

---

*This method will be particularly useful in obtaining rapidly the relations between the cross sections for various processes of scattering and generation of mesons (see problem No. 9, Chapter XII).

As expected, these equations contain the result (obvious beforehand) that, for $M_1 = L_1$ and $M_2 = L_2 = +\frac{1}{2}$ (the upper sign in the formulas), the total angular momentum L has only one definite value $L = L_1 + L_2 = L_1 + \frac{1}{2}$, whereas the value $L = L_1 - \frac{1}{2}$ is impossible.

14. In the notation adopted in [1], Section 97 and in problem No. 11, we have:

$$\hat{A} \to \text{набор } \hat{M}_1^2, \hat{M}_2^2, \hat{M}_{1z}, \hat{M}_{2z}; \ \hat{B} \to \text{ set } \hat{M}_1^2, \hat{M}_2^2, (\hat{\boldsymbol{M}}_1 + \hat{\boldsymbol{M}}_2)^2, (\hat{\boldsymbol{M}}_1 + \hat{\boldsymbol{M}}_2)_z; \ a \to \text{ set } j_1, j_2, m_1, m_2; \ b \to \text{ set } j_1, j_2, j, m = m_1 + m_2; \ \psi_a(q) \to \psi^{(1)}_{j_1 m_1}\psi^{(2)}_{j_2 m_2}, \ \varphi_b(q) \to \Psi_{jm}.$$

Here, q — the set of independent variables of the two subsystems (1) and (2) — is quite arbitrary.

In complete agreement with (1′) (problem No. 24, Chapter III), we have* [1, Section 97]

$$\psi^{(1)}_{j_1 m_1}\psi^{(2)}_{j_2 m_2} = \sum_j c^j_{m_1 m_2}\Psi_{j,\, m_1+m_2}. \tag{1}$$

The set of coefficients $c^j_{m_1 m_2}$ for all j ($m = m_1 + m_2$ single-valuedly) represents the eigenfunction of the set of quantities (j_1, m_1, j_2, m_2) in the (j_1, j_2, j, m)-space; i.e., it is $\psi_a(b)$.

Conversely (cf. (3′) in problem No. 24, and [1, Section 97]),

$$\Psi_{jm} = \sum_{m_1} (c^j_{m_1,\, m-m_1})^* \psi^{(1)}_{j_1 m_1}\psi^{(2)}_{j_2,\, m-m_1}. \tag{2}$$

The set of coefficients $(c^j_{m_1,\, m-m_1})^*$ for all m_1 represents the eigenfunction $\varphi_b(a)$. As can be seen by comparing (2) with (1), it is the complex conjugate of $\psi_a(b)$, in complete agreement with (5) (problem No. 24).

Consequently [cf. (6′)], in an "a-state" with a specific pair of values m_1, m_2, the probability of measuring some value j is equal to the probability of obtaining the same pair of values (m_1, m_2) in a "b-state" with the same j and with $m = m_1 + m_2$, Namely, this probability is $|c^j_{m_1, m_2}|^2$.

Thus, in problem No. 11, we obtained that (for $j_1 = 1, j_2 = \frac{1}{2}$) in the state $j = \frac{1}{2}, m = \frac{1}{2}$, the probability of the pair of values $\left(m_1 = 1, m_2 = -\frac{1}{2}\right)$ is equal to $\frac{2}{3}$, while the probability of the pair of values $\left(m_1 = 0, m_2 = \frac{1}{2}\right)$ is equal to $\frac{1}{3}$.

---

*For concision, in a number of quantities we omit the indices j_1 and j_2, which are constant and common to both "a-states" and "b-states."

From equation (6′) of problem No. 24, it follows that (for the same j_1 and j_2):

1) in the state $m_1 = 1$, $m_2 = -\frac{1}{2}$, the probability of obtaining the value $j = \frac{1}{2}$ $\left(\text{and, automatically, } m = m_1 + m_2 = \frac{1}{2}\right)$ is $\frac{2}{3}$; the remaining $\frac{1}{3}$ of the total probability goes to the values $\left(j = \frac{3}{2},\ m = \frac{1}{2}\right)$;

2) in the state $m_1 = 0$, $m_2 = \frac{1}{2}$, the probability of obtaining the value $j = \frac{1}{2}$ $\left(\text{and } m = \frac{1}{2} \text{ automatically}\right)$ is $\frac{1}{3}$; the remaining $\frac{2}{3}$ of the total probability go to the values $\left(j = \frac{3}{2},\ m = \frac{1}{2}\right)$.

Another, very similar, application of (5′) and (6′) to the addition of angular momenta (isotropic) is contained in problem No. 9, Chapter XII.

CHAPTER V

Variation of States in Time. Operators in the Heisenberg Space

1. It is necessary to find a solution of the time-dependent Schrödinger equation

$$\hat{H}\Psi(\varphi, t) = i\hbar \frac{\partial \Psi(\varphi, t)}{\partial t} \qquad \left(\hat{H} = -\frac{\hbar^2}{2I}\frac{\partial^2}{\partial \varphi^2}\right)$$

satisfying the given initial condition.

Separating the variables φ and t, we find a particular solution of this equation (the wave function for a stationary state of a rotator) in the form

$$\Psi_m(\varphi, t) = e^{im\varphi - \frac{i\hbar m^2}{2I}t} \qquad (m = 0, \pm 1, \pm 2, \ldots).$$

The general solution has the form

$$\Psi(\varphi, t) = \sum_m c_m \Psi_m(\varphi, t),$$

where the constants c_m are determined from the initial condition

$$\Psi(\varphi, 0) = \sum_m c_m e^{im\varphi} = A \sin^2 \varphi.$$

Finding from this the Fourier coefficients c_m and substituting them into the general solution, we obtain the desired wave function

$$\Psi(\varphi, t) = \frac{A}{2}\left(1 - \cos 2\varphi \cdot e^{-\frac{2i\hbar}{I}t}\right). \tag{1}$$

At the moments of time t satisfying the condition

$$\frac{2\hbar}{I} t = 2\pi n \quad (n = 0, 1, 2, \ldots), \quad \text{i.e.,} \; t = t_n = \frac{\pi I}{\hbar} n,$$

the rotator passes through its initial state.

From the normalization condition $\int_0^{2\pi} |\Psi(\varphi, t)|^2 d\varphi = 1$, which is observed for all values of t, we have $\frac{A}{2} = \frac{1}{\sqrt{3\pi}}$.

2. According to the conditions of the problem, we have to solve (for the given initial condition) the one-dimensional wave equation for a free particle

$$-\frac{\hbar^2}{2m} \frac{\partial^2 \Psi(x, t)}{\partial x^2} = i\hbar \frac{\partial \Psi(x, t)}{\partial t}. \tag{1}$$

To solve equation (1), we can use its formal analogy with the one-dimensional diffusion equation

$$\frac{\partial n}{\partial t} = D \frac{\partial^2 n}{\partial x^2}, \tag{2}$$

which, as we know, has, for a given initial distribution $n(x, 0)$, a solution in the form*

$$n(x, t) = \frac{1}{2\sqrt{\pi D t}} \int_{-\infty}^{\infty} e^{-\frac{(x-\xi)^2}{4Dt}} n(\xi, 0)\, d\xi. \tag{3}$$

In the case with which we are concerned, as we can see by comparing (1) with (2), the role of the diffusion coefficient D is played by the imaginary number

$$D' \equiv \frac{i\hbar}{2m}. \tag{4}$$

In equation (3), replacing $n(x, t)$ by $\Psi(x, t)$, and D by D', we obtain the desired solution of equation (1), i.e., the wave function of the particle for $t > 0$:

$$\Psi(x, t) = \frac{1}{2\sqrt{\pi D' t}} \int_{-\infty}^{\infty} e^{-\frac{(x-\xi)^2}{4D't}} \Psi(\xi, 0)\, d\xi. \tag{5}$$

---

*See for instance [7, Section 51] or [8, Chapter VI, Section 1]. Another method of solving similar problems, which is connected with the expansion of $\Psi(x, t)$ into a Fourier series (or integral) of eigenfunctions of the stationary Schrödinger equation, is presented in problems No. 1 and No. 3 of this chapter. For the given problem, this method of solution is presented, for instance, in [9, Chapter I, Section 9].

Determining the constant in Ψ from the normalization condition $\int_{-\infty}^{\infty} |\Psi|^2 dx = 1$ (this constant is equal to $\frac{1}{\pi^{1/4} a^{1/2}}$) and substituting $\Psi(\xi, 0)$ into (5), we obtain the expression

$$\Psi(x, t) = \frac{1}{2\sqrt{\pi D' t}} \cdot \frac{1}{\pi^{1/4} a^{1/2}} \int_{-\infty}^{\infty} \exp\left\{-\frac{(x-\xi)^2}{4D't} - \frac{\xi^2}{2a^2} + \frac{imv_0\xi}{\hbar}\right\} d\xi.$$

Setting

$$\frac{(x-\xi)^2}{4D't} + \frac{\xi^2}{2a^2} - \frac{imv_0}{\hbar}\xi = (\alpha\xi - \beta)^2 - \gamma,$$

where the coefficients α, β, and γ are obviously equal to

$$\left.\begin{aligned} \alpha &= \sqrt{\frac{1}{4D't} + \frac{1}{2a^2}}, \\ \beta &= \frac{1}{2\alpha}\left(\frac{x}{2D't} + \frac{imv_0}{\hbar}\right), \\ \gamma &= \frac{1}{4\alpha^2}\left[\frac{1}{D't}\left(\frac{imv_0}{\hbar}x - \frac{x^2}{2a^2}\right) - \frac{m^2 v_0^2}{\hbar}\right], \end{aligned}\right\} \qquad (6)$$

we finally obtain

$$\Psi(x, t) = \frac{e^{\gamma}}{2\sqrt{\pi D't}\,\pi^{1/4} a^{1/2}} \int_{-\infty}^{\infty} e^{-\alpha^2\left(\xi - \frac{\beta}{\alpha}\right)^2} d\xi = \frac{e^{\gamma}}{2\alpha\sqrt{D't}\,\pi^{1/4} a^{1/2}},$$

where we have used the formula

$$\int_{-\infty}^{\infty} e^{-\alpha^2 y^2} dy = \frac{1}{\alpha}\sqrt{\pi}. \qquad (7)$$

The distribution function of the probability density has the form

$$|\Psi(x, t)|^2 = \frac{e^{\gamma+\gamma^*}}{4\sqrt{\pi}\, a\, |\alpha|^2\, |D'|\, t},$$

After the substitution of γ, α, and D' from (6) and (4), and after a simple computation, this gives

$$|\Psi(x, t)|^2 = \frac{1}{a\sqrt{\pi}\sqrt{1 + \left(\frac{\hbar t}{ma^2}\right)^2}} \exp\left\{-\frac{(x - v_0 t)^2}{a^2\left[1 + \left(\frac{\hbar t}{ma^2}\right)^2\right]}\right\}. \qquad (8)$$

As can easily be verified from (7), $\int_{-\infty}^{\infty} |\Psi(x, t)|^2 dx = 1$ for all t; i.e., the total probability is constant in time, as expected.

However, the distribution function of the probability density (8) changes considerably with increasing time. For any given t, the maximum of the distribution function is at $x = v_0 t$; i.e., the center of gravity of the wave packet moves with the initial velocity v_0.

The width of the packet, which is determined from the denominator of the exponent in (8), increases with time according to the equation

$$a' = a\sqrt{1 + \left(\frac{\hbar t}{ma^2}\right)^2}, \tag{9}$$

being equal to twice its initial width ($a' = a$ at $t = 0$) at a time $t = t_1$, corresponding to $\sqrt{1 + \left(\frac{\hbar t_1}{ma^2}\right)^2} = 2$, i.e., at a time

$$t_1 = \sqrt{3}\,\frac{ma^2}{\hbar}. \tag{10}$$

Correspondingly, the probability of the maximum, given by the factor in front of the exponential term, decreases.

For $t \gg t_1$, the width of the packet increases proportionally to the time

$$a' \approx \frac{\hbar}{ma} t \equiv v_1 t. \tag{11}$$

As is apparent from (9)-(11), the spreading out of the wave packet represents a purely quantum-mechanical effect, which disappears totally in the limiting transition to classical mechanics ($\hbar \to 0$).

We also note the velocity with which the packet spreads out, $v_1 = \frac{\hbar}{ma}$ [see (11)], can be evaluated from simple considerations based on the uncertainty principle. Indeed, the initial state is characterized by a spread of the momenta $\Delta p \sim \frac{\hbar}{a}$, i.e., a spread of the velocities $\Delta v \sim \frac{\hbar}{ma}$, which causes the subsequent spreading out of the wave packet.

Let us determine the "spreading-out" time of the packet t_1 for several characteristic values of the mass of the particle m and of the accuracy of its initial localization a.

For a macroscopic particle ($m \sim 1$ g, $a \sim 10^{-3}$ cm) equation (10) yields $t_1 \sim 10^{21}$ sec $\sim 10^{14}$ years!

On the contrary, for a microscopic particle such as an electron ($m \approx 10^{-27}$ g), if it is initially localized in a region of space with dimensions of the order of an atomic diameter ($a \sim 10^{-8}$ cm), $t_1 \sim 10^{-16}$ sec. Thus, the packet spreads out very rapidly (in a time of the order of the atomic periods).

From equations (10) and (11), it follows that, the more accurate the localization of the particle at the time $t=0$, the sooner it will be possible to find it with an appreciable probability far away from the corresponding position of the center of gravity of the wave packet. This fact is obviously in complete agreement with the uncertainty principle $\Delta p\,\Delta x \sim \hbar$.

3. The general solution of the wave equation for an oscillator

$$\left(-\frac{\hbar^2}{2\mu}\frac{\partial^2}{\partial x^2}+\frac{1}{2}\mu\omega^2x^2\right)\Psi(x,\ t)=i\hbar\frac{\partial\Psi(x,\ t)}{\partial t} \tag{1}$$

can be represented in the form of a superposition of stationary solutions

$$\psi_n(x)\,e^{-\frac{iE_nt}{\hbar}}$$

with arbitrary constant coefficients A_n:

$$\Psi(x,\ t)=\sum_{n=0}^{\infty}A_n\psi_n(x)\,e^{-\frac{iE_nt}{\hbar}}. \tag{2}$$

We can easily convince ourselves of this by substituting (2) into (1) and remembering that

$$\left(-\frac{\hbar^2}{2\mu}\frac{\partial^2}{\partial x^2}+\frac{1}{2}\mu\omega^2x^2\right)\psi_n(x)=E_n\psi_n(x).$$

We shall use functions $\psi_n(x)$ normalized to unity. As we know, they have the form

$$\psi_n(x)=\sqrt{\frac{\alpha}{2^nn!\sqrt{\pi}}}\,e^{-\frac{1}{2}(\alpha x)^2}H_n(\alpha x), \tag{3}$$

where

$$H_n(\xi)=(-1)^ne^{\xi^2}\frac{d^n}{d\xi^n}(e^{-\xi^2})$$

is a Hermite polynomial of the n-th order. These functions satisfy the orthonormal condition

$$\int_{-\infty}^{\infty}\psi_m^*(x)\,\psi_n(x)\,dx=\int_{-\infty}^{\infty}\psi_m\psi_n\,dx=\delta_{mn}. \tag{4}$$

From the specified conditions, we have for the normalized wave function of the initial state

$$\Psi(x, 0) = \frac{\alpha^{1/2}}{\pi^{1/4}} e^{-\frac{1}{2}\alpha^2(x-b)^2} = \psi_0(x-b). \tag{5}$$

This is a wave function having the form of the ψ-function of the ground state of the oscillator, but with the center of gravity shifted a distance b from the equilibrium position $(x=0)$ [cf. (3)].

The set of coefficients A_n and consequently the wave function $\Psi(x, t)$ for which we are looking are uniquely defined by the given initial condition (5):

$$\sum_{m=0}^{\infty} A_m \psi_m(x) = \frac{\alpha^{1/2}}{\pi^{1/4}} e^{-\frac{1}{2}\alpha^2(x-b)^2}.$$

By multiplying this equation by $\psi_n^*(x) = \psi_n(x)$ and integrating over all x, we obtain, according to (4) and (3):

$$A_n = \frac{\alpha}{\sqrt{\pi \cdot 2^n n!}} \int_{-\infty}^{\infty} e^{-\frac{1}{2}(\alpha x)^2 - \frac{1}{2}\alpha^2(x-b)^2} H_n(\alpha x)\, dx,$$

or, transforming to the dimensionless variable $\xi = \alpha x$ and introducing $\xi_0 = \alpha b$,

$$A_n = \frac{1}{\sqrt{\pi \cdot 2^n n!}} \int_{-\infty}^{\infty} e^{-\left(\xi^2 - \xi_0\xi + \frac{1}{2}\xi_0^2\right)} H_n(\xi)\, d\xi. \tag{6}$$

To compute integral (6), we shall use the following method. If it were possible to replace the $H_n(\xi)$ under the integration sign by a generating function of Hermite polynomials (see for instance [6], p. 579)

$$e^{-t^2+2t\xi} = \sum_{n=0}^{\infty} \frac{H_n(\xi)}{n!} t^n, \tag{7}$$

the integral would immediately reduce to $\int_{-\infty}^{\infty} e^{-y^2} dy = \sqrt{\pi}$. Accordingly, we multiply both sides of equation (6) by $\frac{t^n}{n!}\sqrt{2^n n!}$ (t is an arbitrary parameter) and sum over all n. Consequently, after integrating and expanding the result into a series of powers of t, we obtain

$$\sum_{n=0}^{\infty} A_n \sqrt{2^n n!}\frac{t^n}{n!} = \frac{1}{\sqrt{\pi}} \sum_{n=0}^{\infty} \frac{t^n}{n!} \int_{-\infty}^{\infty} H_n(\xi)\, e^{-\left(\xi^2-\xi_0\xi+\frac{1}{2}\xi_0^2\right)} d\xi =$$

$$= \frac{1}{\sqrt{\pi}} \int_{-\infty}^{\infty} e^{-t^2+2t\xi} e^{-\left(\xi^2-\xi_0\xi+\frac{1}{2}\xi_0^2\right)} d\xi = e^{-\frac{1}{4}\xi_0^2+\xi_0 t} =$$

$$= e^{-\frac{1}{4}\xi_0^2} \sum_{n=0}^{\infty} \frac{(\xi_0 t)^n}{n!}.$$

By equating the coefficients of identical powers of t in both members of the equation, we find A_n:

$$A_n = \frac{e^{-\frac{1}{4}\xi_0^2}\xi_0^n}{\sqrt{2^n n!}}. \tag{8}$$

We substitute into (2) this value (8) for A_n, $\psi_n(x)$ from (3), and $E_n = \left(n+\frac{1}{2}\right)\hbar\omega$; We use equation (7) for the generating function in summing over n and separate the real and imaginary parts in the resulting exponent, thus obtaining the final expression for the wave function we have been determining:

$$\Psi(x, t) = \frac{\alpha^{1/2}}{\pi^{1/4}} \exp\left(-\frac{1}{2}\xi^2 - \frac{1}{4}\xi_0^2 - \frac{1}{2}i\omega t\right) \times$$

$$\times \sum_{n=0}^{\infty} \frac{H_n(\xi)}{n!}\left(\frac{1}{2}\xi_0 e^{-i\omega t}\right)^n =$$

$$= \frac{\alpha^{1/2}}{\pi^{1/4}} \exp\left(-\frac{1}{2}\xi^2 - \frac{1}{4}\xi_0^2 - \frac{1}{2}i\omega t - \frac{1}{4}\xi_0^2 e^{-2i\omega t} + \xi\xi_0 e^{-i\omega t}\right) =$$

$$= \frac{\alpha^{1/2}}{\pi^{1/4}} \exp\left[-\frac{1}{2}(\xi - \xi_0\cos\omega t)^2 - \right.$$

$$\left. - i\left(\frac{1}{2}\omega t + \xi\xi_0 \sin\omega t - \frac{1}{4}\xi_0^2 \sin 2\omega t\right)\right]. \tag{9}$$

The squared modulus of the Ψ-function gives the probability density of the position x for any time t. Substituting $\xi = \alpha x$ and $\xi_0 = \alpha b$, we have

$$|\Psi(x, t)|^2 = \frac{\alpha}{\sqrt{\pi}} e^{-\alpha^2(x - b\cos\omega t)^2}. \tag{10}$$

At the time t, this probability density has a maximum at $x = b\cos\omega t$.

Moreover, comparing (10) and (6), we see that the wave function which we have found represents a wave packet, which oscillates without changing its shape about the equilibrium position ($x = 0$) with an amplitude b and a frequency equal to the angular frequency of the oscillator ω.

Let us consider the two limiting cases.

If the initial deflection b is small relative to the width of the packet $\sim \frac{1}{\alpha} = \sqrt{\frac{\hbar}{\mu\omega}}$ then $\xi_0 \ll 1$. Therefore, according to (9), for all t, the state of the oscillator is described approximately by the Ψ-function for the normal state

$$\psi_0(x) e^{-\frac{1}{2} i\omega t}$$

as expected.

As b increases in the Ψ-function (2) or (9), the increasingly large number of stationary states ψ_n begins to play a significant role, and the maximum of A_n [as a function of n, see (8)] is shifted in the direction of larger n.

In the limiting case of extremely large deflections, i.e., for $b \gg \frac{1}{\alpha}$ ($\xi_0 \gg 1$), A_n has a maximum at $n = n_0 \gg 1$.* In looking for n, this makes it possible to express $n!$ according to Stirling's formula

$$n! \approx \left(\frac{n}{e}\right)^n \sqrt{2\pi n}.$$

Taking the logarithm of A_n, we have, neglecting terms of the order of $\ln n$ and lower,

$$\ln A_n \approx n\left(\ln \xi_0 - \frac{1}{2} \ln 2\right) - \frac{1}{2} n (\ln n - 1) - \frac{1}{4} \xi_0^2.$$

Equating $\frac{\partial \ln A_n}{\partial n}$ to zero, we obtain

$$n_0 \approx \frac{1}{2} \xi_0^2 = \frac{1}{2} \alpha^2 b^2 = \frac{1}{2} \frac{\mu\omega b^2}{\hbar} \gg 1.$$

Thus, we arrive at an extremely striking result: for large deflections b, the energy of the state which is most important in the sum (the wave packet) (2) or (9) is approximately equal to the energy of a classical oscillator with an amplitude b. Indeed,

$$E_{n_0} = \hbar\omega\left(n_0 + \frac{1}{2}\right) \approx \hbar\omega n_0 = \frac{1}{2} \mu\omega^2 b^2 = E_{\text{cl}}.$$

---

*This is obvious beforehand because of the quasi-classical nature of the motion, which is the result of the narrowness of the packet relative to the dimensions of the region of motion. It is confirmed by the further computations.

4. 1. The wave equation for the function $\Psi(x, t)$ has the form

$$i\hbar\frac{\partial\Psi}{\partial t}=-\frac{\hbar^2}{2\mu}\frac{\partial^2\Psi}{\partial x^2}\qquad(0\leqslant x\leqslant a)\tag{1}$$

and the boundary conditions are

$$\Psi(0, t)=\Psi(a, t)=0,$$

where, from the specified conditions,

$$a=a(t)=a_0f(t)\qquad[f(t)\text{ is a given function}].$$

Introducing the new variable $y=\frac{x}{f(t)}$, we transform (1) to the form

$$i\hbar[f(t)]^2\frac{\partial\Psi}{\partial t}+\frac{\hbar^2}{2\mu}\frac{\partial^2\Psi}{\partial y^2}=\frac{i\hbar y}{2}\frac{d}{dt}(f^2)\frac{\partial\Psi}{\partial y},\tag{2}$$

for which the function $\Psi(y, t)$ satisfies the usual boundary conditions for rigid walls

$$\Psi(0, t)=\Psi(a_0, t)=0.\tag{3}$$

Moreover, introducing the new variable $\tau=\int\limits_c^t\frac{dt}{[f(t)]^2}$, where c is a constant, and setting $f(t)\equiv\varphi(\tau)$, we have

$$i\hbar\frac{\partial\Psi}{\partial\tau}=-\frac{\hbar^2}{2\mu}\frac{\partial^2\Psi}{\partial y^2}+i\hbar\frac{d}{d\tau}[\ln\varphi(\tau)]\,y\frac{\partial\Psi}{\partial y}.\tag{4}$$

Thus, we have reduced the problem to a solution of equation (4), with a Hamiltonian depending explicitly on the "time"

$$\hat{H}(y, \tau)=-\frac{\hbar^2}{2\mu}\frac{\partial^2}{\partial y^2}+i\hbar\frac{d}{d\tau}[\ln\varphi(\tau)]\,y\frac{\partial}{\partial y}\tag{4'}$$

and with the usual boundary conditions (3).

It is clear that an exact solution of equation (4) for an arbitrary $f(t)\equiv\varphi(\tau)$ is impossible. An approximate solution can be found from perturbation theory in the case where $f(t)$ has a weak dependence on time. Thus, in the given problem, the slow perturbation of the boundary conditions reduces to a small time-dependent perturbation of the Hamiltonian.

We note that, in using the equations of perturbation theory, it is necessary to generalize them somewhat in consideration of the fact that the Hamiltonian is non-Hermitian. It was unavoidable that this

Hamiltonian would be non-Hermitian, since the normalizing integral of the function $\Psi(y, t)$ [or $\Psi(y, \tau)$] depends explicitly on the time. Indeed, for any time t,

$$\int_0^{a(t)} |\Psi(x, t)|^2 dx = 1, \qquad dx = f(t)\, dy,$$

so that

$$\int_0^{a_0} |\Psi(y, t)|^2 dy = \frac{1}{f(t)}. \tag{5}$$

2. From (2) or (4), the special choice of $f(t)$ for which the variables y and t (or y and τ) separate is immediately apparent. A particular instance is*

$$f(t) = \sqrt{1 + \frac{t}{t_0}}, \tag{6}$$

where t_0 is an arbitrary constant. Indeed, substituting (6) into (2) and shifting the origin of the time by the substitution $t + t_0 \equiv t'$, we obtain

$$i\hbar t' \frac{\partial \Psi}{\partial t'} + \frac{\hbar^2 t_0}{2\mu} \frac{\partial^2 \Psi}{\partial y^2} = \frac{i\hbar}{2} y \frac{\partial \Psi}{\partial y}. \tag{7}$$

In this equation, the variables obviously separate (n is the number of the eigenfunction):

$$\Psi_n(y, t') = Y_n(y)\, T_n(t'). \tag{8}$$

We shall not solve here the equations obtained for the functions $Y_n(y)$ and $T_n(t')$. We only note that the former functions appear as superpositions of Hermite functions satisfying the boundary conditions $Y_n(0) = Y_n(a_0) = 0$, while the time dependence of the modulus of the latter functions is easily obtained from (5), (6) and (8):

$$|T_n(t')| = \text{const}\,(t')^{-1/4} = \text{const}\left(1 + \frac{t}{t_0}\right)^{-1/4}. \tag{9}$$

Because of the orthogonality of the functions $Y_n(y)$, function (9) is also correct for the root-square modulus $\sqrt{|\Psi|^2}$ of the complete wave function $\Psi(x, t)$, which is a superposition of particular solutions (8):

---

*This choice of $f(t)$ satisfies in particular the initial condition $f(0) = 1$; i.e., $a(0) = a_0$.

$$\Psi(x, t) = \sum_{n=1}^{\infty} C_n Y_n \left[\frac{x}{f(t)}\right] T_n(t + t_0).$$

It is clear that the corresponding decrease in the probability density takes place simply because of the increase in the width of the well for

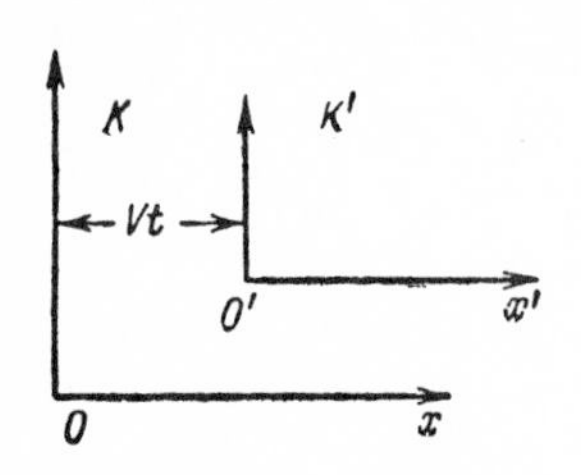

$$\int_0^{a(t)} |\Psi(x, t)|^2 dx = \text{const}.$$

5. Let us consider two inertial frames of reference $K(x, t)$ and $K'(x', t')$,* which move relative to each other with a velocity V.

Let the potential energy of a particle in the field of the forces acting on it be $U'(x', t')$ in the frame of reference K'. Then, from Galileo's transformations,

$$\left.\begin{aligned} x &= x' + Vt', \\ t &= t' \end{aligned}\right\} \tag{1}$$

the potential energy in the frame of reference K turns out to be equal to

$$U'(x - Vt, t) \equiv U(x, t). \tag{2}$$

The Schrödinger equation for a particle of mass m in the frame of reference K' has the form

$$-\frac{\hbar^2}{2m}\frac{\partial^2 \Psi'}{\partial x'^2} + U'\Psi' = i\hbar\frac{\partial \Psi'}{\partial t'}. \tag{3}$$

We have to prove that the Schrödinger equation

$$-\frac{\hbar^2}{2m}\frac{\partial^2 \Psi}{\partial x^2} + U\Psi = i\hbar\frac{\partial \Psi}{\partial t} \tag{4}$$

is also correct in the frame of reference K, the function U being given by equation (2), and the function Ψ being entirely analogous to the function Ψ' in terms of its physical meaning [namely, the quantity $|\Psi(x, t)|^2 \equiv w(x, t)$ is the probability density of the particle at

*For simplicity, we have confined ourselves to the case of one-dimensional motion. The generalization to the three-dimensional case is obvious.

the point x at the time t]. This fact implies the existence of a definite connection between Ψ and Ψ'.

Indeed, the fact of finding the particle at a definite point in space at a given moment of time does not depend on the choice of the frame of reference. Therefore, the corresponding probabilities must be equal:

$$w'(x', t') = w(x, t) \tag{5}$$

or, according to (1),

$$w'(x - Vt, t) = w(x, t). \tag{5'}$$

Hence, it follows that the wave functions Ψ and Ψ' must differ from one another only by a phase factor (whose modulus is equal to unity):

$$\Psi(x, t) = e^{iS}\Psi'(x', t') = e^{iS(x, t)}\Psi'(x - Vt, t). \tag{6}$$

Moreover, the fact that the particle has a velocity v' in the frame of reference K' implies that in the frame K its velocity is equal to $v = v' + V$. Hence, for the momentum $p = mv$ and $p' = mv'$, we have

$$p = p' + mV. \tag{7}$$

From the existence of this reciprocally single-valued relation between p and p', a requirement analogous to (5) follows:

$$w'(p', t') = w(p, t), \tag{8}$$

or, according to (7) and (1):

$$w'(p - mV, t) = w(p, t). \tag{8'}$$

Let us now derive an equation for the function $\Psi(x, t)$, which is defined by equation (6).

In equation (3), performing the substitution

$$\Psi' = e^{-iS(x, t)}\Psi(x, t), \tag{9}$$

substituting (2), and transforming to the independent variables (x, t) by means of (1), we obtain

$$\begin{aligned} -\frac{\hbar^2}{2m}\frac{\partial^2\Psi}{\partial x^2} + i\hbar\left(\frac{\hbar}{m}\frac{\partial S}{\partial x} - V\right)\frac{\partial\Psi}{\partial x} + \Big[U(x, t) + i\frac{\hbar^2}{2m}\frac{\partial^2 S}{\partial x^2} + \\ + \frac{\hbar^2}{2m}\left(\frac{\partial S}{\partial x}\right)^2 - \hbar V\frac{\partial S}{\partial x} - \hbar\frac{\partial S}{\partial t}\Big]\Psi = i\hbar\frac{\partial\Psi}{\partial t}. \end{aligned} \tag{10}$$

So far, the function $S(x, t)$ (more accurately, $e^{iS(x, t)}$) has played the part of an arbitrary phase factor. We shall now select this function in such a way that equation (10) reduces to the Schrödinger equation (4). From a comparison of (10) and (4), it is clear that for this the function S must satisfy the equations

$$\frac{\hbar}{m}\frac{\partial S}{\partial x}-V=0, \tag{11}$$

$$i\frac{\hbar^2}{2m}\frac{\partial^2 S}{\partial x^2}+\frac{\hbar^2}{2m}\left(\frac{\partial S}{\partial x}\right)^2-\hbar V\frac{\partial S}{\partial x}-\hbar\frac{\partial S}{\partial t}=0. \tag{11'}$$

These equations are easily integrated. From (11), we have

$$S=\frac{mV}{\hbar}x+\varphi(t),$$

where $\varphi(t)$ is an arbitrary function of t.

Substituting this expression into (11), we determine $\varphi(t)$. As a result, we have

$$S=\frac{mV}{\hbar}x-\frac{mV^2}{2\hbar}t, \tag{12}$$

where we have discarded the arbitrary additive constant in S, which, according to (6), appears in Ψ only as an unimportant phase factor.

Finally, according to (6) and (12), the wave function in the frame of reference K is equal to

$$\Psi(x, t)=e^{i\left(\frac{mV}{\hbar}x-\frac{mV^2}{2\hbar}t\right)}\Psi'(x-Vt, t). \tag{13}$$

As we should have expected, this Ψ-function appears as the product of the wave function Ψ' in the frame of reference K' and the function $\exp\left(i\frac{mV}{\hbar}x-i\frac{mV^2}{2\hbar}t\right)$, which describes the free motion of a particle together with the system K' relative to the system K.

We note that the Ψ-function we have found automatically satisfies requirement (8′). Indeed, the probability density of the momentum p at the time t is equal to

$$w(p, t)=|c(p, t)|^2,$$

where

$$c(p, t)=\frac{1}{\sqrt{2\pi\hbar}}\int_{-\infty}^{\infty}\Psi(x, t)\,e^{-\frac{ipx}{\hbar}}dx. \tag{14}$$

Substituting $\Psi(x, t)$ from (13) into this, we easily find

$$c(p, t)=e^{i\left(\frac{mV^2}{2\hbar}-\frac{pV}{\hbar}\right)t}\cdot\frac{1}{\sqrt{2\pi\hbar}}\int_{-\infty}^{\infty}\Psi'(x', t)\,e^{-\frac{i}{\hbar}(p-mV)x'}dx'.$$

The integral on the right is obviously equal to $c'(p-mV, t)$ [cf. (14)]. Thus,

$$c(p, t) = e^{i\left(\frac{mV^2}{2\hbar} - \frac{pV}{\hbar}\right)t} c'(p - mV, t).$$

Thus, we have proved the invariance of the nonrelativistic Schrödinger equation relative to Galileo's transformation.

6. The problem consists in transforming the operator $\hat{L}(t)$ from the energy space to the A-space. For this, as known from [11], it is necessary to take the matrix element $\hat{L}_E(t)$ between the eigenfunctions of the operator $\hat{A}$ in the energy space (we write the variable on which the operator operates as a subscript). Assuming that the energy spectrum is discrete, we write these functions in the form $\psi_A(n)$ (as usual, we have written the eigenvalue to which the function corresponds as a subscript). Thus,

$$L_{AA'}(t) = \sum_{n, m} \psi_A^*(n) L_{nm}(t) \psi_{A'}(m). \tag{1}$$

This expression is the matrix element if the spectrum of A is discrete, and the kernel of the integral operator (a "continuous matrix") if the spectrum of A is continuous. We shall assume the latter case to be true. However, this does not restrict the generality of the proof.

Suppose the transformation to the Hiesenberg energy space was made from the A-space. Then,

$$\begin{aligned} L_{AA'}(t) = \\ = \sum_{n, m} \psi_A^*(n) e^{\frac{i}{\hbar}(E_n - E_m)t} \int \psi_n^*(A'') \hat{L}_{A''} \psi_m(A'') d\tau_{A''} \psi_{A'}(m) = \\ = \int d\tau_{A''} \sum_n e^{\frac{i}{\hbar}E_n t} \psi_A^*(n) \psi_n^*(A'') \hat{L}_{A''} \sum_m e^{-\frac{i}{\hbar}E_m t} \psi_m(A'') \psi_{A'}(m). \end{aligned} \tag{2}$$

We shall now use the equation (see problem No. 24, Chapter III)

$$\psi_A(n) = \psi_n^*(A), \tag{3}$$

where $\psi_n(A)$ is an eigenfunction of the Hamiltonian corresponding to the n-th eigenvalue, in the A-space:

$$\hat{H}_A \psi_n(A) = E_n \psi_n(A). \tag{4}$$

This makes it possible for us to transform the sum appearing in (2) to the form

$$\begin{aligned} \sum_n \psi_A^*(n) \psi_n^*(A'') e^{\frac{i}{\hbar}E_n t} = \sum_n e^{\frac{i}{\hbar}E_n t} \psi_n^*(A'') \psi_n(A) = \\ = e^{\frac{i}{\hbar}\hat{H}_A t} \sum_n \psi_n^*(A'') \psi_n(A) = e^{\frac{i}{\hbar}\hat{H}_A t} \delta(A - A''), \end{aligned}$$

$$\sum_m \psi_m(A'') \psi_{A'}(m) e^{-\frac{i}{\hbar}E_m t} = e^{-\frac{i}{\hbar}\hat{H}_{A''} t} \delta(A'' - A'),$$

where we have used the equation $\sum_n \psi_n^*(A_1)\psi_n(A_2)=\delta(A_1-A_2)$, which is a consequence of (3), and of the normalization of the functions $\psi_A(n)$. Thus, the kernel of the integral operator assumes the form

$$L_{AA'}(t)=e^{\frac{i}{\hbar}\hat{H}_A t}\int d\tau_{A''}\,\delta(A-A'')\,\hat{L}_{A''}\,e^{-\frac{i}{\hbar}\hat{H}_{A''}t}\delta(A''-A')= \\ =e^{\frac{i}{\hbar}\hat{H}_A t}\hat{L}_A e^{-\frac{i}{\hbar}\hat{H}_A t}\,\delta(A-A'). \tag{5}$$

Consequently, the application of the operator to an arbitrary function $\psi(A)$ yields

$$\hat{L}_A(t)\,\psi(A)=\int dA' L_{AA'}(t)\,\psi(A')= \\ =e^{\frac{i}{\hbar}\hat{H}_A t}\hat{L}_A e^{-\frac{i}{\hbar}\hat{H}_A t}\int dA'\,\delta(A-A')\,\psi(A')= \\ =e^{\frac{i}{\hbar}\hat{H}_A t}\hat{L}_A e^{-\frac{i}{\hbar}\hat{H}_A t}\psi(A).$$

Hence,

$$\hat{L}_A(t)=e^{\frac{i}{\hbar}\hat{H}_A t}\hat{L}_A e^{-\frac{i}{\hbar}\hat{H}_A t}, \tag{6}$$

Q.E.D.

7. In the Heisenberg energy space [11],

$$\hat{x}(t)=e^{\frac{i}{\hbar}\hat{H}t}\,\hat{x}e^{-\frac{i}{\hbar}\hat{H}t}.$$

In our case, $\hat{H}=\frac{\hat{p}^2}{2\mu}$. Therefore,

$$\hat{x}(t)=e^{i\frac{\hat{p}^2}{2\mu\hbar}t}\,\hat{x}e^{-i\frac{\hat{p}^2}{2\mu\hbar}t}.$$

Let us carry out the computation in the momentum space. Then, $\hat{x}=i\hbar\frac{\partial}{\partial p}$, and

$$\hat{x}e^{-i\frac{\hat{p}^2}{2\mu\hbar}t}=i\hbar\frac{\partial}{\partial p}e^{-i\frac{p^2}{2\mu\hbar}t}=e^{-i\frac{p^2}{2\mu\hbar}t}\,i\hbar\frac{\partial}{\partial p}+\frac{pt}{\mu}e^{-i\frac{p^2}{2\mu\hbar}t},$$

or

$$\hat{x}e^{-i\frac{\hat{p}^2}{2\mu\hbar}t}=e^{-i\frac{\hat{p}^2}{2\mu\hbar}t}\left(\hat{x}+t\frac{\hat{p}}{\mu}\right).$$

Substituting this into the original equation, we obtain

$$\hat{x}(t) = \hat{x} + t\frac{\hat{p}}{\mu},$$

Thus, the relation between the operators is the same as that between the corresponding classical quantities.

8. The equations of motion for the operators have the form

$$\left.\begin{aligned} \frac{d\hat{x}}{dt} &= \frac{i}{\hbar}[\hat{H},\ \hat{x}(t)], \\ \frac{d\hat{p}}{dt} &= \frac{i}{\hbar}[\hat{H},\ \hat{p}(t)]. \end{aligned}\right\} \tag{1}$$

In the case of the Heisenberg space, the derivatives on the left are understood to be derivatives with respect to time, which appears explicitly in the Heisenberg operators. Equations (1) can be verified directly by differentiating equation (6) of problem No. 6. Since the operators $e^{\pm\frac{i}{\hbar}\hat{H}t}$ commute with the Hamiltonian, equations (1) can be written in the form

$$\left.\begin{aligned} \frac{d\hat{x}}{dt} &= \frac{i}{\hbar}e^{\frac{i}{\hbar}\hat{H}t}[\hat{H},\ \hat{x}]e^{-\frac{i}{\hbar}\hat{H}t}, \\ \frac{d\hat{p}}{dt} &= \frac{i}{\hbar}e^{\frac{i}{\hbar}\hat{H}t}[\hat{H},\ \hat{p}]e^{-\frac{i}{\hbar}\hat{H}t}. \end{aligned}\right\} \tag{2}$$

Carrying out the necessary commutations, we obtain

$$\left.\begin{aligned} \frac{d\hat{x}}{dt} &= \frac{\hat{p}(t)}{\mu}, \\ \frac{d\hat{p}}{dt} &= -\mu\omega^2\hat{x}(t). \end{aligned}\right\} \tag{3}$$

Because these equations are linear, they can be solved in the same way as equations for ordinary, nonoperator quantities. Thus, we obtain:

$$\left.\begin{aligned} \hat{x}(t) &= \hat{c}_1\cos\omega t + \hat{c}_2\sin\omega t, \\ \hat{p}(t) &= \hat{c}_2\mu\omega\cos\omega t - \hat{c}_1\mu\omega\sin\omega t. \end{aligned}\right\} \tag{4}$$

The integration constants $\hat{c}_1$ and $\hat{c}_2$ are constants only with regard to their independence of time. They can be determined from the initial conditions. Indeed, from the definition of a Heisenberg operator, it follows that

$$\hat{L}(t)\big|_{t=0} = e^{\frac{i}{\hbar}\hat{H}t}\hat{L}e^{-\frac{i}{\hbar}\hat{H}t}\big|_{t=0} = \hat{L}.$$

Consequently,

$$\hat{x}(t)\big|_{t=0} = \hat{x} = \hat{c}_1,$$
$$\hat{p}(t)\big|_{t=0} = \hat{p} = \hat{c}_2\mu\omega.$$

Hence, we finally have:

$$\left.\begin{aligned}\hat{x}(t) &= \hat{x}\cos\omega t + \frac{\hat{p}}{\mu\omega}\sin\omega t,\\ \hat{p}(t) &= \hat{p}\cos\omega t - \mu\omega\hat{x}\sin\omega t.\end{aligned}\right\} \tag{5}$$

These equations are correct in any Heisenberg space. In particular, for the position space, we obtain:

$$\left.\begin{aligned}\hat{x}_x(t) &= x\cos\omega t + \frac{\hbar}{i\mu\omega}\sin\omega t\frac{\partial}{\partial x},\\ \hat{p}_x(t) &= \frac{\hbar}{i}\cos\omega t\frac{\partial}{\partial x} - \mu\omega x\sin\omega t.\end{aligned}\right\} \tag{6}$$

9. According to the Schrödinger equation

$$i\hbar\frac{\partial\Psi}{\partial t} = \hat{H}\Psi$$

any state changes with time according to the equation

$$\Psi(\xi, t) = e^{-\frac{i}{\hbar}\hat{H}t}\Psi(\xi, 0), \tag{1}$$

where ξ denotes the set of independent variables on which the wave function of the system depends.

In the Heisenberg space, the operator $\hat{A}$ has the form

$$\hat{A}(t) = e^{\frac{i}{\hbar}\hat{H}t}\hat{A}e^{-\frac{i}{\hbar}\hat{H}t}, \tag{2}$$

where $\hat{A}$ is the operator for a physical quantity A in the Schrödinger space. From the conditions specified in the problem,

$$\hat{A}\Psi(\xi, 0) = A\Psi(\xi, 0). \tag{3}$$

Substituting into this $\Psi(\xi, 0) = e^{\frac{i}{\hbar}\hat{H}t}\Psi(\xi, t)$ and operating with the operator $e^{-\frac{i}{\hbar}\hat{H}t}$ from the left, we obtain:

$$e^{-\frac{i}{\hbar}\hat{H}t}\hat{A}e^{\frac{i}{\hbar}\hat{H}t}\Psi(\xi, t) = A\Psi(\xi, t). \tag{4}$$

By comparing the operator in the left member of this equation with (2), we find

$$\hat{A}(-t)\Psi(\xi, t) = A\Psi(\xi, t).$$

The proof we have given applies to the case where the Hamiltonian of the system $\hat{H}$ does not depend on the time explicitly. For generalization to the case of a time-dependent Hamiltonian, it is sufficient to replace $e^{-\frac{i}{\hbar}\hat{H}t}$ by $\hat{U}(t, t_0)$, the operator transforming the Ψ-function at the time t_0 to the Ψ-function at the time t.

10. From the conditions specified in the problem, Green's function at the initial time is equal to

$$G(r, t; r_0)|_{t=0} = \delta(r - r_0);$$

i.e., it is an eigenfunction of the position operator, corresponding to the eigenvalue r_0. Consequently, from the results of problem No. 9, at any time t, Green's functions will be an eigenfunction of the position operator, taken at the time $-t$, in the Heisenberg space. Therefore, the following simple equation can be written for Green's function:

$$\left(\hat{r} - t\frac{\hat{p}}{\mu}\right)G = r_0 G,$$

or

$$\left(x - \frac{t\hbar}{i\mu}\frac{\partial}{\partial x}\right)G = x_0 G,$$

$$\left(y - \frac{t\hbar}{i\mu}\frac{\partial}{\partial y}\right)G = y_0 G,$$

$$\left(z - \frac{t\hbar}{i\mu}\frac{\partial}{\partial z}\right)G = z_0 G.$$

Representing G in the form of the product

$$G = G_x(x)\,G_y(y)\,G_z(z),$$

we obtain for the functions similar equations of the form

$$\left(x + it\frac{\hbar}{\mu}\frac{\partial}{\partial x}\right)G_x = x_0 G_x.$$

Hence,

$$G_x = C_x e^{i\frac{\mu(x - x_0)^2}{2\hbar t}}$$

or

$$G = Ce^{i\frac{\mu(r-r_0)^2}{2\hbar t}}.$$

The value of the constant C can be determined from the initial condition

$$\int G\,dV \to 1, \quad t \to 0.$$

Computing the integral of G, we obtain

$$\int G\,dV = C\left(-\frac{2\pi\hbar t}{\mu i}\right)^{3/2}.$$

Consequently,

$$C = \left(\frac{-\mu i}{2\pi\hbar t}\right)^{3/2}.$$

Thus, finally,

$$G(r, t; r_0) = \left(\frac{-\mu i}{2\pi\hbar t}\right)^{3/2} e^{i\frac{\mu(r-r_0)^2}{2\hbar t}} \tag{1}$$

This same expression can also be obtained by directly solving the Schrödinger equation. Indeed, the obvious generalization of equation (5) of problem No. 2 to the three-dimensional case gives [considering equation (4) of the same problem]:

$$\Psi(r, t) = \left(\frac{-\mu i}{2\pi\hbar t}\right)^{3/2} \int e^{i\frac{\mu(r-r_0)^2}{2\hbar t}} \Psi(r_0, 0)\,dr_0. \tag{2}$$

On the other hand, the definition of Green's function given in the formulation of the present problem is equivalent to the relation

$$\Psi(r, t) = \int G(r, t; r_0)\Psi(r_0, 0)\,dr_0. \tag{3}$$

Indeed, from (3), we have

$$\Psi(r, 0) = \int G(r, 0; r_0)\Psi(r_0, 0)\,dr_0.$$

Hence, obviously,

$$G(r, 0; r_0) = \delta(r - r_0).$$

Moreover, applying the operator $\hat{L} \equiv \left(\hat{H} - i\hbar\frac{\partial}{\partial t}\right)$ to equation (3), we can easily convince ourselves that because of the arbitrariness of the initial function $\Psi(r_0, 0)$ from $\hat{L}\Psi = 0$ implies $\hat{L}G = 0$, which is what we had to prove.

Finally, comparing (2) and (3), we necessarily obtain equation (1).

11. At first, the problem is solved following problem No. 10. To find G, it is necessary to solve the equation

$$\hat{x}(-t)\,G = x_0 G, \tag{1}$$

or, in explicit form,

$$\left(x\cos\omega t - \frac{\hbar}{i\mu\omega}\sin\omega t\,\frac{\partial}{\partial x}\right)G = x_0 G. \tag{2}$$

Its solution has the form

$$G = G_0(t)\,e^{i\frac{\mu\omega}{2\hbar}\cdot\frac{x^2\cos\omega t - 2xx_0}{\sin\omega t}}, \tag{3}$$

where G_0 is a constant of integration depending on time. To determine this function, we substitute the above value of G into the Schrödinger equation

$$\left(-\frac{\hbar^2}{2\mu}\frac{\partial^2}{\partial x^2} + \frac{\mu\omega^2 x^2}{2}\right)G = i\hbar\,\frac{\partial G}{\partial t}. \tag{4}$$

As a result of the substitution, all the terms containing the variable x in the equation cancel out. This confirms that the dependence of G on x which we have found is correct. For G_0, we obtain the equation

$$\frac{dG_0}{dt} + \left(\frac{\omega}{2}\operatorname{ctg}\omega t + i\,\frac{\mu\omega^2 x_0^2}{2\hbar\sin^2\omega t}\right)G_0 = 0, \tag{5}$$

whose solution is

$$G_0 = \frac{c}{\sqrt{\sin\omega t}}\,e^{i\frac{\mu\omega x_0^2}{2\hbar}\operatorname{ctg}\omega t}. \tag{6}$$

Here c is a constant which does not depend on x or t. Thus, for G, we obtain

$$G = \frac{c}{\sqrt{\sin\omega t}}\,e^{i\frac{\mu\omega}{2\hbar}\operatorname{ctg}\omega t\,(x^2 - 2xx_0\sec\omega t + x_0^2)}. \tag{7}$$

The constant c can be determined in different ways, as from the initial condition $\int G\,dx\,\big|_{t=0} = 1$. However, it is more simple to require that for small times $t \ll \frac{1}{\omega}$, G reduces to Green's function for one-dimensional free motion

$$G(x, t;\ x_0) = \sqrt{-\frac{\mu i}{2\pi\hbar t}}\,e^{i\frac{\mu(x-x_0)^2}{2\hbar t}}. \tag{8}$$

Hence, we obtain for c the value

$$c=\sqrt{-\frac{i\mu\omega}{2\pi\hbar}}\,.$$

Consequently we finally have

$$G(x,t;x_0)=\sqrt{-\frac{i\mu\omega}{2\pi\hbar\sin\omega t}}\,e^{i\frac{\mu\omega}{2\hbar}\operatorname{ctg}\omega t\,(x^2-2xx_0\sec\omega t+x_0^2)}\,. \tag{9}$$

12. The Hamiltonian of the system has the form

$$\hat{H}=\frac{\hat{p}^2}{2\mu}+\frac{\mu\omega^2}{2}(x-x_0(t))^2.$$

The problem consists in finding the wave function $\Psi(x, t)$ satisfying the equation

$$\hat{H}\Psi=i\hbar\frac{\partial\Psi}{\partial t} \tag{1}$$

and the initial condition

$$\Psi(x,0)=\Psi_0(x).$$

Let $\hat{U}(t, t_0)$ be the operator changing $\Psi(t_0)$ to $\Psi(t)$:

$$\Psi(t)=\hat{U}\Psi(t_0).$$

Substituting this equation into the Schrödinger equation (1) and considering that $\Psi(t_0)$ can be arbitrary, we obtain

$$\hat{H}\hat{U}=i\hbar\frac{\partial\hat{U}}{\partial t}\,.$$

Taking the Hermitian conjugate of this equation, we obtain

$$\hat{U}^+\hat{H}=-i\hbar\frac{\partial\hat{U}^+}{\partial t}\,.$$

We now introduce the operators $\hat{x}$ and $\hat{p}$ in the Heisenberg space [11]:

$$\hat{x}(t,t_0)=\hat{U}^+(t,t_0)\,\hat{x}\hat{U}(t,t_0),$$
$$\hat{p}(t,t_0)=\hat{U}^+(t,t_0)\,\hat{p}\hat{U}(t,t_0).$$

The following equations for $\hat{x}(t, t_0)$ and $\hat{p}(t, t_0)$ are easily obtained (differentiation with respect to time is indicated by a dot):

$$\dot{\hat{x}}(t,t_0)=\frac{i}{\hbar}\hat{U}^+[\hat{H},\hat{x}]\,\hat{U},$$
$$\dot{\hat{p}}(t,t_0)=\frac{i}{\hbar}\hat{U}^+[\hat{H},\hat{p}]\,\hat{U}.$$

Computing the corresponding commutators, we find a system of equations for $\hat{x}(t, t_0)$ and $\hat{p}(t, t_0)$:

$$\dot{\hat{x}} = \frac{1}{\mu}\hat{p}, \quad \dot{\hat{p}} = -\mu\omega^2(\hat{x} - x_0(t)) \quad \text{or} \quad \ddot{\hat{x}} + \omega^2\hat{x} = \omega^2 x_0. \tag{2}$$

These equations have a "classical" form.

Because they are linear, they can be solved in the same way as equations for ordinary functions (rather than operators):

$$\hat{x} = \hat{c}_1 \sin\omega(t - t_0) + \hat{c}_2 \cos\omega(t - t_0) + x_1,$$
$$\hat{p} = \mu\omega\hat{c}_1 \cos\omega(t - t_0) - \mu\omega\hat{c}_2 \sin\omega(t - t_0) + p_1,$$

where x_1 and p_1 are the solutions of the inhomogeneous equations (2), becoming zero for $t = t_0$:

$$\left.\begin{aligned} x_1(t, t_0) &= \omega\int_{t_0}^{t} x_0(t')\sin\omega(t - t')\,dt', \\ p_1(t, t_0) &= \mu\omega^2\int_{t_0}^{t} x_0(t')\cos\omega(t - t')\,dt'. \end{aligned}\right\} \tag{3}$$

From the definition of the operators in the Heisenberg space, it follows that

$$\hat{x}(t_0, t_0) = \hat{x}, \quad \hat{p}(t_0, t_0) = \hat{p}.$$

Satisfying these initial conditions, we obtain:

$$\left.\begin{aligned} \hat{x}(t, t_0) &= \hat{x}\cos\omega(t - t_0) + \frac{\hat{p}}{\mu\omega}\sin\omega(t - t_0) + x_1(t, t_0), \\ \hat{p}(t, t_0) &= \hat{p}\cos\omega(t - t_0) - \mu\omega\hat{x}\sin\omega(t - t_0) + p_1(t, t_0). \end{aligned}\right\} \tag{4}$$

Using these expressions, we easily find the solution of the problem.

Let us write the equation satisfied by the zero-point function:

$$\hat{H}_0\Psi_0 = E_0\Psi_0. \tag{5}$$

Here,

$$\hat{H}_0 = \frac{\hat{p}^2}{2\mu} + \frac{\mu\omega^2\hat{x}^2}{2}.$$

From the definition of $\hat{U}(t, t_0)$, we can write

$$\Psi(t) = \hat{U}(t, 0)\Psi_0, \quad \text{or} \quad \Psi_0 = \hat{U}(0, t)\Psi(t),$$

where $\Psi(t)$ is the function for which we are looking.

Substituting this expression for Ψ_0 into equation (5), we find

$$\hat{U}^+(0, t)\hat{H}_0\hat{U}(0, t)\Psi(t) = E_0\Psi(t). \tag{6}$$

The Hamiltonian of this system is the Hamiltonian $\hat{H}_0$, which is formed from our operators $\hat{x}(0, t)$ and $\hat{p}(0, t)$:

$$\hat{U}^+(0, t)\hat{H}_0\hat{U}(0, t) = \frac{\hat{p}^2(0, t)}{2\mu} + \frac{\mu\omega^2\hat{x}^2(0, t)}{2}.$$

By using the relations following from (4) and (3):

$$\hat{x} = \hat{x}(0, t)\cos\omega t + \frac{\hat{p}(0, t)}{\mu\omega}\sin\omega t + x_1(t, 0),$$

$$\hat{p} = \hat{p}(0, t)\cos\omega t - \mu\omega\hat{x}(0, t)\sin\omega t + p_1(t, 0),$$

or simply by substitution, we can easily convince ourselves that

$$\frac{\hat{p}^2(0, t)}{2\mu} + \frac{\mu\omega^2\hat{x}^2(0, t)}{2} = \frac{[\hat{p} - p_1(t, 0)]^2}{2\mu} + \frac{\mu\omega^2[\hat{x} - x_1(t, 0)]^2}{2}.$$

Thus, equation (6) for $\Psi(t)$ becomes

$$\frac{[\hat{p} - p_1(t, 0)]^2}{2\mu}\Psi + \frac{\mu\omega^2[\hat{x} - x_1(t, 0)]^2}{2}\Psi = E_0\Psi$$

with the solution*

$$\Psi(x, t) = e^{\frac{ip_1(t, 0)[x - x_1(t, 0)]}{\hbar}}\Psi_0[x - x_1(t, 0)]. \tag{7}$$

We could have selected another method of determining $\Psi(t)$, as by looking for Green's function for the Schrödinger equation (see problem No. 11).

We selected the method used above, because the initial state was a state with a definite energy.

Function (7), which we have obtained, represents the former (zero-point) distribution function relative to the classical position of the particle [see (2) and (3)] in the coordinate system moving with the particle.

To find w_n — the probability of excitation to the n-th level — it is necessary to expand $\Psi(t)$ in terms of eigenfunctions of the Hamiltonian at a time $t (t > T)$. These eigenfunctions, normalized to unity, have the form

$$\Psi_n(x) = \left(\frac{\mu\omega}{\pi\hbar}\right)^{1/4}\frac{1}{\sqrt{2^n n!}}e^{-\frac{\mu\omega}{2\hbar}(x - x_0)^2}H_n\left[\sqrt{\frac{\mu\omega}{\hbar}}(x - x_0)\right]. \tag{8}$$

*Since t is a parameter in our equation, Ψ can contain a phase factor depending on t arbitrarily. However, this phase factor will not affect the probability, with which we are concerned.

where

$$H_n(\xi) = (-1)^n e^{\xi^2} \frac{d^n e^{-\xi^2}}{d\xi^n} \tag{9}$$

is a Hermite polynomial. The coefficients of the expansion are equal to

$$c_n(t) = \int_{-\infty}^{\infty} \Psi(x, t) \Psi_n^*(x)\, dx.$$

Substituting $\Psi(x, t)$ from (7) and $\Psi_n^* = \Psi_n$ from (8) and (9), and transforming to the variable $\xi = (x - x_0)\sqrt{\frac{\mu\omega}{\hbar}}$ in the integral, we find in succession

$$c_n = \frac{1}{\sqrt{2^n n! \pi}} e^{i \frac{p_1(t, 0)(x_0 - x_1)}{\hbar}} \int_{-\infty}^{\infty} e^{i \frac{p_1(t, 0)}{\sqrt{\mu\hbar\omega}} \xi} e^{-\frac{1}{2}\left(\xi + \frac{x_0 - x_1}{\sqrt{\hbar/\mu\omega}}\right)^2} e^{-\frac{\xi^2}{2}} \times$$

$$\times H_n(\xi)\, d\xi = \frac{(-1)^n}{\sqrt{2^n n! \pi}} \exp\left[-\frac{\mu\omega(x_1 - x_0)^2}{2\hbar} + i \frac{p_1(x_0 - x_1)}{\hbar}\right] \times$$

$$\times \int_{-\infty}^{\infty} d\xi \exp\left\{\xi\left[i \frac{p_1}{\sqrt{\mu\omega\hbar}} + \sqrt{\frac{\mu\omega}{\hbar}}(x_1 - x_0)\right]\right\} \frac{d^n e^{-\xi^2}}{d\xi^n} =$$

$$= \frac{1}{\sqrt{2^n n! \pi}} \exp\left[-\frac{\mu\omega(x_1 - x_0)^2}{2\hbar} + i \frac{p_1(x_0 - x_1)}{\hbar}\right] \times$$

$$\times \left[i \frac{p_1}{\sqrt{\mu\omega\hbar}} + \sqrt{\frac{\mu\omega}{\hbar}}(x_1 - x_0)\right]^n \times$$

$$\times \int_{-\infty}^{\infty} \exp\left\{-\xi^2 + \xi\left[i \frac{p_1}{\sqrt{\mu\omega\hbar}} + \sqrt{\frac{\mu\omega}{\hbar}}(x_1 - x_0)\right]\right\} d\xi =$$

$$= \frac{1}{\sqrt{2^n n!}} \left[i \frac{p_1}{\sqrt{\mu\omega\hbar}} + \sqrt{\frac{\mu\omega}{\hbar}}(x_1 - x_0)\right]^n \times$$

$$\times \exp\left\{-\frac{\mu\omega(x_1 - x_0)^2}{2\hbar} + i \frac{p_1(x_0 - x_1)}{\hbar} + \right.$$

$$\left. + \frac{1}{4}\left[\sqrt{\frac{\mu\omega}{\hbar}}(x_1 - x_0) + i \frac{p_1}{\sqrt{\mu\omega\hbar}}\right]^2\right\} =$$

$$= \frac{1}{\sqrt{2^n n!}} \left[\sqrt{\frac{\mu\omega}{\hbar}}(x_1 - x_0) + i \frac{p_1}{\sqrt{\mu\omega\hbar}}\right]^n \times$$

$$\times \exp\left\{-\frac{\frac{p_1^2}{2\mu} + \frac{\mu\omega^2(x_1 - x_0)^2}{2}}{2\hbar\omega} - i \frac{p_1(x_1 - x_0)}{2\hbar}\right\}.$$

Hence,

$$w_n = |c_n|^2 = \frac{1}{n!}\left[\frac{\frac{p_1^2}{2\mu}+\frac{\mu\omega^2(x_1-x_0)^2}{2}}{\hbar\omega}\right]^n \times$$

$$\times \exp\left[-\frac{\frac{p_1^2}{2\mu}+\frac{\mu\omega^2(x_1-x_0)^2}{2}}{\hbar\omega}\right].$$

We now note that $\left[\frac{p_1^2}{2\mu}+\frac{\mu\omega^2(x_1-x_0)^2}{2}\right]$ is the energy imparted to a classical particle at rest at the initial time as a result of the process we have considered. Denoting this quantity by ϵ, we obtain

$$w_n = \frac{\left(\frac{\varepsilon}{\hbar\omega}\right)^n}{n!} e^{-\frac{\varepsilon}{\hbar\omega}},$$

i.e., the Poisson distribution with a mean n equal to

$$\overline{n} = \frac{\varepsilon}{\hbar\omega}.$$

Let us now examine the limiting cases.

In the case of rapid change of position of the equilibrium point, x_1 and p_1 are approximately equal to

$$x_1 = x_0(1-\cos\omega t), \quad p_1 = \mu\omega x_0 \sin\omega t.$$

Substituting these values into the expression for c_n, we obtain

$$c_n = \frac{(-1)^n}{\sqrt{2^n n!}}\left[x_0\sqrt{\frac{\mu\omega}{\hbar}}\right]^n \times$$

$$\times \exp\left(-in\omega t - \frac{\mu\omega^2 x_0^2}{2\hbar\omega} + i\,\frac{\mu\omega x_0^2}{\hbar}\sin\omega t\cos\omega t\right).$$

This result differs only by the over-all phase factor $\exp\left(i\,\frac{\mu\omega x_0^2}{\hbar}\sin\omega t\cos\omega t\right)$ from the result obtained by re-expanding the zero-point function into eigenfunctions of the Hamiltonian for $t>0$.*

In the case of slow changes, it is possible to use the zero order approximation $x_1 \approx x_0$, $p_1 \approx 0$. Consequently,

$$\Psi(x, t) \approx \Psi_0(x - x_0(t)).$$

This procedure can be used for solving problems regarding an oscillator with other time-dependent parameters.

---

*This expression can be obtained by setting $p_1 = 0$ and $x_1 = 0$ in the general expression for c_n.

CHAPTER VI

Perturbation Theory. Sudden and Adiabatic Changes

1. As we already pointed out in problem No. 13, Chapter II, the potential energy of an electron in the field of a nucleus which has a charge evenly distributed throughout its volume has the form (see figure)

$$U(r)=\begin{cases} -\dfrac{Ze^2}{R}\left(\dfrac{3}{2}-\dfrac{1}{2}\dfrac{r^2}{R^2}\right) & \text{for } 0\leqslant r\leqslant R, \\ -\dfrac{Ze^2}{r} & \text{for } r\geqslant R. \end{cases} \tag{1}$$

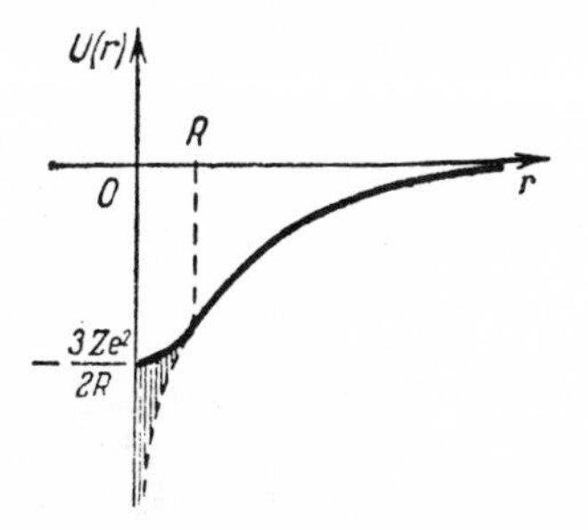

From Equations (1) and the figure, it is clear that the perturbing term H' in the Hamiltonian of the system is the difference between the potential energy of the electron and the quantity $\left(-\dfrac{Ze^2}{r}\right)$, which corresponds to the unperturbed problem (i.e., to the case of a point nucleus):

$$H'=\begin{cases} -\dfrac{Ze^2}{R}\left(\dfrac{3}{2}-\dfrac{1}{2}\dfrac{r^2}{R^2}\right)-\left(-\dfrac{Ze^2}{r}\right) & \text{for } 0\leqslant r\leqslant R, \\ 0 & \text{for } r\geqslant R. \end{cases} \tag{2}$$

On the figure, the magnitude of H' corresponds to the lengths of the ordinates in the shaded area.

According to perturbation theory, in the first approximation the correction to the ground-state energy level $E_0^{(0)}$* is equal to the average value of the perturbation in the state ψ_0:

$$E_0^{(1)} = \overline{H'} = \int \psi_0^{(0)*} H' \psi_0^{(0)} \, dV, \tag{3}$$

where

$$\psi_0^{(0)}(r) = \frac{1}{\sqrt{\pi a^3}} e^{-\frac{r}{a}} \tag{4}$$

is the normalized unperturbed ψ-function of the ground state of a hydrogenlike atom or ion, while

$$a = \frac{\hbar^2}{Zme^2} \tag{5}$$

is the radius of the first Bohr orbit.

Because of (2), expression (3) reduces to a volume integral throughout a sphere of radius R. Considering that the radii of even the heaviest nuclei are small relative to the radii of the Bohr orbits of electrons,** we can conclude that throughout the region of integration $e^{-\frac{r}{a}} \approx 1$; i.e., the ψ-function is practically constant.

In accordance with this, we have

$$E_0^{(1)} \approx \frac{1}{\pi a^3} \int_0^R \left\{ \frac{Ze^2}{r} - \frac{Ze^2}{R} \left\{ \frac{3}{2} - \frac{1}{2} \frac{r^2}{R^2} \right\} 4\pi r^2 \, dr = \frac{2}{5} \frac{Ze^2}{a} \left(\frac{R}{a} \right)^2. \tag{6}$$

We could have predicted that $E_0^{(1)} > 0$ (the energy level is raised) on the basis of the fact that the "smearing" of the nucleus over a finite volume reduces the depth of the electron's potential well (see figure).

The unperturbed energy of the ground state is

$$E_0^{(0)} = -\frac{Z^2 me^4}{2\hbar^2}.$$

---

*From now on, a subscript zero will indicate the ground state, while a superscript will indicate the order of approximation.

**Indeed, for all the elements in Mendeleyev's table, $R \leq 10^{-12}$ cm, whereas, according to (5), $a \approx \frac{0.5 \cdot 10^{-8}}{Z}$ cm. Thus, for $Z = Z_{max} \approx 100$, the ratio $\frac{a}{R} \sim 50$.

Therefore, for the perturbed energy, we finally obtain [see (5) and (6)]

$$E_0 \approx E_0^{(0)} + E_0^{(1)} = E_0^{(0)}\left\{1 - \frac{4}{5}\left(\frac{R}{a}\right)^2\right\}.$$

It is easily seen that if we had taken into account the change of the ψ-function inside the nucleus, we would have obtained additional terms of the order of $\left(\frac{R}{a}\right)^3$ inside the braces.

Finally, considering that R is approximately proportional to $Z^{\frac{1}{3}}$ and $\frac{1}{a}$ is proportional to Z, we can conclude that the relative magnitude of the shift of the ground-state energy level increases with increasing Z approximately as $Z^{4/3}$.

2. Adding to the Hamiltonian for the unperturbed problem (see problem No. 2, Chapter II) the operator for the perturbation energy

$$\hat{H}' = -\boldsymbol{d}\cdot\boldsymbol{\mathcal{E}} = -d\cdot\mathcal{E}\cos\varphi,$$

we can write the Schrödinger equation in the form

$$\frac{d^2\psi}{d\varphi^2} + \frac{2I}{\hbar^2}(E + d\cdot\mathcal{E}\cos\varphi)\psi = 0,$$

where φ is the angle of rotation, and E is the energy of the rotator.

The energy levels of the unperturbed problem

$$E_m^{(0)} = \frac{\hbar^2 m^2}{2I} \qquad (m = 0, \pm 1, \pm 2, \ldots)$$

are twofold degenerate (except for the lowest level) with respect to the directions of the angular momentum $M_z = m\hbar$. However, since this degeneracy is not removed until orders of perturbation higher than the second are used, it is possible to use (up to the second order) the perturbation theory for nondegenerate levels.* In other words, the unperturbed wave functions

$$\psi_m^{(0)} = \frac{1}{\sqrt{2\pi}}e^{im\varphi}$$

are correct functions in the zero-order approximation.

The matrix elements of the perturbation operator are

$$H'_{mm'} \equiv \int_0^{2\pi} \psi_m^{(0)*}\hat{H}'\psi_{m'}^{(0)}\,d\varphi =$$

$$= -\frac{d\mathcal{E}}{2\pi}\int_0^{2\pi} e^{i(m'-m)\varphi}\cos\varphi\,d\varphi = \begin{cases} 0 \text{ for } m' \neq m \pm 1, \\ -\frac{d\mathcal{E}}{2} \text{ for } m' = m \pm 1. \end{cases}$$

---

*An exception is the energy level with $m = \pm 1$, which splits (pointed out by B. A. Trubnikov).

Hence, it is apparent that the first-order correction to any energy level is equal to zero:

$$E_m^{(1)} = H'_{mm} = 0.$$

For the second-order correction to the m-th level, we obviously obtain

$$E_m^{(2)} = \frac{|H'_{m,\,m-1}|^2}{E_m^{(0)} - E_{m-1}^{(0)}} + \frac{|H'_{m,\,m+1}|^2}{E_m^{(0)} - E_{m+1}^{(0)}} = \frac{Id^2\mathcal{E}^2}{\hbar^2(4m^2-1)},$$

Accordingly, to a second-order approximation, the energy levels of a plane rotator in a weak electric field are

$$E_m = E_m^{(0)} + E_m^{(1)} + E_m^{(2)} = \frac{\hbar^2 m^2}{2I} + \frac{Id^2\mathcal{E}^2}{\hbar^2(4m^2-1)}.$$

There is a simple interpretation of this result. Defining, as usual, the polarizability of the rotator α as the ratio of the induced dipole moment to the intensity of the external field, we obtain that the energy of the induced dipole in a field $\mathcal{E}$ is $-\frac{1}{2}\alpha\mathcal{E}^2$ (since it is equal to the work of polarization $-\alpha\int_0^{\mathcal{E}}\mathcal{E}\,d\mathcal{E}$). Comparing this additional energy with the first nonvanishing correction to the level computed above, we obtain the following equation for the polarizability:

$$\alpha_m = -\frac{2Id^2}{\hbar^2(4m^2-1)}.$$

We see that, for $m \neq 0$, the polarizability $\alpha < 0$; i.e., the electric dipole moment of the rotator $\boldsymbol{d}$ is oriented antiparallel to the field $\boldsymbol{\mathcal{E}}$. The reverse picture ($\alpha > 0$) is obtained for $m = 0$.

This result is entirely analogous to the classical effect of antiparallel polarization of a plane rotator in rapid rotation (sufficient for a complete revolution), and of parallel polarization in slow rotation.

3. Taking the direction of $\boldsymbol{\mathcal{E}}$ to be the polar axis of the spherical-coordinate system, we can write the perturbation operator in the form

$$\hat{V} = V = -\boldsymbol{d}\boldsymbol{\mathcal{E}} = -d\cdot\mathcal{E}\cos\theta, \tag{1}$$

where θ is the angle between the axis of the rotator (which is parallel to $\boldsymbol{d}$) and the field $\boldsymbol{\mathcal{E}}$.

According to the result of problem No. 3, Chapter II, the wave functions of the unperturbed stationary states have the form

$$\psi_{lm}^{(0)}(\theta, \varphi) = Y_{lm}(\theta, \varphi) = \sqrt{\frac{(2l+1)(l+m)!}{4\pi(l-m)!}} P_l^m(\cos\theta) e^{im\varphi}, \tag{2}$$

where θ is the polar angle defined above, and φ is the azimuthal angle of the rotator's axis.

The functions (2) are orthonormal:

$$\int_0^{2\pi}\int_0^{\pi} Y_{lm}^*(\theta, \varphi) Y_{l'm'}(\theta, \varphi) \sin\theta \, d\theta \, d\varphi = \delta_{ll'}\delta_{mm'}. \tag{3}$$

In particular, the wave function of the ground state, whose perturbation we are studying, has the form

$$\psi_{00}^{(0)}(\theta, \varphi) = Y_{00} = \frac{1}{\sqrt{4\pi}}. \tag{4}$$

The unperturbed energy levels of the stationary states (including the ground state) are

$$E_l^{(0)} = \frac{l(l+1)\hbar^2}{2I}; \qquad E_0^{(0)} = 0. \tag{5}$$

Let us form the matrix element of the perturbation operator for a transition from the ground state (0, 0) to an excited state (l, m):

$$V_{lm}^{00} = (V_{00}^{lm})^* = \int_0^{2\pi}\int_0^{\pi} [\psi_{00}^{(0)}(\theta, \varphi)]^* \hat{V} \psi_{lm}^{(0)}(\theta, \varphi) \sin\theta \, d\theta \, d\varphi.$$

Substituting (1), (2), and (4) into this, replacing $\cos\theta$ by $\sqrt{\frac{4\pi}{3}}\, Y_{10}(\theta, \varphi)$ and using the orthonormal condition (3), we obtain:

$$(V_{lm}^{00})^* = V_{00}^{lm} = -d \cdot \mathcal{E} \sqrt{\frac{4\pi}{3}} \times$$
$$\times \frac{1}{\sqrt{4\pi}} \int_0^{2\pi}\int_0^{\pi} Y_{lm}^*(\theta, \varphi) Y_{10}(\theta, \varphi) \sin\theta \, d\theta \, d\varphi = -\frac{d \cdot \mathcal{E}}{\sqrt{3}} \delta_{l1}\delta_{m0}. \tag{6}$$

Thus, only one matrix element is different from zero, namely the element corresponding to a transition from the normal state $l = m = 0$ to the state $l = 1$, $m = 0$. Since this matrix element is nondiagonal, the first-order correction to the energy level is equal to zero.

From the general formulas of perturbation theory and from (5) and (6), the second-order correction to the energy level is

$$E_0^{(2)} = \sum_l{}' \sum_m \frac{|V_{lm}^{00}|^2}{E_0^{(0)} - E_l^{(0)}} = \frac{|V_{10}^{00}|^2}{E_0^{(0)} - E_1^{(0)}} = -\frac{(d\cdot\mathscr{E})^2 I}{3\hbar^2}. \qquad (7)$$

Thus, the shift of the ground-state level of a spatial rotator is negative (the same is true for the second-order correction to the ground state of any quantum-mechanical system).

The condition which must be satisfied for perturbation theory to be valid is that the computed change (7) be small relative to the distance $|E_0^{(0)} - E_1^{(0)}|$ between the ground state and the first excited level. Solving this condition with respect to $\mathscr{E}$, we have

$$\mathscr{E} \ll \sqrt{3}\,\frac{\hbar^2}{dI}.$$

As we should have expected, this inequality also implies the smallness of the perturbation ($\sim\mathscr{E}d$) relative to the distance between neighboring levels $\left(\sim\frac{\hbar^2}{I}\right)$.

In conclusion, we note that recursion relations of the form

$$\cos\theta\cdot Y_{lm} = a_{lm}Y_{l-1,\,m} + b_{lm}Y_{l+1,\,m} \quad [6,\ 14]$$

permit easy solving of the problem of the perturbation of excited states of a rotator with any values of l and m.

4. Designating the radius vectors of the electrons relative to the nucleus by $\boldsymbol{r}_1$ and $\boldsymbol{r}_2$, we have the following Schrödinger equation for a stationary state of the given two-electron ("heliumlike") system:

$$\hat{H}\Psi(\boldsymbol{r}_1,\ \boldsymbol{r}_2) = E\Psi(\boldsymbol{r}_1,\ \boldsymbol{r}_2), \qquad (1)$$

where the Hamiltonian $\hat{H}$ has the form

$$\hat{H} = -\frac{\hbar^2}{2m}(\Delta_{r_1} + \Delta_{r_2}) - Ze^2\left(\frac{1}{r_1} + \frac{1}{r_2}\right) + \frac{e^2}{r_{12}}. \qquad (2)$$

According to the conditions specified in the problem, the last term is to be regarded as a perturbation. We denote it by $\hat{H}'$.

We shall carry out the subsequent computations in atomic units ($\hbar = 1,\ e = 1,\ m = 1$).

Since the unperturbed Hamiltonian $\hat{H}^{(0)} \equiv \hat{H} - \hat{H}'$ decomposes into two one-electron Hamiltonians, the unperturbed wave function of the ground state of the given system is equal to the product of two hydrogenlike functions in the field of the nucleus Z*:

---

*Since the ground state of a hydrogenlike atom lies much lower than the excited states, it is clear that the ground state of a helium-like system will be constructed from the ground states of the corresponding hydrogenlike systems.

$$\Psi^{(0)}(r_1, r_2) = \psi_0(r_1)\psi_0(r_2) = \frac{Z^{3/2}}{\sqrt{\pi}} e^{-Zr_1} \cdot \frac{Z^{3/2}}{\sqrt{\pi}} e^{-Zr_2} = \frac{Z^3}{\pi} e^{-Z(r_1+r_2)}, \tag{3}$$

while the unperturbed ground-state energy is equal to the sum of the ground-state energies of the hydrogenlike atoms

$$E^{(0)} = -\frac{Z^2}{2} - \frac{Z^2}{2} = -Z^2. \tag{4}$$

The first-order correction to the ground-state energy is equal to the average value of the perturbation energy H' in the unperturbed state (3):

$$E^{(1)} = \overline{H'} = \int\int \Psi_0^*(r_1, r_2)\hat{H}'\Psi_0(r_1, r_2)\,dr_1\,dr_2 = \frac{Z^6}{\pi^2}\int\int e^{-2Z(r_1+r_2)}\frac{1}{r_{12}}\,dr_1\,dr_2. \tag{5}$$

The resulting integral can be computed by various methods. We shall use one of the simplest.*

The quantity $\frac{1}{r_{12}} = \frac{1}{|r_1 - r_2|}$ is a generating function of Legendre polynomials:

$$\frac{1}{|r_1 - r_2|} = \begin{cases} \frac{1}{r_1}\sum_{l=0}^{\infty}\left(\frac{r_2}{r_1}\right)^l P_l(\cos\theta) & \text{for } r_1 > r_2, \quad (6') \\ \frac{1}{r_2}\sum_{l=0}^{\infty}\left(\frac{r_1}{r_2}\right)^l P_l(\cos\theta) & \text{for } r_1 < r_2, \quad (6'') \end{cases}$$

where θ is the angle between r_1 and r_2.

For instance, integrating first over r_2 and breaking up the region of integration over r_2 in accordance with (6′) and (6″), we have

$$E^{(1)} = \frac{Z^6}{\pi^2}\int dr_1\, e^{-2Zr_1}\left\{\int_{r_2=0}^{r_1} dr_2\, e^{-2Zr_2}\frac{1}{r_1}\sum_{l=0}^{\infty}\left(\frac{r_2}{r_1}\right)^l P_l(\cos\theta) + \int_{r_2=r_1}^{\infty} dr_2\, e^{-2Zr_2}\frac{1}{r_2}\sum_{l=0}^{\infty}\left(\frac{r_1}{r_2}\right)^l P_l(\cos\theta)\right\}.$$

*Another method, based on the computation of the electrostatic interaction of two spherically symmetric charge distributions, is presented in [16].

Selecting r_1 as the polar axis of the spherical-coordinate system in integrating over r_2, and using the orthogonality of the Legendre polynomials

$$\int_0^{\pi} P_l(\cos\theta)\sin\theta\, d\theta = \int_0^{\pi} P_l(\cos\theta)\, P_0(\cos\theta)\sin\theta\, d\theta = \frac{2}{2l+1}\delta_{l0},$$

we can convince ourselves that, after we have integrated over the angles, only two terms (corresponding to $l=0$) are left in the braces:

$$E^{(1)} = \frac{Z^6}{\pi^2}\int dr_1\, e^{-2Zr_1}\cdot 4\pi\left\{\frac{1}{r_1}\int_0^{r_1} e^{-2Zr_2} r_2^2\, dr_2 + \int_{r_1}^{\infty} e^{-2Zr_2} r_2\, dr_2\right\}.$$

Performing the remaining elementary integration, we find finally

$$E^{(1)} = \frac{5}{8}Z. \tag{7}$$

The positive sign of this correction corresponds, as it should, to the mutual repulsion of the electrons.

According to (4) and (7), the energy of the ground state of a heliumlike atom in a first-order approximation is equal to

$$E \approx E^{(0)} + E^{(1)} = -\left(Z^2 - \frac{5}{8}Z\right), \tag{8}$$

or, in ordinary units,

$$E \approx -\left(Z^2 - \frac{5}{8}Z\right)\frac{me^4}{\hbar^2} = -\left(Z^2 - \frac{5}{8}Z\right) 27.1 \text{ ev}. \tag{8'}$$

The first ionization potential V_1 means the energy necessary for removing one of the electrons to a state in the continuous spectrum with an energy equal to zero.

Obviously, this equantity is equal to the difference between the total ionization energy $-E$ [see (8)] and the ionization energy of a one-electron atom (ion) $\frac{1}{2}Z^2$ A. U.:

$$V_1 = \left(Z^2 - \frac{5}{8}Z\right) - \frac{1}{2}Z^2 = \left(\frac{1}{2}Z^2 - \frac{5}{8}Z\right) \text{ A. U.} = \left(\frac{1}{2}Z^2 - \frac{5}{8}Z\right) 27.1 \text{ ev}. \tag{9}$$

The condition which must be satisfied for perturbation theory to be valid in the given problem is the inequality $Z \gg 1$, as is apparent from (8).*

---

*In the given simple example, the condition for validity of perturbation theory does not require more rigorous consideration

It is interesting to note that, even for $Z = 2$, the value (8) of the total binding energy obtained in our relatively rough computation agrees with the experimental value within 5%. For larger Z ($Z = 3$ — a Li^+ ion, $Z = 4$ — a Be^{++} ion, etc.), the agreement is naturally even better.

For the first ionization potential computed from equation (9), the agreement with experiment is considerably rougher. Thus, for a helium atom ($Z = 2$), the discrepancy is about 15%.

5. First of all, we shall show that the characteristic time parameter τ appears in the perturbing field in such a way that the total momentum P imparted to an oscillator (classical) by the electric field during the entire duration of the perturbation does not depend on τ:

$$P = \int_{-\infty}^{\infty} e\mathscr{E}(t)\,dt = \frac{eA}{\sqrt{\pi\tau}} \int_{-\infty}^{\infty} e^{-\left(\frac{t}{\tau}\right)^2} dt = eA = \text{const.} \tag{1}$$

Graphically, this implies that the areas under the curves are identical for all τ (see figure).

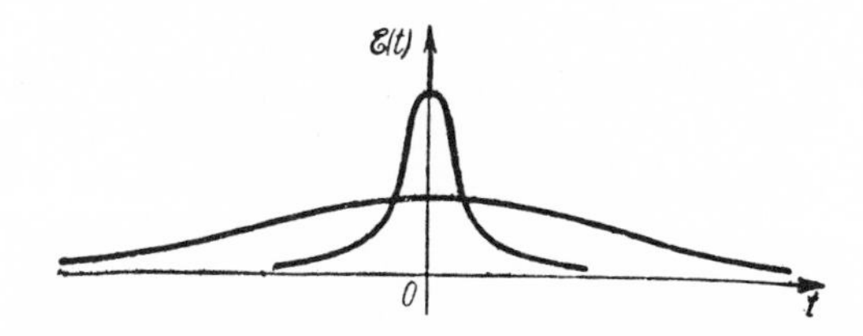

The probability of a transition from the n-th stationary state in the discrete spectrum to the k-th is [1, 6]

$$w_{nk} = \frac{1}{\hbar^2} \left| \int_{-\infty}^{\infty} V_{kn} e^{i\omega_{kn}t}\,dt \right|^2. \tag{2}$$

Here, $V_{kn} = \int_{-\infty}^{\infty} \psi_k^{(0)*} \hat{V} \psi_n^{(0)}\,dx$ is the matrix element of the perturbation $\hat{V}$, and $\omega_{kn} = \frac{1}{\hbar}\left[E_k^{(0)} - E_n^{(0)}\right]$, where $\psi_k^{(0)}$, $\psi_n^{(0)}$, $E_k^{(0)}$, $E_n^{(0)}$ are the wave functions and energy levels of the corresponding (unperturbed) stationary states.

(finding the first-order correction to the Ψ-function or the second-order correction to the energy).

We let e, μ, and ω denote the charge, mass, and natural frequency of the oscillator respectively, and x its deviation from its equilibrium position. In the given case of a uniform field, the perturbation operator is

$$\hat{V}(x, t) = -ex\mathcal{E}(t) \sim x.$$

It is known that, in the matrix of the position of the oscillator (energy space), the only nonzero elements are those immediately adjacent to the diagonal elements and that $x_{n, n+1} = x_{n+1, n} = \sqrt{\frac{(n+1)\hbar}{2\mu\omega}}$. Since, according to the specified conditions, the initial state of the oscillator is the ground state ($n = 0$), the nonzero elements of the perturbation matrix are

$$V_{01} = V_{10} = -\frac{P}{\sqrt{\pi}\tau}\sqrt{\frac{\hbar}{2\mu\omega}}\, e^{-\left(\frac{t}{\tau}\right)^2}. \tag{3}$$

Thus, in the first approximation using perturbation theory, a uniform field can produce a transition of the oscillator only to the first excited level ($k = n + 1 = 1$).*

Substituting expression (3) and $\omega_{kn} = \omega_{10} \equiv \frac{1}{\hbar}[E_1^{(0)} - E_0^{(0)}] = \omega$ into (2), we obtain the probability of excitation

$$w_{01} = \frac{P^2}{2\pi\tau^2\mu\hbar\omega}\left|\int_{-\infty}^{\infty} e^{i\omega t - \left(\frac{t}{\tau}\right)^2} dt\right|^2. \tag{4}$$

By computing the integral from the well-known relation

$$\int_{-\infty}^{\infty} e^{i\beta x - \alpha x^2}\, dx = \sqrt{\frac{\pi}{\alpha}}\, e^{-\frac{\beta^2}{4\alpha}},$$

we finally find

$$w_{01} = \frac{P^2}{2\mu\hbar\omega}\, e^{-\frac{1}{2}(\omega\tau)^2}. \tag{5}$$

---

*To compute the probability of a transition to the second excited level, it is necessary to use the second-order approximation of perturbation theory (the transition $n=0 \to n = 2$ takes place as though it passed through the "intermediate" state $n = 1$), and so on. Each number of a level is related to the corresponding order of approximation of perturbation theory and to the correspondingly increasing number of intermediate states. From the fact that all the elements of the position matrix are immediately adjacent to the diagonal, it follows that all of these intermediate states are adjacent (for instance, the transition $0 \to 1 \to 2 \to 3$, etc.). With reference to this subject, see the end of problem No. 9.

Thus, for a given classically imparted total momentum P (specified in the problem), the probability of excitation decreases with the increase of the effective duration of the perturbation τ, and, for $\tau \gg \frac{1}{\omega}$ (the duration of the perturbation is many times greater than the classical period of the oscillator), this probability is extremely small. This is the case of a so-called adiabatic perturbation.

On the contrary, for a rapid perturbation ($\tau \ll \frac{1}{\omega}$), the probability of excitation (5) is practically constant. In the limit as $\tau \to 0$, for which, according to the well-known expression for the δ-function,

$$\lim_{\tau \to 0} \mathscr{E}(t) = A\delta(t) = \frac{P}{e}\delta(t),$$

we have the so-called sudden (instantaneous, ballistic) perturbation. In this case, the probability assumes the value

$$\lim_{\tau \to 0} w_{01} = \frac{P^2}{2\mu\hbar\omega}, \qquad (5')$$

which is equal to the ratio of the classically imparted energy $\frac{1}{2\mu}P^2$ to the difference between the energy levels of the oscillator $\hbar\omega$.

The criterion for the applicability of perturbation theory [equation (2)] is that the probability of excitation be small relative to the probability that the oscillator will remain in the normal state:

$$w_{01} \ll (1 - w_{01}), \quad \text{or} \quad w_{01} \ll 1. \qquad (6)$$

It is apparent from (5) that a sufficient condition for requirement (6) to be satisfied is

$$\frac{P^2}{2\mu} = \frac{(eA)^2}{2\mu} \ll \hbar\omega. \qquad (6')$$

However, it is clear that, if the change of the field is sufficiently adiabatic, i.e., if $\tau \gg \frac{1}{\omega}$, condition (6′) is too rigorous and perturbation theory will be applicable simply if $\frac{1}{2\mu}P^2$ is of the order of $\hbar\omega$.

We emphasize that the excitation of the oscillator when condition (6′) is satisfied is a purely quantum-mechanical effect. Indeed, according to classical mechanics, the excitation of the oscillator by $\hbar\omega$ would be impossible because of the law of conservation of energy. According to quantum mechanics, the excitation is possible, although its probability is small [cf. (5), (5′)]. This does not of course contradict the law of conservation of energy, since, generally speaking, it is no longer possible in quantum mechanics to interpret the quantity $\frac{P^2}{2\mu}$ classically as the energy imparted to the oscillator by the field.*

6. The perturbation given in the problem has a form qualitatively similar to the "Gaussian" perturbation of the preceding problem. It is easily verified that the condition $P = \int_{-\infty}^{\infty} e\mathcal{E}(t)\,dt =$ const leads to the following equation for the time-dependent electric field

$$\mathcal{E}(t) = \frac{P}{e}\,\frac{\tau}{\pi}\,\frac{1}{\tau^2 + t^2}. \tag{1}$$

All of the equations of the preceding problem hold without change up to equation (3), which is replaced by

$$V_{01} = V_{10} = -P\frac{\tau}{\pi}\sqrt{\frac{\hbar}{2\mu\omega}}\,\frac{1}{\tau^2 + t^2}. \tag{2}$$

Therefore, for the probability of a transition to the first excited level, we obtain, instead of (4):

$$w_{01} = \frac{P^2\tau^2}{2\pi^2\mu\hbar\omega}\left|\int_{-\infty}^{\infty}\frac{e^{i\omega t}\,dt}{t^2 + \tau^2}\right|^2. \tag{3}$$

The integral appearing in (3) is computed most conveniently by using the theory of residues. For this, we transform to the complex plane of the variable t (see figure) and supplement the real axis [along which the integration in (3) takes place] with a semicircle of infinitely large radius in the upper half plane. When the integration contour is closed in this way, the value of integral (3) will not change, since the integral over the arc tends toward zero because of the presence of the factor $e^{i\omega t}$.** Inside the closed integration contour we have obtained, the only isolated singular point (in the given case, a first-order role) of the function under the integral sign is the point $t = +i\tau$. The integral over t is equal to the product of $2\pi i$ and the residue of the function under the integral size at this point:

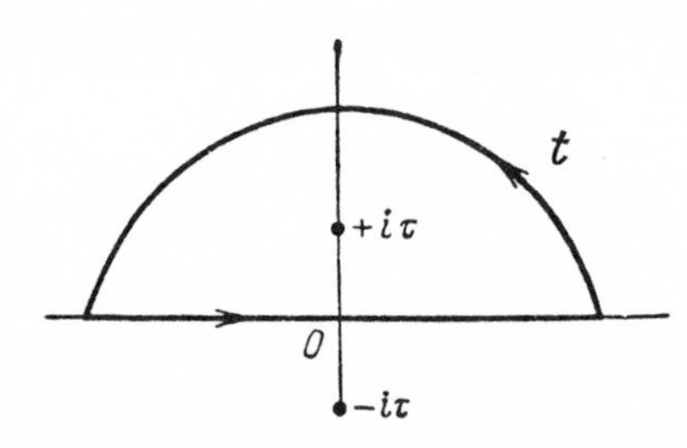

---

*Compare, however, with the first footnote to problem No. 9.

**It is essential that the remaining part of the function being integrated also tend toward zero as $|t| \to \infty$ [10].

$$\int_{-\infty}^{\infty} \frac{e^{i\omega t}\,dt}{t^2+\tau^2} = 2\pi i \operatorname{Res} \frac{e^{i\omega t}}{t^2+\tau^2}\bigg|_{t=i\tau} = 2\pi i \frac{e^{-\omega\tau}}{2i\tau} = \frac{\pi}{\tau} e^{-\omega\tau}.$$

Substituting this into (3), we find finally

$$w_{01} = \frac{P^2}{2\mu\hbar\omega} e^{-2\omega\tau}. \tag{4}$$

With regard to the qualitative dependence of this transition probability on the effective duration of the perturbation τ, and with regard to the requirement for validity of perturbation theory, it is possible to repeat exactly what we said in the preceding problem. We note that in the limiting case of a sudden perturbation ($\tau \to 0$), for which, from equation (1) and from one of the expressions for the δ-function $\lim\limits_{\tau\to 0} \mathscr{E}(t) = \frac{1}{e} P\delta(t)$, the transition probability tends toward $\frac{P^2}{2\mu\hbar\omega}$. This is exactly the same as equation (5′) of the preceding problem. We should have expected this, since, for a given $\int_{-\infty}^{\infty} \mathscr{E}(t)\,dt$, the probability of a transition caused by a sudden perturbation cannot depend on the specific form of the "impulse" function $\mathscr{E}(t)$. The formal expression of this is that there exists a number of different "impulse" functions transforming to the same function $\delta(t)$ as $\tau \to 0$.*

In the limiting case of an adiabatic perturbation ($\omega\tau \gg 1$), the transition probability is small, as we would expect. However, as we can see by comparing (4) with equation (5) of the preceding problem, it decreases less rapidly as the "adiabatic parameter" $\omega\tau$ decreases.

7. The general equation for the transition probability (per unit time) from a state in the discrete spectrum to a differential interval of a state in the continuous spectrum under the action of a periodic perturbation of frequency ω has the form [1, 6]:

$$dw_{n\nu} = \frac{2\pi}{\hbar} |F_{\nu n}|^2 \delta(E_\nu - E_n^{(0)} - \hbar\omega)\,d\nu. \tag{1}$$

Here n represents the set of quantum numbers characterizing the state in the discrete spectrum; ν represents the set of quantities for a state in the continuous spectrum, and $d\nu$ the corresponding interval;

---

*It is interesting to compare the case of sudden on-off switching of an infinitely large perturbation of "impulse" form ⊥ which we have considered here with the case of sudden switching of a perturbation of finite magnitude, but infinite duration, of the form _|¯ (a "step") considered in the general case in [1, p. 173].

$E_n^{(0)}$ and E_ν represent the unperturbed energy level of the discrete spectrum and the energy level of the continuous spectrum respectively; and $F_{\nu n}$ is the matrix element of the perturbation operator for the transition (for its definition, see below). The ψ-functions of the discrete spectrum are normalized to unity, while the ψ-functions of the continuous spectrum are normalized to $\delta(\nu - \nu')$.

We denote by $\boldsymbol{r}$ and $-e$ the radius vector and charge of the atom's electron, and by $\mathcal{E}_0$ the intensity of the uniform electric field. From the conditions specified in the problem, the perturbation operator has the form

$$\hat{V} = e\mathcal{E}(t)\boldsymbol{r} = e\mathcal{E}_0\boldsymbol{r}\sin\omega t = \hat{F}e^{-i\omega t} + \hat{F}^* e^{i\omega t}. \tag{2}$$

Hence,

$$\hat{F} = \frac{i}{2} e\mathcal{E}_0\boldsymbol{r}. \tag{2'}$$

The δ-function appearing in (1) points to the resonance nature of the possible transitions. Namely, the electron can be excited only to a state in the continuous spectrum with an energy*

$$E_\nu = E_n^{(0)} + \hbar\omega \tag{3}$$

(the absorption of a "quantum" of frequency ω). Since for a hydrogen atom in the normal state, $(E_\nu - E_n^{(0)})_{\min} = \frac{me^4}{2\hbar^2}$, the following minimum frequency necessary for ionization is obtained from (3):

$$\omega_{\min} = \frac{me^4}{2\hbar^3} \equiv \omega_0.$$

We shall now compute the matrix element

$$F_{\nu n} = \int \psi_\nu^* \hat{F} \psi_n^{(0)}\, d\tau \tag{4}$$

by substituting into it (2′) and (in accordance with the above-mentioned normalization of the ψ-functions)

$$\psi_n^{(0)} = \psi_{100} = (\pi a^3)^{-1/2} e^{-r/a}, \qquad \psi_\nu \approx \psi_k = (2\pi)^{-3/2} e^{i\boldsymbol{kr}}.$$

For the set of quantities ν, we have selected the propagation vector $\boldsymbol{k}$ of the ejected electron. It is clear that, strictly speaking, the use of a plane wave for ψ_ν is legitimate only if the inequality $\omega \gg \omega_0$ is satisfied (i.e., if the ejected electron is fast).

---

*Strictly speaking, equation (3) should contain the sign of approximate equality (see end of problem).

As a result of the above substitutions, (4) becomes

$$F_{\nu n}=\frac{ie}{2}(2\pi)^{-3/2}(\pi a^3)^{-1/2}\int e^{-ikr-r/a}(\mathcal{E}_0 r)\,dr. \tag{4'}$$

To compute the integral, we introduce a spherical-coordinate system $(r,\ \vartheta,\ \varphi)$ with the polar axis along $\boldsymbol{k}$, and we denote the angle between $\boldsymbol{k}$ and $\mathcal{E}_0$ by Θ. Then,

$$\mathcal{E}_0 \boldsymbol{r}=\mathcal{E}_0 r\,[\cos\Theta\cos\vartheta+\sin\Theta\sin\vartheta\cos(\varphi-\varphi_0)],$$

where φ_0 is the azimuth of $\mathcal{E}_0$ in the coordinate system we have selected. If we substitute this expression into (4′), the second term will obviously equal zero when it is integrated over φ. Thus, we obtain (setting $\cos\vartheta\equiv x$):

$$F_{\nu n}=\frac{ie}{2^{5/2}\pi^2 a^{3/2}}\,2\pi\mathcal{E}_0\cos\Theta\int_{-1}^{1}\left(\int_0^\infty e^{-ikrx-\frac{r}{a}}r^3\,dr\right)x\,dx=$$

$$=\frac{ie\mathcal{E}_0\cos\Theta}{\pi(2a)^{3/2}}\int_{-1}^{1}\frac{3!\,x\,dx}{\left(\frac{1}{a}+ikx\right)^4}=-\frac{e\mathcal{E}_0\cos\Theta}{\pi(2a)^{3/2}}\,\frac{16ka^5}{(1+k^2a^2)^3}.$$

Substituting into (1) the value of $|F_{\nu n}|^2$ obtained from this, as well as

$$d\nu=d\boldsymbol{k}=k^2dk\,d\Omega_k=k^2\frac{dk}{dE_\nu}\,d\Omega_k\,dE_\nu=\frac{mk}{\hbar^2}\,d\Omega_k\,dE_\nu$$

(where we have used the equation $E_\nu=\frac{\hbar^2k^2}{2m}$), we obtain

$$dw_{n\nu}=\frac{2^6}{\pi}\cdot\frac{ma^7e^2}{\hbar^3}\cdot\frac{\mathcal{E}_0^2k^3\cos^2\Theta}{(1+k^2a^2)^6}\,\delta\left(E_\nu-E_n^{(0)}-\hbar\omega\right)d\Omega_k\,dE_\nu,$$

where $d\Omega_k$ is an element of a solid angle whose axis lies along $\boldsymbol{k}$. Finally, integrating $dw_{n\nu}$ in terms of E_ν, we find the probability of ionization with ejection of the electron in the given direction $\boldsymbol{k}$ (within the element $d\Omega_k$). In this integration, it is obvious that only the point $E_\nu=E_n^{(0)}+\hbar\omega$, plays a part, i.e., $k^2=\frac{2mE_\nu}{\hbar^2}=\frac{2m}{\hbar}(\omega-\omega_0)$, from which $(1+k^2a^2)=\frac{\omega}{\omega_0}$ (we have substituted $E_n^{(0)}=-\frac{me^4}{2\hbar^2}=-\hbar\omega_0$). Moreover, considering that $a=\frac{\hbar^2}{me^2}$, we find finally

$$dw_k=\frac{64a^3}{\pi\hbar}\,\mathcal{E}_0^2\left(\frac{\omega_0}{\omega}\right)^6\left(\frac{\omega}{\omega_0}-1\right)^{3/2}\cos^2\Theta\,d\Omega_k. \tag{5}$$

Thus, as we would expect on the basis of the spherical symmetry of the initial state of the atom, the angular distribution of the electrons ejected from the atom by a high-frequency field is axially symmetric about the only preferred direction — that of the field $\mathcal{E}$. Moreover, this angular distribution is also symmetric with respect to the plane $\Theta = \frac{\pi}{2}$, where it becomes zero (impossibility of ejection of electrons perpendicular to the field $\mathcal{E}$). In other words, the distribution extends identically "forward" ($\Theta \approx 0$) and "backward" ($\Theta \approx \pi$).

This fact is also a natural consequence of the fact that the field $\mathcal{E}(t)$ oscillates in magnitude and in direction with a frequency exceeding the natural frequency ω of the electron in the atom. However, it is useful to note how this result (which is explainable qualitatively in classical mechanics) follows automatically from the quantum-mechanical computation. In equation (5), the appearance of the factor $\cos^2 \Theta$, which is symmetric relative to the directions $\mathcal{E}_0$ and $-\mathcal{E}_0$, is simply the result of the structure of the matrix element $F_{\nu n}$ [see (4′)], which does not depend on the time at all and which would therefore seem to be in no way connected with a sufficiently high frequency of the field. In reality, however, this high frequency is "contained" in the energy δ-function [see (1)], while for frequencies of the field less than ω_0, the probability (1) is strictly zero.*

Integrating (5) over all the ejection angles of the electron (which obviously yields $4\pi \overline{\cos^2 \Theta} = \frac{4\pi}{3}$), we obtain the total probability w_i of ionization of the atom per unit time as a function of the frequency of the field:

$$w_i(\omega) = \frac{256}{3} \frac{a^3}{\hbar} \mathcal{E}_0^2 \left(\frac{\omega_0}{\omega}\right)^6 \left(\frac{\omega}{\omega_0} - 1\right)^{3/2}. \tag{6}$$

For $\omega \gtrsim \omega_0$, i.e., near the ionization threshold, this probability increases from zero as $(\omega - \omega_0)^{3/2}$. For $\omega \gg \omega_0$, it decreases rapidly (as $\omega^{-9/2}$) with increasing ω. As we can easily see by differentiating function (6), it has one maximum at $\omega = \frac{4}{3} \omega_0$.

In conclusion, let us consider the range of validity of the equations of perturbation theory we have used above. First of all, in accordance with the actual derivation of equation (1), the time t elapsed since the time $t = 0$ must be sufficiently large. Moreover

---

*In other words, we can say that for $\omega < \omega_0$ the δ-function in (1) makes it impossible for the physical meaning of matrix element (4′) to manifest itself with a real value of k; i.e., in this case, the transition to the continuous spectrum is impossible.

[1, Section 44], the effective spread ΔE_ν of the energies of the possible final states of the electron is connected with the value of t by the uncertainty principle

$$\Delta E_\nu \cdot t \sim \hbar.$$

On the other hand, the time t must not be too great, so that the distortion of the initial ψ-functions of the atom is still relatively small. This is equivalent to the requirement that the probability of ionization $w_i t$ "accumulated" in the entire interval of time t be much smaller than unity. Hence, from (6), it is easy to obtain the restrictions placed by perturbation theory on the changes of each of the quantities t, $\mathscr{E}_0$, and ω for fixed values of the two remaining ones.

8. The wave function for the initial state of the electron (in atomic units) has the form

$$\psi_0 = \frac{Z^{3/2}}{\sqrt{\pi}} e^{-Zr}.$$

The final state, because of the electron's large velocity, is described by a plane wave

$$\psi_1 = \frac{1}{(2\pi)^{3/2}} e^{ikr}.$$

The perturbing interaction has the form (also in atomic units)

$$V = -\sum_p \frac{1}{|r - r_p|},$$

where the sum is taken over all the protons of the nucleus.

Designating the wave functions of the initial and final states of the nucleus by Ψ_0 and Ψ_1 respectively, we write the matrix element of the perturbation in the form

$$V_{01} = -\int\int dV\, d\tau\, \Psi_1^* \frac{1}{(2\pi)^{3/2}} e^{-ikr} \sum_p \frac{1}{|r - r_p|} \Psi_0 \frac{Z^{3/2}}{\sqrt{\pi}} e^{-Zr}, \qquad (1)$$

where $d\tau$ is the product of the differentials of all the coordinates of the nucleus, and dV is the product of the differentials of all the coordinates of the electron.

Let us expand the potential of the Coulomb interaction into a Fourier integral:

$$\sum_p \frac{1}{|r - r_p|} = \frac{1}{2\pi^2} \int \frac{dq}{q^2} \sum_p e^{iq(r - r_p)} = \frac{1}{2\pi^2} \int \frac{dq}{q^2} e^{iqr} \sum_p e^{-iqr_p}. \qquad (2)$$

Substituting this expansion into the matrix element (1) and changing the order of integration, we have

$$V_{01} = -\frac{Z^{3/2}}{2^{5/2}\pi^4}\int\frac{d\boldsymbol{q}}{q^2}\int d\tau\,\Psi_1^*\sum_p e^{-i\boldsymbol{q}\boldsymbol{r}_p}\Psi_0\int dV e^{-i\boldsymbol{k}\boldsymbol{r}+i\boldsymbol{q}\boldsymbol{r}-Zr}.$$

According to (2), $q_{\text{eff}}r \sim 1$. Moreover, since $r \gg r_p$ (the dimensions of the K-orbit are much greater than the dimensions of the nucleus), we have $|\boldsymbol{q}\boldsymbol{r}_p| \ll 1$. Accordingly, in the integral over the variables of the nucleus, we expand the exponential into a series of powers of $\boldsymbol{q}\boldsymbol{r}_p$ and discard all terms after the second one:

$$\int d\tau\,\Psi_1^*\sum_p e^{-i\boldsymbol{q}\boldsymbol{r}_p}\Psi_0 \approx \int d\tau\,\Psi_1^*\left(Z - i\boldsymbol{q}\sum_p \boldsymbol{r}_p\right)\Psi_0 =$$

$$= -i\boldsymbol{q}\int d\tau\,\Psi_1^*\sum_p \boldsymbol{r}_p\Psi_0 = -i\boldsymbol{q}\boldsymbol{d}_{01},$$

where we have used the mutual orthogonality of the functions of the nucleus Ψ_1 and Ψ_0, and where we have let $\boldsymbol{d}_{01}$ denote the matrix element of the dipole moment of the nucleus.

Computing the integral over the electron's coordinates, we obtain

$$\int dV\, e^{i(\boldsymbol{q}-\boldsymbol{k})\boldsymbol{r}-Zr} = \frac{8\pi Z}{[Z^2+(\boldsymbol{q}-\boldsymbol{k})^2]^2}.$$

Thus,

$$V_{01} = i\frac{Z^{5/2}\sqrt{2}}{\pi^3}\boldsymbol{d}_{01}\int\frac{d\boldsymbol{q}}{q^2}\frac{\boldsymbol{q}}{[Z^2+(\boldsymbol{q}-\boldsymbol{k})^2]^2}.$$

In the integral over $\boldsymbol{q}$, we define the new variable $\boldsymbol{q}' = \boldsymbol{q} - \boldsymbol{k}$:

$$\int\frac{\boldsymbol{q}'+\boldsymbol{k}}{(\boldsymbol{q}'+\boldsymbol{k})^2}\cdot\frac{d\boldsymbol{q}'}{[Z^2+q'^2]^2}.$$

The function under the integral has a maximum in the neighborhood of $q' = 0$. The width of this maximum is of the order of Z. From the conditions specified in the problem, the velocity of the ejected electron is much greater than the velocity of the electron: $k \gg Z$. Therefore, in the first fraction we can neglect the term $\boldsymbol{q}'$, as a result of which we obtain

$$\frac{\boldsymbol{k}}{k^2}\int\frac{d\boldsymbol{q}'}{(Z^2+q'^2)^2} = \frac{\pi^2}{Z}\frac{\boldsymbol{k}}{k^2}.$$

Thus, finally

$$V_{01} = i\frac{\sqrt{2}}{\pi}Z^{3/2}\frac{\boldsymbol{k}\boldsymbol{d}_{01}}{k^2}.$$

From the general formula for the probability of a transition under the effect of a constant perturbation the probability that the electron will be ejected within the solid angle $d\Omega$ is

$$dw = 2\pi|V_{01}|^2 k^2\frac{dk}{dE}d\Omega = 2\pi\frac{2}{\pi^2}Z^3\frac{|\boldsymbol{k}\boldsymbol{d}_{01}|^2}{k^4}k\,d\Omega = \frac{4Z^3}{\pi}\frac{|\boldsymbol{k}\boldsymbol{d}_{01}|^2}{k^3}d\Omega.$$

Integrating over all the angles, we obtain the total probability that an electron will be ejected per unit time

$$w = \frac{16}{3}\frac{Z^3}{k}\,|\boldsymbol{d}_{01}|^2,$$

or transforming to the usual units,

$$w = \frac{16}{3}\frac{m^3e^6}{\hbar^7}\frac{Z^3e^2}{\hbar v}\,|\boldsymbol{d}_{01}|^2.$$

On the other hand, the probability of dipole radiation is [17, p. 22]

$$w_{\text{rad}} = \frac{4}{3}\frac{\omega^3}{\hbar c^3}\,|\boldsymbol{d}_{01}|^2,$$

where ω is the frequency of the radiation.

Hence, the internal-conversion coefficient defined as

$$\alpha = \frac{w}{w + w_{\text{изл}}} = \frac{\dfrac{w}{w_{\text{изл}}}}{1 + \dfrac{w}{w_{\text{изл}}}}$$

is equal to

$$\alpha = \frac{4\left(\dfrac{Ze^2}{\hbar c}\right)^3 \dfrac{e^2}{\hbar v}\left(\dfrac{mc^2}{\hbar\omega}\right)^3}{1 + 4\left(\dfrac{Ze^2}{\hbar c}\right)^3 \dfrac{e^2}{\hbar v}\left(\dfrac{mc^2}{\hbar\omega}\right)^3}.$$

9. Let us take the moment when the field is switched on to be $t = 0$. The wave function of the oscillator up to this time, i.e., for $t \leq 0$, has the form $\psi_0(x)e^{-\frac{iE_0t}{\hbar}}$, where $\psi_0(x)$ is the function of the ground state, and $E_0 = \frac{1}{2}\hbar\omega$ is the zero point energy of the oscillator.

If the field is switched on suddenly at the time $t = 0$,* the ψ-function of the oscillator does not change instantaneously, and at $t = +0$ it is equal to its value at $t = -0$:

$$\psi_0(x) = \frac{\alpha^{1/2}}{\pi^{1/4}} e^{-\frac{1}{2}(\alpha x)^2}, \tag{1}$$

where $\alpha = \sqrt{\frac{\mu\omega}{\hbar}}$ (μ and ω are the mass and frequency of the oscillator).

---

*More accurately, if the duration of the time Δt in which the field is turned on is small relative to the natural "period" of the oscillator $\hbar/E_0 \sim 1/\omega$.

Meanwhile, the Hamiltonian of the oscillator changes discontinuously at $t = 0$ by the quantity $-e\mathcal{E}x$, and, from the results of problem No. 12, Chapter II, its eigenfunctions have the form

$$\varphi_n(x) \equiv \psi_n(x - x_0) = \frac{\alpha^{1/2}}{\pi^{1/4}} \frac{1}{\sqrt{2^n n!}} e^{-\frac{\alpha^2 (x-x_0)^2}{2}} H_n[\alpha(x - x_0)], \quad (2)$$

where $x_0 = \frac{e\mathcal{E}}{\mu\omega^2}$ is the displacement of the point of equilibrium of the oscillator after the field $\mathcal{E}$ is applied.

The initial ψ-function (1) is no longer an eigenfunction of the new Hamiltonian, but it does represent some superposition of the eigenfunctions (2) of this Hamiltonian:

$$\psi_0(x) = \sum_{n=0}^{\infty} c_n \varphi_n(x) = \sum_{n=0}^{\infty} c_n \psi_n(x - x_0), \quad (3)$$

where the c_n are constants.

This superposition corresponds to the time $t = +0$. At succeeding moments of time ($t > 0$), each of the eigenfunctions $\psi_n(x - x_0)$ is multiplied by $\exp\left(-\frac{iE_n t}{\hbar}\right)$, and the complete Ψ-function of the oscillator has the form

$$\Psi(x, t) = \sum_{n=0}^{\infty} c_n \psi_n(x - x_0) e^{-\frac{iE_n t}{\hbar}}, \quad (4)$$

where $E_n = \hbar\omega\left(n + \frac{1}{2}\right)$. The state described by function (4) is nonstationary.*

The probability that, for $t > 0$, the oscillator will be in the n-th level (i.e., the probability that it will be excited to this level as a result of the sudden switching on of the field $\mathcal{E}$) is given by $|c_n|^2$. Fourier's techniques for expansion (3) yield

$$c_n = \int_{-\infty}^{\infty} \psi_0(x)\, \psi_n^*(x - x_0)\, dx,$$

or, after substitution of (1) and (2),

$$c_n = \frac{\alpha}{\sqrt{\pi \cdot 2^n n!}} \int_{-\infty}^{\infty} \exp\left[-\frac{1}{2}(\alpha x)^2 - \frac{1}{2}\alpha^2 (x - x_0)^2\right] \times \quad (5)$$
$$\times H_n[\alpha(x - x_0)]\, dx.$$

---

*The explicit form of the Ψ-function is easily established on the basis of problem No. 3, Chapter V.

We have already computed this integral (except for an unimportant difference in notation) in problem No. 3, Chapter V. There, we had

$$\frac{\alpha}{\sqrt{\pi \cdot 2^n n!}} \int_{-\infty}^{\infty} \exp\left[-\frac{1}{2}(\alpha x)^2 - \frac{1}{2}\alpha^2 (x-b)^2\right] H_n(\alpha x)\, dx =$$

$$= \frac{(\alpha b)^n \exp\left(-\frac{1}{4}\alpha^2 b^2\right)}{\sqrt{2^n n!}}.$$

After replacing q by $(-x_0)$ in this equation and changing the variable of integration $x \to (x - x_0)$, we find the value of (5):

$$c_n = (-1)^n \frac{(\alpha x_0)^n \exp\left(-\frac{1}{4}\alpha^2 x_0^2\right)}{\sqrt{2^n n!}}.$$

Hence, for the probability w_n, we have

$$w_n = |c_n|^2 = \frac{(\alpha x_0)^{2n} \exp\left(-\frac{1}{2}\alpha^2 x_0^2\right)}{2^n n!}. \tag{6}$$

Thus, the probability distribution function w_n represents a Poisson distribution $\frac{1}{n!}(\bar{n})^n e^{-\bar{n}}$ with a mean n equal to

$$\bar{n} = \frac{1}{2}(\alpha x_0)^2 = \frac{e^2 \mathcal{E}^2}{2\mu \hbar \omega^3}. \tag{7}$$

Since the Poisson distribution is normalized to unity $\left(\sum_{n=0}^{\infty} \frac{e^{-\bar{n}}(\bar{n})^n}{n!} = e^{-\bar{n}} \cdot e^{\bar{n}} = 1\right)$, the distribution of the probabilities of excitation to the different levels automatically satisfies the normalization condition $\sum_{n=0}^{\infty} w_n = 1$ (as we would expect since all the ψ-functions used were normalized to unity).

We emphasize (also in regard to the next problem) that, generally speaking, a sudden change of the Hamiltonian (a "shock") may be a far from small perturbation. Therefore, in the general case, the probability of excitation is not small.

Thus, for a sufficiently large intensity of the field $\mathcal{E}$, satisfying the inequality

$$\mathcal{E} \gg \frac{1}{e}\sqrt{\mu \hbar \omega^3}, \quad \text{i.e.,} \quad \bar{n} \gg 1, \tag{8}$$

the probability that the oscillator will remain in the normal state after the field is turned off is $w_0 = e^{-\bar{n}} \ll 1$ from (6) and (7), while the probability that it will be excited is

$$\sum_{n=1}^{\infty} w_n = 1 - w_0 = 1 - e^{-\bar{n}} \approx 1.$$

This fact has a very evident physical cause. Inequality (8) can be rewritten in the form

$$e\mathcal{E} \cdot \frac{1}{\omega} \gg \sqrt{\mu\hbar\omega}. \qquad (8')$$

This means that the impulse acting on the oscillator from the electric field during a time of the order of the oscillator's period $\left(\frac{2\pi}{\omega}\right)$ is large relative to the quantum-mechanical amplitude of the zero-point oscillations of the momentum (or relative to the root-mean-square momentum), which is of the order of $\sqrt{\mu\hbar\omega}$. It is clear that under this condition the excitation must take place with a probability close to unity.*

At the same time, it follows from the elementary property of the Poisson distribution (see also problem No. 3, Chapter V) that excitation to the level with $n \approx \bar{n} \gg 1$ will occur with greatest probability. The larger n is, the sharper this maximum in the distribution (6) will be (its width is of the order of $\sqrt{\bar{n}}$). In other words, the group of levels with energies near

$$E_{\bar{n}} = \hbar\omega\left(\bar{n} + \frac{1}{2}\right) \approx \frac{1}{2\mu}\left(\frac{e\mathcal{E}}{\omega}\right)^2 \qquad (9)$$

is excited with greatest probability.

Since the motion of the oscillator is quasi-classical for $n_{\text{eff}} \approx \bar{n} \gg 1$, the value of the quasi-classical amplitude $a_{\bar{n}}$ of the oscillations performed by the oscillator when it is excited by the field has a meaning. Equating the total energy (9) of the oscillator to its maximum potential energy $\frac{1}{2}\mu\omega^2 a_{\bar{n}}^2$, we obtain

$$a_{\bar{n}} = \frac{e\mathcal{E}}{\mu\omega^2} = x_0. \qquad (10)$$

As we should have expected on the basis of the quasi-classical nature of the motion for $\bar{n} \gg 1$, equations (9) and (10) are identical with the classical equations. Indeed, if a field $\mathcal{E}$ is applied to an oscillator in the "lowest energy state" (i.e., at rest), the amplitude a of the oscillations produced will be equal to a displacement x_0 of

---

*We emphasize that, as distinguished from the case of a small perturbation (see below, and also problems No. 5 and No. 6), it is possible to talk in the classical terms of the impulse (or energy) imparted, if condition (8) is satisfied, since this condition implies that the motion of the oscillator is quasi-classical after the field is applied.

the point of equilibrium,* and correspondingly the oscillation energy $E = \frac{1}{2}\mu\omega^2 a^2$ will be equal to $\frac{1}{2\mu}\left(\frac{e\mathcal{E}}{\omega}\right)^2$, in full agreement with (9) and (10).**

In the opposite limiting case, i.e., for $\bar{n} \ll 1$, the probability of excitation, which (6) is approximately equal to $w_n \approx \frac{1}{n!}(\bar{n})^n$, decreases monotonically (and extremely rapidly) with increasing n. Therefore, only the probability of a transition to the first excited level is at all significant:

$$w_1 \approx \bar{n} = \frac{e^2\mathcal{E}^2}{2\mu\hbar\omega^3} \ll 1.$$

As expected, this result is exactly the same as that obtained in first-order perturbation theory for the case of "sudden" turning on of a perturbing potential [1, equation (41.4)].

Moreover, it is clear that, if the probabilities of excitation to higher levels — w_2, w_3, etc. (each of which is smaller than the preceding one by a factor of approximately $1/\bar{n}$) — are computed for $\bar{n} \ll 1$ according to the exact formula (6), they will be exactly the same as those computed from approximations of the second order, third order, and so on (see the first footnote to Problem No. 5).

10. The first inequality given in the problem implies that the ψ-function of the atom (i.e., the ψ-function of the electronic shell) is not able to change significantly during the duration τ of the impulse. The second inequality implies that the nucleus can be regarded as having stayed in practically the same place during the duration of the impulse.

To find the probability of the transition, it is necessary to expand the initial wave function of the electronic shell ψ_0 (cf. the first condition!) into a series of eigenfunctions of the shell for the moving nucleus. Each of these functions describes a stationary state of the moving atom.*** According to the general rules of quantum mechanics, the coefficients of this expansion give the probability of the corresponding states of the atom.

---

*This is easily demonstrated by writing the law of conservation of energy for the accelerated and retarded parts of one half-period of oscillation $\left(\frac{1}{2}\mu v^2\right)_{\max} = \int_0^{x_0} (e\mathcal{E} - \mu\omega^2 x)\,dx = \int_{x_0}^{x_1} (\mu\omega^2 x - e\mathcal{E})\,dx.$

Hence, $x_1 = \frac{2e\mathcal{E}}{\mu\omega^2} = 2x_0$, which is what had to be proved.

**Concerning (9), i.e., the classically imparted energy, compare with problem No. 12, Chapter V.

***The system of these functions obviously includes functions belonging to the continuous spectrum, i.e., functions describing the states of the ionized atom.

This expansion can be carried out either in the system of coordinates in which the nucleus was initially at rest, or, more conveniently, in a system of coordinates moving together with the nucleus after the jolt. In the latter system, the eigenfunctions of the possible final states appear as the set of the ordinary stationary ψ-functions of an atom at rest:

$$\psi_n(\mathbf{r}_1, \mathbf{r}_2, \dots, \mathbf{r}_i, \dots, \mathbf{r}_N), \tag{1}$$

where the $\mathbf{r}_i$ represent the coordinates of the i-th electron of the shell relative to the nucleus, while the subscript n designates the set of quantum numbers characterizing a stationary state of the atom.

In this system, the initial ψ-function transforms to

$$\psi_0' = e^{-\frac{imv\sum\limits_i \mathbf{r}_i}{\hbar}} \psi_0(\mathbf{r}_1, \mathbf{r}_2, \dots, \mathbf{r}_i, \dots, \mathbf{r}_N), \tag{2}$$

where m is the mass of the electron.

Indeed, the exponential factor represents the ψ-function of the center of mass of the electronic shell, which in the coordinate system we have selected obviously moves with a velocity $-\mathbf{v}$,* while $\psi_0(\mathbf{r}_1, \dots, \mathbf{r}_N)$ is the ψ-function of the shell in the system of its center of mass. Because of the second condition of the problem, the $\mathbf{r}_i$ in (2) are measured from the same origin as in (1).

The required expansion of ψ_0' has the form

$$\psi_0'(\mathbf{r}_1, \dots, \mathbf{r}_i, \dots, \mathbf{r}_N) = \sum_n c_n \psi_n(\mathbf{r}_1, \dots, \mathbf{r}_i, \dots, \mathbf{r}_N).$$

Multiplying both sides of this equation by

$$\psi_n^* d\tau_1 \dots d\tau_i \dots d\tau_N \qquad (d\tau_i = dx_i\, dy_i\, dz_i)$$

and integrating over the entire configuration space of the electrons,** we obtain, assuming that the functions $\psi_n, \psi_m, \dots$ are normalized to δ_{nm},

$$c_n = \int \dots \int \psi_n^*(\mathbf{r}_1, \dots, \mathbf{r}_i, \dots, \mathbf{r}_N) \times$$

$$\times e^{iq\sum\limits_i \mathbf{r}_i} \psi_0(\mathbf{r}_1, \dots, \mathbf{r}_i, \dots, \mathbf{r}_N)\, d\tau_1 \dots d\tau_i \dots d\tau_N.$$

---

*We have

$$\psi_{c.m} = \exp\left\{\frac{i}{\hbar} \mathbf{P}_{c.m} \mathbf{R}_{c.m}\right\} = \exp\left\{\frac{i}{\hbar} \sum_i m_i(-\mathbf{v}) \frac{\sum\limits_i m_i \mathbf{r}_i}{\sum\limits_i m_i}\right\}.$$

Hence, the required expression for $\psi_{c.m}$ follows, since $m_1 = m_2 = \dots = m_i = \dots \equiv m$.

**Including a summation over the spin suffixes.

The probability of a transition to the state n is

$$w_n = |c_n|^2 = \left| \int \psi_n^* e^{iq \sum_{i=1}^{N} r_i} \psi_0 \, d\tau \right|^2, \tag{3}$$

where the following notation is used:

$$q = -\frac{mv}{\hbar}, \quad d\tau = \prod_{i=1}^{N} d\tau_i.$$

This result is easily generalized to the case of a transition to the continuous spectrum, i.e., to the case of ionization of the atom [18].

We note that, if the inequality $qa \ll 1$ is satisfied, the probability (3) that the atom will be excited by the "jarring" is proportional to the probability of the corresponding transition in the optical spectrum. Indeed, in this case, we can expand the exponential factor and retain only two of its terms:

$$e^{iq \sum_i r_i} \approx 1 + iq \sum_i r_i.$$

Then, the integral of the zeroth power term will be zero, since the wave functions ψ_0 and ψ_n are orthogonal. Moreover, taking the direction of $\boldsymbol{q}$ to be the z-axis, we obtain

$$w_n \approx q^2 \left| \int \psi_n^* \left(\sum_i z_i \right) \psi_0 \, d\tau \right|^2,$$

which is proportional to the probability of the optical transition $0 \to n$.

11. According to equation (3) of the preceding problem, the probability of a transition of the hydrogen atom to the n-th stationary state is

$$w_n = \left| \int \psi_n^* e^{i\boldsymbol{qr}} \psi_0 \, dr \right|^2, \tag{1}$$

where $\psi_0 = (\pi a^3)^{-1/2} e^{-r/a}$ $\left(a = \frac{\hbar^2}{me^2} \text{ is the Bohr radius} \right)$, and $\boldsymbol{q} = \frac{m\boldsymbol{v}}{\hbar}$ ($\boldsymbol{v}$ is the velocity delivered to the proton). Since $\boldsymbol{v} = \frac{\boldsymbol{p}}{M}$, where M is the mass of the proton, we have

$$\boldsymbol{q} = -\frac{m}{M} \frac{\boldsymbol{p}}{\hbar}. \tag{2}$$

The total probability of excitation and ionization of the atom is obviously equal to $1 - w_0$, where, according to (1), w_0 — the probability that the atom will remain in the ground state — is equal to

$$w_0 = \left| \int \psi_0^2 e^{iqr}\, dr \right|^2,$$

which after substituting ψ_0 becomes

$$w_0 = \frac{1}{(\pi a^3)} \left| \int e^{-\frac{2r}{a} + iqr}\, dr \right|^2. \tag{3}$$

We have computed the integral appearing in this expression several times (problems No. 9 of Chapter III and No. 8 of this chapter). It is equal to

$$\int e^{-\frac{2r}{a} + iqr}\, dr = \frac{16\pi a^3}{(4 + q^2 a^2)^2}.$$

Thus, the probability that the atom will remain in the ground state is

$$w_0 = \frac{1}{\left(1 + \frac{1}{4} q^2 a^2\right)^4}, \tag{4}$$

while the total probability of excitation and ionization of the atom is

$$1 - w_0 = 1 - \frac{1}{\left(1 + \frac{1}{4} q^2 a^2\right)^4}. \tag{5}$$

As we would expect, in the limiting cases of weak $\left(\frac{1}{2} qa \ll 1\right)$ and strong $\left(\frac{1}{2} qa \gg 1\right)$ jarring, probability (5) tends toward zero and unity respectively. The corresponding limiting expressions have the form

$$\frac{1}{2} qa \ll 1: \quad 1 - w_0 \approx q^2 a^2,$$

$$\frac{1}{2} qa \gg 1: \quad 1 - w_0 \approx 1 - \left(\frac{2}{qa}\right)^8.$$

We note that qualitatively these results are obvious without any computations from equation (3) for w_0: this quantity is close to unity or it is small depending on the speed of the oscillations of the factor e^{iqr} over the lengths of the attenuation factor $e^{-2r/a}$. The measure of this speed is precisely the quantity $\frac{qa}{2}$.

The criteria for the applicability of the approximation used here are given in the formulation of the preceding problem. Since ionization of the atom plays an important role in the present problem, it is necessary to define further the first of these criteria — the criterion for the suddenness (ballistic nature) of the action. Namely, the duration of the jolt τ must be small relative to the Bohr periods for the important transitions:

$$\tau \ll \frac{\hbar}{|E_k - E_0|}, \tag{6}$$

where E_0 and E_k are the energies of the initial and final states of the atom respectively. In our case, $E_0 = -\frac{me^4}{2\hbar^2}$, while E_k is equal to the kinetic energy of the ejected electron.

The effective values of E_k can be evaluated from (1). Thus, for $qa \gg 1$, the integral in (1) is appreciably different from zero only for states whose ψ-functions (ψ_n) contain a factor of the type $e^{i\boldsymbol{kr}}$ with $\boldsymbol{k} \approx \boldsymbol{q}$ (only under this condition do the rapid oscillations of the function under the integral cancel each other out). Therefore, here,

$$(E_k)_{\text{eff}} \sim \frac{\hbar^2 q^2}{m} \sim \frac{m}{M} E_p, \tag{7}$$

where E_p is the energy imparted to the proton.

For $qa \ll 1$, it is easily understood that the integral in (1) is basically determined by the degree of overlapping of ψ_0 and ψ_n^*. Thus, an appreciable transition probability is obtained only for final states $k \lesssim \frac{1}{a}$. Hence,

$$(E_k)_{\text{eff}} \sim \frac{\hbar^2}{ma^2} \sim E_0. \tag{8}$$

The set of equations (6) and (7) or (6) and (8) (depending on qa, i.e., on p) thus represents the condition for the range of applicability of the "ballistic" approximation.

12. The state of the system is described by the wave function $\Psi(t)$, which satisfies the wave equation

$$i\hbar \frac{\partial \Psi}{\partial t} = \hat{H}(t) \Psi, \tag{1}$$

for which, from the conditions specified in the problem,

$$\hat{H}(t) \psi_n(t) = E_n(t) \psi_n(t). \tag{2}$$

Because of the finiteness of the motion, the spectrum of "levels" E_n* is discrete, and since the motion is confined to one dimension,

---

*The concept of "energy level" has a purely formal meaning here, since energy is not conserved for explicitly time-dependent Hamiltonians.

these levels are not degenerate. This latter factor in turn implies ([1], p. 70) that the functions $\psi_n(t)$ are real (except for an unimportant phase factor).

According to the requirements of the problem, we must expand the wave function $\Psi(t)$ into a series of "instantaneous" eigenfunctions $\psi_n(t)$ of the Hamiltonian. Regarding the Ψ-function for $t = 0$ as known, we can represent this expansion for $t \geq 0$ in the form

$$\Psi = \sum_n c_n(t)\,\psi_n(t)\exp\left[-\frac{i}{\hbar}\int_0^t E_n(t')\,dt'\right]. \tag{3}$$

The set of coefficients of this expansion $c_n(t)$ represents the wave function in the required space. The writing of the wave equation in this space means finding the system of equations connecting the coefficients c_n with their time derivatives $\dot{c}_n$.

Substituting (3) into (1), we have

$$i\hbar\sum_n\left(\dot{c}_n\psi_n + c_n\dot{\psi}_n - \frac{i}{\hbar}c_n\psi_n E_n\right)\exp\left[-\frac{i}{\hbar}\int_0^t E_n(t')\,dt'\right] =$$

$$= \hat{H}\sum_n c_n\psi_n\exp\left[-\frac{i}{\hbar}\int_0^t E_n(t')\,dt'\right].$$

Because of (2), the right member of this equation cancels with the last term of the left member. Multiplying both sides by $\psi_k^* = \psi_k$ from the left and integrating over the coordinates of the system q, we obtain as a consequence of the orthonormal nature of the functions ψ_n:

$$\dot{c}_k = -\sum_n c_n\exp\left[\frac{i}{\hbar}\int_0^t (E_k - E_n)\,dt'\right]\int\psi_k\dot{\psi}_n\,dq. \tag{4}$$

Let us transform the last integral in this equation. First of all, for $n = k$, we have $\int\psi_k\dot{\psi}_k\,dq = \frac{1}{2}\frac{d}{dt}\int\psi_k^2\,dq = 0$, since $\int\psi_k^2\,dq = 1$.

Moreover, differentiating (2) with respect to t, multiplying from the left by $\psi_k^* = \psi_k$, and integrating over q, we have, for $n \neq k$:

$$\int\psi_k\frac{\partial\hat{H}}{\partial t}\psi_n\,dq + \int\psi_k\hat{H}\dot{\psi}_n\,dq = E_n\int\psi_k\dot{\psi}_n\,dq. \tag{5}$$

Because the Hamiltonian is Hermitian (and real), and because of equation (2), we have

$$\int \psi_k \hat{H} \dot{\psi}_n \, dq = \int (\hat{H} \psi_k) \dot{\psi}_n \, dq = E_k \int \psi_k \dot{\psi}_n \, dq.$$

Substituting this into (5), we obtain

$$\int \psi_k \dot{\psi}_n \, dq = -\frac{\int \psi_k \left(\frac{\partial \hat{H}}{\partial t} \right) \psi_n \, dq}{E_k - E_n} \qquad (n \neq k). \tag{6}$$

Finally, substituting into (4) equation (6) (concerning which we remember that the least term with $n = k$ is equal to zero), and using the notation

$$E_k - E_n = \hbar \omega_{kn}, \qquad \int \psi_k \left(\frac{\partial \hat{H}}{\partial t} \right) \psi_n \, dq = \left(\frac{\partial H}{\partial t} \right)_{kn}, \tag{7}$$

we arrive at the desired system of equations:

$$\dot{c}_k = \sum_n{}' \frac{c_n}{\hbar \omega_{kn}} \left(\frac{\partial H}{\partial t} \right)_{kn} e^{i \int_0^t \omega_{kn} \, dt'}, \tag{8}$$

where the prime on the summation sign shows that the term with $n = k$ is not included in the summation. According to (7), the quantity $\left(\frac{\partial H}{\partial t} \right)_{kn}$ represents the matrix element of the time derivative of the Hamiltonian for the transition $k \rightarrow n$.

It is apparent from our derivation that the set of equations (8) for all k is exactly equivalent to the initial wave equation (1).

Let us compare our equations with the initial time-dependent equations of ordinary perturbation theory [1, 6]. There, we have $\hat{H}(t) = \hat{H}_0 + \hat{V}(t)$, where $\hat{H}_0$ is the part of the Hamiltonian which does not depend on time with eigenvalues $E_n^{(0)}$ and corresponding eigenfunctions $\psi_n^{(0)}(q)$. These eigenfunctions are selected as the eigenvectors for the expansion*

$$\Psi = \sum_n a_n(t) \psi_n^{(0)} \exp\left(-\frac{i}{\hbar} E_n^{(0)} t \right). \tag{9}$$

Substituting (9) into (1) and going through the usual process, we obtain the following system of equations for the coefficients a_n:

$$a_k = \frac{1}{i\hbar} \sum_n a_n V_{kn} e^{i \omega_{kn}^{(0)} t}, \tag{10}$$

---

*A natural generalization of this expansion is obviously expansion (3).

where

$$V_{kn} = \int \psi_k^{(0)*} \hat{V}(t) \psi_n^{(0)} dq, \qquad \hbar\omega_{kn}^{(0)} = E_k^{(0)} - E_n^{(0)}. \tag{11}$$

As distinguished from the similar equation (8), the summation in (10) also includes the term with $n = k$, while the transition frequencies $\omega_{kn}^{(0)}$ do not depend on the time.

Like (8), the system of equations (10) for all k is exactly equivalent to the wave equation (1). It is clear that, in the general case, the exact solution of any of these systems presents a problem of the same difficulty as the solution of equation (1) itself. However, equations (8) and (10) are extremely convenient for an approximate solution if their right members contain small factors. In this case, with an accuracy of the second order of smallness, it is possible to replace the unknowns c_n or a_n by their unperturbed (or initial) values, i.e., by given quantities.

It is obvious that (10) represents an adequate initial system of equations in the case of sufficiently small matrix elements V_{kn}, i.e., in the case where the time-dependent term in the Hamiltonian is small ("ordinary" perturbation theory). On the other hand, the "range of adequacy" of system (8) is that of small values of the matrix elements $\left(\frac{\partial H}{\partial t}\right)_{kn}$, i.e., the range in which the Hamiltonian $\hat{H}(t)$ changes sufficiently slowly. The method of consecutive approximations which is used in this last case is sometimes called the adiabatic perturbation theory (see next problem).*

13. We shall start from the exact equations (8) of the preceding problem. If the Hamiltonian of the system were completely independent of time $\left(\frac{\partial \hat{H}}{\partial t} = 0\right)$, then, according to (7) and (8), we would have $\dot{c}_k = 0$; i.e., $c_k = \text{const}$ for all k. If the derivative $\frac{\partial H}{\partial t}$ is sufficiently close to zero, the quantities c_n in the right part of (8) can be regarded as approximately constant, with $c_n = \delta_{nm}$ from the conditions specified in the problem. Thus, for all $k \neq m$, we have

$$\dot{c}_k \approx \frac{1}{\hbar\omega_{km}} \left(\frac{\partial H}{\partial t}\right)_{km} e^{i\int_0^t \omega_{km}\, dt'} \tag{1}$$

(for $k = m$ we obviously have $\dot{c}_m = 0$ in the same approximation). Integrating (1) for the given initial condition, we obtain

---

*The adiabatic perturbation theory was developed by M. Born and V. A. Fok (1926-1928). It is described together with the theory of "sudden" effects in [19] and [20]. Concerning its application to collision theory, see for instance [9, p. 190].

$$c_k(t) = \frac{1}{\hbar}\int_0^t \frac{1}{\omega_{km}}\left(\frac{\partial H}{\partial t}\right)_{km} e^{i\int_0^{t'}\omega_{km}\,dt''}\,dt' \qquad (k \neq m). \tag{2}$$

It follows from the derivation that this adiabatic equation is correct only if the probability amplitudes of states other than the initial one are small:

$$|c_k(t)| \ll 1 \quad \text{for} \quad k \neq m. \tag{3}$$

To evaluate the order of magnitude of $|c_k(t)|$, it is sufficient to regard the quantities ω_{km} and $\left(\frac{\partial H}{\partial t}\right)_{km}$ in (2) as approximately constant. As a result, equation (2) simplifies, yielding

$$|c_k| \sim \left|\frac{\frac{\partial H}{\partial t}\frac{1}{\omega_{km}}}{E_k - E_m}\right| \qquad (k \neq m).$$

The term on the right is obviously the ratio of the change of the Hamiltonian during a time of the order of the Bohr period $\frac{1}{\omega_{km}}$ for the transition $m \to k$ to the difference between the energies of the states m and k. According to (3), the smallness of this ratio represents the condition for the range of validity of the adiabatic perturbation theory.

Thus, if during a time of the order of the Bohr period for a certain transition, the Hamiltonian changes by an amount which is small compared with the "transition energy," the probability of this transition will be small (by analogy with the classical case, this is sometimes called adiabatic invariance).

14. For $t \geq 0$, the Hamiltonian of the oscillator has the form

$$\hat{H}(t) = \frac{1}{2\mu}\hat{p}^2 + \frac{1}{2}\mu\omega^2[x - a(t)]^2, \tag{1}$$

where $a(t)$ is the position of the equilibrium point, equal to $v_0 t$ from the given condition (v_0 = const is the velocity of the motion of the equilibrium point). The eigenfunctions ("instantaneous") of the Hamiltonian (1) have the form

$$\psi_n = \left(\frac{\mu\omega}{\pi\hbar}\right)^{1/4}\frac{1}{\sqrt{2^n n!}}e^{-\frac{\mu\omega}{2\hbar}[x-a(t)]^2}H_n\left\{\sqrt{\frac{\mu\omega}{\hbar}}[x - a(t)]\right\}.$$

Obviously, the matrix element of the operator $\frac{\partial \hat{H}}{\partial t} = -\mu\omega^2[x - a(t)]\dot{a} = -\mu\omega^2 v_0\,[x - a(t)]$ computed from these functions is different from zero only for the transition $n = 0 \to n = 1$ (we recall that the initial state is the ground state), being equal to

$$\left(\frac{\partial H}{\partial t}\right)_{10} = -\mu\omega^2 v_0\sqrt{\frac{\hbar}{2\mu\omega}}. \tag{2}$$

It is clear from (1) (see also problem No. 12, Chapter II) that the spectrum of energy levels of the oscillator does not change during the motion of the equilibrium point; i.e., all the ω_{km} are constant.

Because of this and because quantity (2) is constant, we can carry the computation with equation (2) of the preceding problem to its end. Thus, for the probability amplitude of the first excited state, substituting $\omega_{10}=\omega$, we obtain

$$c_1(t)\approx-\frac{1}{i\hbar\omega^2}\mu\omega^2 v_0\sqrt{\frac{\hbar}{2\mu\omega}}(e^{i\omega t}-1)=iv_0\sqrt{\frac{\mu}{2\hbar\omega}}(e^{i\omega t}-1).$$

Correspondingly, the probability that at the time t the oscillator will be in the first excited state is

$$w_1(t)=|c_1(t)|^2=\frac{\mu v_0^2}{\hbar\omega}(1-\cos\omega t);$$

This probability oscillates with time. The probability of excitation as a result of the process given in the problem (i.e., for $t\geq T$) is

$$w_1(T)=\frac{\mu v_0^2}{\hbar\omega}(1-\cos\omega T).$$

In order that the adiabatic approximation we have used be valid, it is necessary that the inequality $w_1(t)\ll 1$ hold for all t. This is equivalent to the condition

$$v_0\ll\sqrt{\frac{\hbar\omega}{\mu}}. \tag{3}$$

In other words, the adiabatic theory is valid over the range of velocities of the equilibrium point which are small relative to the characteristic velocity of the oscillator in the ground state.

15. Let $x_1=0$ and $x_2=a(t)$ be the positions of the walls of the well. The "instantaneous" ψ-functions and energy levels of the stationary states have the form

$$\psi_n=\sqrt{\frac{2}{a(t)}}\sin\frac{\pi n x}{a(t)},\quad E_n=\frac{\pi^2\hbar^2 n^2}{2\mu[a(t)]^2}\quad (n=1,2,3,\ldots). \tag{1}$$

However, for computational purposes, it is convenient to consider at first a well of very great but finite depth U_0, and then to take the limiting transition $U_0\to\infty$ (cf. problem No. 11, Chapter III). Suppose that, in the equations for the accurate solution of a symmetric well of finite depth ([1], p. 22), we take the main terms in the expansions in terms of $\frac{1}{\sqrt{U_0}}$, Then, we easily find

$$\psi_n(x)\approx\sqrt{\frac{2}{a}}\sin\left[\frac{n\pi}{a}x-\left(2\frac{x}{a}-1\right)\frac{n\pi}{a}\frac{\hbar}{\sqrt{2\mu U_0}}\right] \tag{2}$$

[for the energy levels, we can use equation (1) directly]. Let us compute the matrix element $\frac{\partial \hat{H}}{\partial t}$ for the transition $n \to m$. It is obvious that $\frac{\partial \hat{H}}{\partial t} = \frac{\partial U_r}{\partial t}$, where $U_r = U(x-a)$ is the potential for the right wall. Moreover, we have

$$\frac{\partial U_{\text{пр}}}{\partial x} = U_0 \delta[x - a(t)],$$
$$\frac{\partial U_{\text{пр}}}{\partial t} = \frac{\partial U_{\text{пр}}}{\partial a}\frac{da}{dt} = -\frac{\partial U_{\text{пр}}}{\partial x}\dot{a} = -U_0\delta[x-a(t)]\,\dot{a}, \tag{3}$$

Therefore, the matrix element $\frac{\partial H}{\partial t}$ between "instantaneous" functions (2) is (as $\epsilon \to 0$)

$$\left(\frac{\partial H}{\partial t}\right)_{mn} = \int_0^{a+\epsilon} \psi_m(x)\frac{\partial \hat{H}}{\partial t}\psi_n(x)\,dx =$$
$$= -U_0\dot{a}\int_0^{a+\epsilon}\psi_m(x)\psi_n(x)\,\delta(x-a)\,dx = -U_0\dot{a}\psi_m(a)\psi_n(a). \tag{4}$$

In (2), setting $x = a$, we obtain

$$\psi_n(a) = \sqrt{\frac{2}{a}}(-1)^{n+1}\frac{n\pi}{a}\frac{\hbar}{\sqrt{2\mu U_0}},$$

After substitution into (4), this yields

$$\left(\frac{\partial H}{\partial t}\right)_{mn} = (-1)^{n+m+1}\,nm\,\frac{\pi^2\hbar^2\dot{a}(t)}{\mu[a(t)]^3}. \tag{5}$$

Thus, in the first approximation of adiabatic perturbation theory, we obtain for c_m the coefficients associated with instantaneous functions (see problem No. 13):

$$\dot{c}_m = 2(-1)^{n+m+1}\frac{nm}{m^2-n^2}\frac{\dot{a}}{a}e^{i\frac{\pi^2\hbar}{2\mu}(m^2-n^2)\int_0^t \frac{dt'}{a^2}} \quad (m \neq n). \tag{6}$$

After integrating and considering the initial condition $c_m(0) = \delta_{mn}$, we obtain for $c_m(t)$ the expression

$$c_m(t) = 2(-1)^{n+m+1}\frac{nm}{m^2-n^2}\int_0^t dt'\,\frac{\dot{a}}{a}\,e^{i\frac{\pi^2\hbar}{2\mu}(m^2-n^2)\int_0^{t'}\frac{dt''}{a^2}} \tag{7}$$
$$(m \neq n).$$

Let us consider the question of when equation (7) yields definite probabilities for a transition from an initial n-th state to an m-th state. First of all, we note that two cases are possible: a) the motion of the wall stops at a time $t = T$; b) the motion of the wall continues for any values of t.

In case (a), equation (7) is correct only for $t \leqslant T$. For larger values of t, after the wall has stopped, the instantaneous functions become exact functions, and consequently their coefficients c_m will not depend on time. From the condition that $\psi(x, t)$ is continuous at $t = T$, we obtain

$$c_m(t > T) = c_m(T), \tag{8}$$

where $c_m(T)$ is the value of c_m obtained from equation (7) for the time $t = T$. Since the probability of finding the particle in the m-th state, which equals $|c_m(t > T)|^2$, does not change with time, in this case there will always be a definite transition probability. This probability is

$$w_{n \to m} = |c_m(T)|^2 = \frac{4n^2m^2}{(m^2 - n^2)^2} \left| \int_0^T dt' \frac{\dot{a}}{a} e^{i \frac{\pi^2 \hbar}{2\mu} (m^2 - n^2) \int_0^{t'} \frac{dt''}{a^2}} \right|^2. \tag{9}$$

Let us now examine case (b), in which the motion of the wall continues until $t \to \infty$. We shall confine ourselves to the consideration of motion in which the width of the well tends toward a finite limit: $a(t) \to a_\infty$ as $t \to \infty$.

Then, the spectrum of the system remains discrete for any t, and the relative position of the levels does not change (the so-called nonintersection of terms). The probability of a transition is given by equation (9), in which the limit as T goes to infinity is taken. To answer the question of whether this probability exists, we shall assume that the wall approaches its limiting value according to the equation

$$a_\infty - a(t) \sim \frac{1}{t^\gamma} \qquad (\gamma > 0). \tag{10}$$

In this case, for sufficiently large t, we can replace a by a_∞ everywhere. As a result, we obtain an integral of the form

$$\int^\infty \frac{dt}{t^{\gamma+1}} e^{i\omega_\infty t}, \tag{11}$$

where $\omega_\infty = \dfrac{\pi^2 \hbar (m^2 - n^2)}{2\mu a_\infty^2}$. We have written only the upper limit to emphasize that the expression under the integral is correct as $t \to \infty$. In our case ($\gamma > 0$), this integral always converges at the upper limit, and thus the existence of the transition probability is secured.

Let us consider the previously obtained result (9) and determine the range of validity of the adiabatic approximation we have used. In the case where T is much smaller than the Bohr period for the transition $n \to m$, i.e., at

$$T \ll \frac{\mu a^2}{\hbar\,|m^2 - n^2|},$$

the exponential term in (9) is obviously ≈ 1. Therefore,

$$w_{n \to m} \approx \frac{4n^2m^2}{(m^2 - n^2)^2}\left(\int_0^T \frac{\dot{a}}{a}\,dt'\right)^2 \sim \frac{4n^2m^2}{(m^2 - n^2)^2}\left(\frac{\Delta a}{a}\right)^2, \tag{9'}$$

where $\Delta a \equiv a(T) - a(0)$.

The range of validity of the adiabatic approximation is $w_{n \to m} \ll 1$; i.e., in the given case,

$$\frac{|\Delta a|}{a} \ll \frac{|m^2 - n^2|}{mn}.$$

The case of prolonged action

$$T \gg \frac{\mu a^2}{\hbar\,|m^2 - n^2|}$$

is more interesting. In this case, the exponential term under the integral in (9) oscillates rapidly. Thus, the integral is of the order of $\frac{|\dot{a}|}{a}\,\frac{\mu a^2}{\hbar\,|m^2 - n^2|}$, and

$$w_{n \to m} \sim \frac{n^2m^2}{(m^2 - n^2)^4}\left(\frac{\mu a \dot{a}}{\hbar}\right)^2. \tag{9''}$$

It is apparent from (9) or (9″) that the transition probability decreases rapidly with increasing $|m - n|$. In the given case, the range of validity of the adiabatic approximation, $w_{n \to m} \ll 1$, has the form

$$|\dot{a}| \ll \frac{(m^2 - n^2)^2}{nm}\,\frac{\hbar}{\mu a}.$$

For $n \sim m \sim 1$, this inequality implies that the velocity of the motion of the wall is small relative to the characteristic velocity of a particle in the lowest level of the well $\left(v \sim \sqrt{\frac{E_1}{\mu}} \sim \frac{\hbar}{\mu a}\right)$ (cf. problem No. 14).

We emphasize that the "adiabatic invariant" in the motion of the wall is the quantum number of the initial level (n), whereas the energy of the particle in this level (E_n) can change considerably [cf. (1)].

We also note that equation (9) is symmetric with respect to reversal of the final and initial states n and m; i.e., it also gives the probability $w_{m \to n}$ for the transition $m \to n$. This circumstance is a consequence of the reversability of quantum mechanics, i.e., the symmetry of the equations of quantum mechanics relative to a change of the sign of time [1, Section 116].

CHAPTER VII

The Quasi-Classical Approximation

1. The energy levels E which we must determine are given by Bohr's rule of quantization

$$\frac{1}{\hbar}\int_a^b p\,dx = \pi\left(n+\frac{1}{2}\right) \qquad (n=0,\ 1,\ 2,\ \ldots). \tag{1}$$

Here $p(x)=\sqrt{2m[E-U(x)]}$ is the momentum; $U(x)$ is the potential energy of the oscillator, having the form $U=\frac{m\omega^2x^2}{2}$ (m is the mass of the oscillator, and ω is its frequency); and a and b are the turning points, determined from the condition that the kinetic energy $(E-U)$ is equal to zero:

$$a=-\sqrt{\frac{2E}{m\omega^2}}, \qquad b=\sqrt{\frac{2E}{m\omega^2}}.$$

Substituting all these quantities into the integral $\int_a^b p\,dx$, we obtain (using the new variable of integration $t=x\sqrt{\frac{m\omega^2}{2E}}$)

$$\int_a^b p\,dx=\frac{2E}{\omega}\int_{-1}^{1}\sqrt{1-t^2}\,dt=\frac{\pi E}{\omega}.$$

Whence, according to (1),

$$E\equiv E_n=\hbar\omega\left(n+\frac{1}{2}\right),$$

which is identical with the exact expression for E_n.

2. The potential energy of the particle has the form*

$$U(z)=\begin{cases}\infty & (z\leqslant 0),\\ mgz & (z\geqslant 0).\end{cases}$$

---

*For the coordinate system, notation, etc., see problem No. 4, Chapter II.

From the given conditions, one of the turning points is $z = 0$. The other is determined from the equation $U(z) = mgz = E$, and consequently has the position

$$z = \frac{E}{mg}.$$

As regards Bohr's quantization rule, it is necessary to alter somewhat the usual expression for the right side $\pi\left(n + \frac{1}{2}\right)$. This is connected with the assumption made in the usual derivation of Bohr's quantization rule [1, Sections 47, 48], according to which the potential energy can be expanded into series of powers of $(z - a)$ and $(z - b)$ beginning with a linear term in the neighborhood of the two classical turning points $z = a$ and $z = b$. As a consequence, a phase factor $\frac{\pi}{4}$ appears in the quasi-classical expressions for the ψ-functions originating at the two turning points:

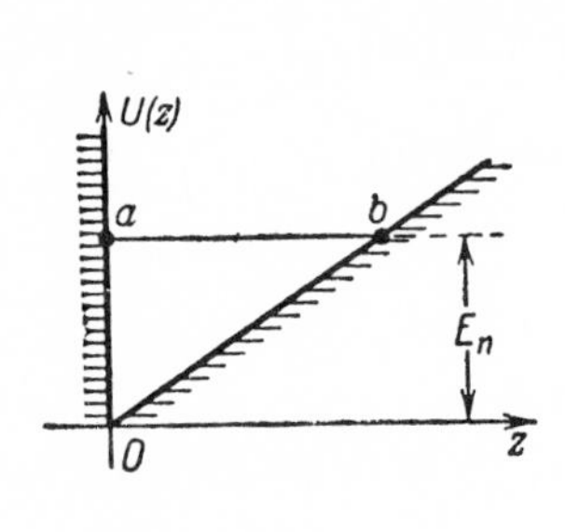

$$\frac{c}{\sqrt{p(z)}} \sin\left[\frac{1}{\hbar}\int_a^z p(z)\,dz + \frac{\pi}{4}\right]$$

and

$$\frac{c'}{\sqrt{p(z)}} \sin\left[\frac{1}{\hbar}\int_z^b p(z)\,dz + \frac{\pi}{4}\right] \qquad (a \leqslant z \leqslant b). \tag{1}$$

The requirement that these two expressions coincide throughout the entire region $a \leqslant z \leqslant b$ leads to the condition

$$\frac{1}{\hbar}\int_a^b p\,dz + \frac{\pi}{2} = (n+1)\pi \qquad (n = 0,\ 1,\ 2,\ \ldots) \tag{2}$$

[the sum of the two phases in (1) is equated to an integral multiple of π].

In the case we are considering, one of the turning points $(z = a = 0)$ is on the "vertical potential wall," so that the first phase in (1) does not contain the term $\frac{\pi}{4}$.* The term $\frac{\pi}{4}$ appears in

---

*As distinguished from the case of an "inclined" potential wall, here the function is quasi-classical right up to the turning point $z = a$, at which it becomes zero. From this, our statements follow.

the second phase in (1) in the usual way. Accordingly, when we add the two phases, we obtain the condition

$$\frac{1}{\hbar}\int_a^b p\,dz+\frac{\pi}{4}=(n+1)\pi$$

instead of (2). Hence, we obtain the quantization rule for which we have been looking:

$$\frac{1}{\hbar}\int_a^b p\,dz=\left(n+\frac{3}{4}\right)\pi \qquad (n=0,\ 1,\ 2,\ \ldots). \tag{3}$$

Substituting

$$p=\sqrt{2m\,[E-U(z)]}=\sqrt{2m\,(E-mgz)},\quad a=0,\quad b=\frac{E}{mg}$$

and carrying out an elementary computation, we obtain

$$E\equiv E_n=\frac{1}{2}\,(9\pi^2 mg^2\hbar^2)^{1/3}\left(n+\frac{3}{4}\right)^{2/3}, \tag{4}$$

which, as we would expect, is exactly the same as the equation in problem No. 4, Chapter II, for the quasi-classical case.

From this problem, we borrow the value for the classical bouncing frequency of the ball [equation (22)]

$$\omega=\frac{2\pi}{T}=\pi g\sqrt{\frac{m}{2E}}$$

and from (4) we compute the distance between neighboring levels ($\Delta n=1$)

$$\Delta E_n=\frac{dE_n}{dn},$$

Thus, we obtain the relation

$$\Delta E=\hbar\omega,$$

which expresses the approximate equidistance of the quasi-classical energy levels.

3. Denoting by m and E the mass and energy of the particle ($E<U_0$), we have for the transmission coefficient (transmittance coefficient) in the quasi-classical approximation the well-known expression

$$D\approx\exp\left\{-2\int_{x_1}^{x_2}\sqrt{\frac{2m}{\hbar^2}\,[U(x)-E]}\,dx\right\}, \tag{1}$$

where x_1 and x_2 are the positions of the classical turning points, obtained from the equation $U(x_{1,2}) = E$:

$$x_2 = -x_1 = a\sqrt{1 - \frac{E}{U_0}}. \tag{2}$$

By substituting the potential $U(x)$ and (2) into (1), performing the change of variables $\frac{x}{x_2} = t$ in the integral, and remembering that $\int_{-1}^{1} \sqrt{1-t^2}\,dt = \frac{\pi}{2}$, we obtain finally

$$D \approx \exp\left\{-\pi\sqrt{\frac{2m}{U_0}}\frac{a(U_0 - E)}{\hbar}\right\}. \tag{3}$$

The criterion for this formula to be valid is that the index of the exponential factor be large

$$\pi\sqrt{\frac{2m}{U_0}}\frac{a(U_0 - E)}{\hbar} \gg 1. \tag{4}$$

For the barrier we are considering, it is easily seen that the legitimacy of taking the coefficient of the exponential factor in (1) to be equal to unity follows from condition (4).

Indeed, this coefficient is equal to unity in the case where the field $U(x)$ satisfies the condition that it be quasi-classical over the whole extent of the barrier, with the exception of the immediate neighborhood of the turning points [1, Section 50]. This condition has the form

$$\left|\frac{d\lambda\!\!\!^{-}}{dx}\right| \equiv \left|\frac{d}{dx}\left\{\frac{\hbar}{\sqrt{2m[E - U(x)]}}\right\}\right| \ll 1, \tag{5}$$

where $\lambda\!\!\!^{-}$ is the de Broglie wavelength.

Inequality (5) can be transformed to

$$\left|\frac{t}{(t^2-1)^{3/2}}\right| \ll \sqrt{\frac{2m}{U_0}}\frac{a(U_0 - E)}{\hbar}, \tag{5'}$$

where $t = \frac{x}{x_2}$.

From (4) it follows directly that the quasi-classical condition (5) or (5$'$) is violated only near $t = \pm 1$ (i.e., $x = \pm x_2$), the width of the nonquasi-classical region being of the order of magnitude of

$$|\Delta x| \equiv |x - x_{1,2}| \sim \frac{a^{1/3}\hbar^{2/3}}{m^{1/3}(U_0 - E)^{1/6}U_0^{1/6}}. \tag{6}$$

For the required "integral" quasi-classical nature of the field $U(x)$ it is obviously necessary that

$$|\Delta x| \ll a. \tag{7}$$

Using (6) and (4), we can easily see that condition (7) is satisfied, and consequently the coefficient of the exponential factor in (1) and (3) is indeed equal to unity.

4. The ψ-function of the particle in well I, corresponding to a decreasing solution for $x > b$, has the form [1]

$$\psi = \frac{c}{\sqrt{p}} \cos\left[\frac{1}{\hbar} \int_x^b p\,dx - \frac{\pi}{4}\right].$$

This expression is easily transformed to

$$\psi = \frac{c}{\sqrt{p}} \cos\left[\frac{1}{\hbar} \int_a^x p\,dx - \frac{\pi}{4} + \alpha\right] =$$

$$= \frac{ce^{i\alpha}}{2\sqrt{p}} e^{i\left[\frac{1}{\hbar}\int_a^x p\,dx - \frac{\pi}{4}\right]} + \frac{ce^{-i\alpha}}{2\sqrt{p}} e^{-i\left[\frac{1}{\hbar}\int_a^x p\,dx - \frac{\pi}{4}\right]},$$

where

$$\alpha = \frac{\pi}{2} - \frac{1}{\hbar} \int_a^b p\,dx. \tag{1}$$

In the case where the barrier is impenetrable, α must be equal to an integral multiple of π:

$$\alpha_0 = \frac{\pi}{2} - \frac{1}{\hbar} \int_{a_0}^{b_0} p_0\,dx = n\pi.$$

In our case, we must find the ψ-function in the region inside the barrier. Using the boundary conditions in the quasi-classical case ([19], p. 156), we obtain

$$\psi = c\frac{\sin\alpha}{\sqrt{|p|}} e^{\frac{1}{\hbar}\int_x^a |p|\,dx} + c\frac{\cos\alpha}{2\sqrt{|p|}} e^{-\frac{1}{\hbar}\int_x^a |p|\,dx} =$$

$$= c\sin\alpha\, e^{\frac{1}{\hbar}\int_0^a |p|\,dx} \cdot \frac{e^{-\frac{1}{\hbar}\int_0^x |p|\,dx}}{\sqrt{|p|}} +$$

$$+ \frac{c}{2}\cos\alpha\, e^{-\frac{1}{\hbar}\int_0^a |p|\,dx} \cdot \frac{e^{\frac{1}{\hbar}\int_0^x |p|\,dx}}{\sqrt{|p|}}.$$

Since the potential $U(x)$ is symmetric, the ψ-functions of the problem must be either even or odd. Hence, we obtain the following equations for determining the energy:

for an even state,

$$\sin\alpha\, e^{\frac{1}{\hbar}\int\limits_0^a |p|\,dx} = \frac{1}{2}\cos\alpha\, e^{-\frac{1}{\hbar}\int\limits_0^a |p|\,dx},$$

for an odd state,

$$\sin\alpha\, e^{\frac{1}{\hbar}\int\limits_0^a |p|\,dx} = -\frac{1}{2}\cos\alpha\, e^{-\frac{1}{\hbar}\int\limits_0^a |p|\,dx},$$

or

$$\sin\alpha = \pm\frac{1}{2}\cos\alpha\, e^{-\frac{2}{\hbar}\int\limits_0^a |p|\,dx} = \pm\frac{1}{2}\cos\alpha\, e^{-\frac{1}{\hbar}\int\limits_{-a}^a |p|\,dx}$$

The quantity $\exp\left(-\frac{1}{\hbar}\int\limits_{-a}^{a}|p|\,dx\right)$ in the right member of this expression is equal to the square root of the probability of penetration of the barrier.

For a completely impenetrable barrier, we obtain

$$\sin\alpha_0 = 0, \quad \text{i.e.,} \quad \alpha_0 = n\pi,$$

as we noted above.

Regarding the change in the energy as small, let us expand α [see (1)] in the neighborhood of values of α_0:

$$\alpha \approx \alpha_0 + \Delta E\left(\frac{\partial\alpha}{\partial E}\right)_0 = \alpha_0 - \frac{\Delta E}{\hbar}\int\limits_{a_0}^{b_0}\frac{\partial p_0}{\partial E_0}\,dx = \\ = \alpha_0 - \frac{T\,\Delta E}{2\hbar} = \alpha_0 - \pi\frac{\Delta E}{\hbar\omega},$$

where T and ω are the period and frequency of the classical motion of the particle in the well.

If we denote the shift in an even level by ΔE_+ and a shift in an odd level by ΔE_-, and if we restrict ourselves to the first power of the quantity $\exp\left(-\frac{1}{\hbar}\int\limits_{-a}^{a}|p|\,dx\right)$, we can find the values of these shifts:

$$\Delta E_{\pm} = \mp \frac{\hbar\omega}{2\pi} e^{-\frac{1}{\hbar}\int_{-a}^{a} |p|\, dx}$$

5. Because of the periodicity of the potential, it follows that the Schrödinger equation has solutions for which

$$\psi(x+a) = z\psi(x).$$

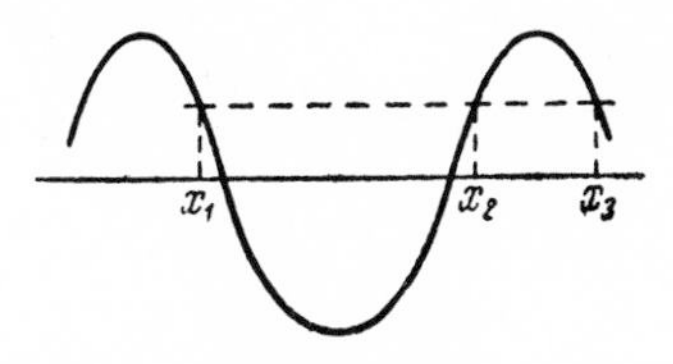

For $|z| \neq 1$, the ψ-function increases without bound in one of the directions. Therefore, the condition defining the permitted zone is $|z| = 1$ or $z = e^{i\varphi}$.

Let us consider one period of the potential (see figure).

It can be divided into three regions: $x_1 < x < x_2$, $x_2 < x < x_3$, and $x_3 < x$. In the first region, the solution can be written in the form

$$\psi_{\mathrm{I}} = \frac{c_1}{\sqrt{p}} e^{\frac{i}{\hbar}\int_{x_1}^{x} p\, dx} + \frac{c_2}{\sqrt{p}} e^{-\frac{i}{\hbar}\int_{x_1}^{x} p\, dx}$$

or, differently,

$$\psi_1 = \frac{c_1'}{\sqrt{p}} e^{-i\left(\frac{1}{\hbar}\int_{x}^{x_2} p\, dx - \frac{\pi}{4}\right)} + \frac{c_2'}{\sqrt{p}} e^{i\left(\frac{1}{\hbar}\int_{x}^{x_2} p\, dx - \frac{\pi}{4}\right)},$$

where

$$c_1' = c_1 e^{i\left(\alpha - \frac{\pi}{4}\right)}, \quad c_2' = c_2 e^{-i\left(\alpha - \frac{\pi}{4}\right)}, \quad \alpha = \frac{1}{\hbar}\int_{x_1}^{x_2} p\, dx.$$

Using the boundary conditions in the quasi-classical case [19], we obtain the solution in the second region

$$\psi_{\mathrm{II}} = \frac{c_2' - c_1'}{i\sqrt{|p|}} e^{\frac{1}{\hbar}\int_{x_2}^{x} |p|\, dx} + \frac{1}{2}\frac{c_2' + c_1'}{\sqrt{|p|}} e^{-\frac{1}{\hbar}\int_{x_2}^{x} |p|\, dx}$$

or

$$\psi_{\mathrm{II}} = \frac{c_1'' e^{-\frac{1}{\hbar}\int_{x}^{x_3} |p|\, dx}}{i\sqrt{|p|}} + \frac{1}{2}\frac{c_2''}{\sqrt{|p|}} e^{\frac{1}{\hbar}\int_{x}^{x_3} |p|\, dx},$$

where

$$c_1'' = (c_2' - c_1')\, e^{\beta}, \quad c_2'' = (c_2' + c_1')\, e^{-\beta}, \quad \beta = \frac{1}{\hbar} \int_{x_2}^{x_3} |p|\, dx.$$

Using the boundary conditions again, we obtain for $x > x_3$:

$$\psi_{III} = -i \frac{\left(c_1'' - \frac{c_2''}{4}\right) e^{-i\frac{\pi}{4}}}{\sqrt{p}} e^{\frac{i}{\hbar}\int_{x_3}^{x} p\, dx} - \\ - i \frac{\left(c_1'' + \frac{c_2''}{4}\right) e^{i\frac{\pi}{4}}}{\sqrt{p}} e^{-\frac{i}{\hbar}\int_{x_3}^{x} p\, dx}$$

The condition for a quasi-periodic solution has the form

$$-i\left(c_1'' - \frac{c_2''}{4}\right) e^{-i\frac{\pi}{4}} = zc_1,$$
$$-i\left(c_1'' + \frac{c_2''}{4}\right) e^{i\frac{\pi}{4}} = zc_2.$$

Expressing c_1'' and c_2'' in terms of c_1 and c_2, we obtain the following system of equations:

$$c_1 e^{i\alpha}(e^{-\beta} + 4e^{\beta}) + ic_2 e^{-i\alpha}(e^{-\beta} - 4e^{\beta}) = 4zc_1,$$
$$c_1 e^{i\alpha}(e^{-\beta} - 4e^{\beta}) + ic_2 e^{-i\alpha}(e^{-\beta} + 4e^{\beta}) = 4izc_2.$$

The quantity z is determined from the condition that this system is solvable (i.e., the condition that its determinant equal zero):

$$z^2 - 2z\left(e^{\beta} + \frac{1}{4} e^{-\beta}\right)\cos\alpha + 1 = 0.$$

Hence,

$$z_{1,2} = \left(e^{\beta} + \frac{1}{4} e^{-\beta}\right)\cos\alpha \pm \sqrt{\left(e^{\beta} + \frac{1}{4} e^{-\beta}\right)^2 \cos^2\alpha - 1}. \quad (1)$$

If the expression underneath the radical is positive, z will be positive and different from unity. In the opposite case, z is complex and its modulus is equal to unity:

$$z_{1,2} = \left(e^{\beta} + \frac{1}{4} e^{-\beta}\right)\cos\alpha \pm i\sqrt{1 - \left(e^{\beta} + \frac{1}{4} e^{-\beta}\right)^2 \cos^2\alpha},$$

$$|z_{1,2}|^2 = \left(e^{\beta} + \frac{1}{4} e^{-\beta}\right)^2 \cos^2\alpha + \\ + \left[1 - \left(e^{\beta} + \frac{1}{4} e^{-\beta}\right)^2 \cos^2\alpha\right] = 1.$$

Thus, the equation giving the permitted zones follows from the condition that the expression under the radical in (1) be negative:

$$\left(e^{\beta}+\frac{1}{4}e^{-\beta}\right)^2\cos^2\alpha\leqslant 1. \tag{2}$$

The range of validity of the quasi-classical approximation is that given by the condition that the $\int p\,dx$ be large relative to $\hbar$, i.e.,

$$\alpha \gg 1, \qquad \beta \gg 1.$$

Accordingly, neglecting the exponential term with the negative index, we can write condition (2) in the form

$$e^{2\beta}\cos^2\alpha\leqslant 1$$

or

$$\cos^2\alpha\leqslant e^{-2\beta}. \tag{2'}$$

In the first approximation, we have

$$\cos^2\alpha=0, \qquad \alpha=n\pi+\frac{\pi}{2}$$

or

$$\int_{x_1}^{x_2} p\,dx=\pi\hbar\left(n+\frac{1}{2}\right).$$

This is Bohr's condition for quantization.

By solving this equation, we obtain a system of energy levels for a well appearing as a depression in a periodic potential with impenetrable walls:

$$E_0,\ E_1,\ E_2,\ \ldots,\ E_n,\ \ldots$$

Let us now expand the left part of (2′) near the value of α_n corresponding to the *n*-th energy level:

$$\cos^2\alpha\approx\sin^2\alpha_n(\Delta\alpha_n)^2\approx(\Delta\alpha_n)^2.$$

From the definition of α, we have

$$\Delta\alpha=\frac{\Delta E}{\hbar}\frac{\partial}{\partial E}\int_{x_1}^{x_2} p\,dx=\frac{\Delta E}{\hbar}\int_{x_1}^{x_2}\frac{\partial p}{\partial E}dx=\frac{\Delta E}{\hbar}\int_{x_1}^{x_2}\frac{dx}{v}=\frac{\Delta E}{\hbar}\frac{T}{2},$$

where T is the period of the motion of a particle in the corresponding level of the well.

Noting that $e^{-2\beta}$ is the probability of passing through the barrier, $W(E)$, we can write condition (2′) in the form

$$(\Delta E_n)^2\leqslant\frac{4\hbar^2}{T_n^2}W(E_n).$$

Hence, for the width of a zone, we obtain

$$\Delta E_n = \frac{2\hbar}{T_n}\sqrt{W(E_n)} \ll \hbar\omega_n.$$

6. To derive the quantization rule for the given case, it is necessary to proceed in the same way as in deriving the ordinary Bohr's quantization rule. Namely, it is necessary to find the exact functions in the neighborhood of the point at which the conditions for validity of the quasi-classical approximation are violated. Comparing these functions with the quasi-classical functions in the region of "overlapping" (i.e., in the region in which both exact and quasi-classical functions are applicable), it is possible to find the quantization rule.

In the quasi-classical case ($n \gg 1$) with which we are concerned, it is easily seen that the exact functions are Coulomb functions for $n \to \infty$ ($E \to 0$), while the region of overlapping $Z^{-1} \ll r \ll Z^{-1/3}$ we are using atomic units). Indeed, for distances $r \ll Z^{-1/3}$ the self-consistent field $\varphi(r)$ in which the electrons of the Thomas-Fermi distribution move is identical with the Coulomb field of the nucleus $\varphi(r) \approx \frac{Z}{r}$. The quasi-classical approximation is valid for distances $r \gg Z^{-1}$.

The Coulomb functions for $l = 0$, $n \to \infty$ (i.e., $E \to 0$) have the form ([1], p. 153)

$$\psi = c\frac{J_1(\sqrt{8r})}{\sqrt{r}} \qquad \text{(in Coulomb units)}$$

or

$$\psi = Z^{3/2}c\,\frac{J_1(\sqrt{8Zr})}{\sqrt{Zr}} \qquad \text{(in atomic units).} \tag{1}$$

For $r \gg Z^{-1}$, i.e., $Zr \gg 1$, we can use the asymptotic expression for the Bessel function J_1, giving

$$\psi = Z^{3/2}c\,\frac{\sin\left(\sqrt{8Zr} - \frac{\pi}{4}\right)}{(2\pi^2 Z^3 r^3)^{1/4}} = c_1\,\frac{\sin\left(\sqrt{8Zr} - \frac{\pi}{4}\right)}{r^{3/4}}. \tag{2}$$

The quasi-classical functions can be written in the form

$$\psi_q = c_q\,\frac{\sin\left(\int_0^r p_r\,dr + \alpha\right)}{r\sqrt{p_r}}. \tag{3}$$

Thus, our problem is to determine the phase α. In the region in which we are interested, the radial momentum $p_r = \sqrt{2[E - U(r)]}$

(there is no centrifugal potential for the given case of $l=0$) is equal to $\sqrt{\frac{2Z}{r}}$, since $|U(r)| \sim \frac{Z}{r} \gg |E|$. This last inequality is a consequence of the fact that the energy of an electron in a Thomas-Fermi distribution is of the order of $Z^{7/3}$. Thus,

$$\int_0^r p_r\,dr = \sqrt{2Z}\int_0^r \frac{dr}{\sqrt{r}} = \sqrt{8Zr},$$

while the ψ-function is

$$\psi_q \approx c_q \frac{\sin(\sqrt{8Zr}+\alpha)}{r\left(\frac{2Z}{r}\right)^{1/4}} = c'_q \frac{\sin(\sqrt{8Zr}+\alpha)}{r^{3/4}}.$$

Comparing these two functions, we obtain $\alpha = -\frac{\pi}{4}$. Thus, the quasi-classical function has the form

$$\psi_q = c_q \frac{\sin\left(\int_0^r p_r\,dr - \frac{\pi}{4}\right)}{r\sqrt{p_r}}. \tag{4}$$

On the other hand, the function satisfying the boundary condition in the neighborhood of the turning point r_0, which limits the motion of the particle on the side of large r, has the form

$$\psi_q = c''_q \frac{\sin\left(\int_r^{r_0} p_r\,dr + \frac{\pi}{4}\right)}{r\sqrt{p_r}}. \tag{5}$$

For expressions (4) and (5) to be identical, it is necessary that the sum of the phases of the sines be a multiple of π. From this, the necessary quantization rule follows:

$$\int_0^{r_0} p_r\,dr = n\pi \quad \text{or} \quad \int_0^{r_0} \sqrt{2\mu[E-U(r)]}\,dr = \pi\hbar n. \tag{6}$$

Thus, the quantization rule which we have obtained differs from Bohr's quantization rule.

It is easily seen that in the special case of a Coulomb field $U(r) = -\frac{Ze^2}{r}$ throughout space, the quantization rule (6) leads to a spectrum of the correct form:

$$E_n = -\frac{Z^2\mu e^4}{2\hbar^2}\frac{1}{n^2}.$$

We can convince ourselves of this by substituting into (6) the quantity r_0 from the condition $E - U(r_0) = E + \frac{Ze^2}{r_0} = 0$, i.e., $r_0 = -\frac{Ze^2}{E}$, and by carrying out the elementary integration.

7. 1. The Schrödinger equation in the p-space has the form

$$\left\{\frac{p^2}{2\mu} + \hat{U}\left(i\hbar\frac{\partial}{\partial p}\right)\right\} G(p) = EG(p),$$

where $\hat{U}\left(i\hbar\frac{\partial}{\partial p}\right) = U(\hat{x})$ is the operator for the potential energy of the particle.

We shall look for a solution of this equation in the form

$$G(p) = e^{-\frac{i}{\hbar}S(p)} \tag{1}$$

by expanding $S(p)$ into powers of $\hbar$:

$$S(p) = S_0(p) + \hbar S_1(p) + \hbar^2 S_2(p) + \dots \tag{2}$$

To find the expansion (into powers of $\hbar$) of the expression obtained as a result of the application of the operator $\hat{U}\left(i\hbar\frac{\partial}{\partial p}\right)$ to the wave function $G(p)$, we shall assume that the potential energy $U(x)$ can be expanded into a series of powers of x. Then,

$$\hat{U}\left(i\hbar\frac{\partial}{\partial p}\right) = \sum_{n=0}^{\infty}\frac{U^{(n)}(0)}{n!}\left(i\hbar\frac{\partial}{\partial p}\right)^n. \tag{3}$$

We shall consider the operation of the individual terms of this series on the function (1):

$$i\hbar\frac{\partial}{\partial p}e^{-\frac{i}{\hbar}S} = e^{-\frac{i}{\hbar}S}\frac{\partial S}{\partial p},$$

$$\left(i\hbar\frac{\partial}{\partial p}\right)^2 e^{-\frac{i}{\hbar}S} = e^{-\frac{i}{\hbar}S}\left\{\left(\frac{\partial S}{\partial p}\right)^2 + i\hbar\frac{\partial^2 S}{\partial p^2}\right\},$$

$$\left(i\hbar\frac{\partial}{\partial p}\right)^3 e^{-\frac{i}{\hbar}S} = e^{-\frac{i}{\hbar}S}\left\{\left(\frac{\partial S}{\partial p}\right)^3 + i\hbar(1+2)\frac{\partial^2 S}{\partial p^2}\frac{\partial S}{\partial p} + O(\hbar^2)\right\}.$$

It can be shown by the method of induction that in general

$$\left(i\hbar\frac{\partial}{\partial p}\right)^n e^{-\frac{i}{\hbar}S} =$$

$$= e^{-\frac{i}{\hbar}S}\left\{\left(\frac{\partial S}{\partial p}\right)^n + i\hbar\left(\sum_{k=1}^{n-1}k\right)\frac{\partial^2 S}{\partial p^2}\left(\frac{\partial S}{\partial p}\right)^{n-2} + O(\hbar^2)\right\} = \tag{4}$$

$$= e^{-\frac{i}{\hbar}S}\left\{\left(\frac{\partial S}{\partial p}\right)^n + i\hbar\frac{n(n-1)}{2}\frac{\partial^2 S}{\partial p^2}\left(\frac{\partial S}{\partial p}\right)^{n-2} + O(\hbar^2)\right\}.$$

According to (3) and (4), we obtain

$$\hat{U}\left(i\hbar\frac{\partial}{\partial p}\right)e^{-\frac{i}{\hbar}S}=e^{-\frac{i}{\hbar}S}\left\{U\left(\frac{\partial S}{\partial p}\right)+\frac{i\hbar}{2}\frac{\partial^2 S}{\partial p^2}U''\left(\frac{\partial S}{\partial p}\right)+\dots\right\}.$$

Thus, the equation for the operator function $S(p)$ has the form

$$\frac{p^2}{2\mu}+U\left(\frac{\partial S}{\partial p}\right)+\frac{1}{2}i\hbar\frac{\partial^2 S}{\partial p^2}U''\left(\frac{\partial S}{\partial p}\right)+\dots=E.$$

Substituting into this S in the form of expansion (2) and collecting terms of the same order of $\hbar$, we obtain the following equations for S_0 and S_1:

$$\frac{p^2}{2\mu}+U\left(\frac{\partial S_0}{\partial p}\right)=E, \tag{5}$$

$$\frac{\partial S_1}{\partial p}U'\left(\frac{\partial S_0}{\partial p}\right)+\frac{i}{2}\frac{\partial^2 S_0}{\partial p^2}U''\left(\frac{\partial S_0}{\partial p}\right)=0. \tag{6}$$

We shall let $x(p)$ denote the dependence of the position on the momentum during motion in the field $U(x)$. Then, solving equation (5) for $\frac{\partial S_0}{\partial p}$, we find

$$\frac{\partial S_0}{\partial p}=x(p).$$

Hence,

$$S_0=\int x(p)\,dp.$$

From equation (6), we obtain

$$\frac{\partial S_1}{\partial p}=-\frac{i}{2}\frac{\partial^2 S_0}{\partial p^2}\frac{U''\left(\frac{\partial S_0}{\partial p}\right)}{U'\left(\frac{\partial S_0}{\partial p}\right)}.$$

We easily see that the right member is the momentum-derivative of

$$-\frac{i}{2}\ln\left|U'\left(\frac{\partial S_0}{\partial p}\right)\right|,$$

and consequently

$$S_1=-\frac{i}{2}\ln\left|U'\left(\frac{\partial S_0}{\partial p}\right)\right|.$$

Thus, finally, the quasi-classical wave function in the momentum space has the form

$$G(p)=\frac{c}{\sqrt{\left|U'\left(\frac{\partial S_0}{\partial p}\right)\right|}}e^{-\frac{i}{\hbar}\int x(p)\,dp}. \tag{7}$$

The meaning of the factor in the denominator becomes clear once it is noted that $\left|U'\left(\frac{\partial S_0}{\partial p}\right)\right|$ is the force expressed in terms of the momentum p; i.e., it is $\left|\frac{dp}{dt}\right|$. This means that, as it should be in the quasi-classical case, the probability of finding the momentum within the interval from p to $p+dp$ is proportional to the corresponding interval of time dt:

$$|G|^2\,dp=\frac{|c|^2}{\left|\frac{dp}{dt}\right|}\,dp=|c|^2\,dt.$$

2. We shall now consider the second part of the problem; that is, we shall show that the wave function $G(p)$ which we have found can be obtained as a Fourier transform of the quasi-classical wave function in the position space.

The quasi-classical function in the x-space has the form

$$\psi(x)=\frac{c_1}{\sqrt{|p(x)|}}e^{\frac{i}{\hbar}\int p(x)\,dx},$$

where $p(x)$ is the momentum as a function of the position $p(x)=\sqrt{2\mu[E-U(x)]}$.

The corresponding function in the momentum space is*

$$\tilde{G}(p)=\frac{1}{\sqrt{2\pi\hbar}}\int dx\,\psi(x)\,e^{-\frac{i}{\hbar}px}=$$
$$=\frac{c_1}{\sqrt{2\pi\hbar}}\int\frac{dx}{\sqrt{|p(x)|}}e^{\frac{i}{\hbar}\left[\int p(x)\,dx-px\right]}. \tag{8}$$

*We denote this function by $\tilde{G}$ to distinguish it for the time being from the quasi-classical function in the momentum space which we have found in part 1. Our problem is to show the identity of these two functions.

Using the fact that the operator $S = \int p\,dx$ is large relative to $\hbar$, let us compute integral (8) by expanding the index of the exponential factor into a series about the maximum (the saddle-point method).

To find this maximum, we equate the first derivative of the expression $\varphi(x) \equiv \int p(x)\,dx - px$ to zero:

$$\frac{d\varphi}{dx} = p(x) - p = \sqrt{2\mu[E - U(x)]} - p = 0. \tag{9}$$

The solution of this equation is $x(p)$ — the position as a function of the momentum in the field U, i.e., the function which we derived in the first part of the problem.

Let us find the second derivative:

$$\frac{d^2\varphi}{dx^2} = -\frac{2\mu U'}{\sqrt{2\mu(E-U)}} = 2\mu\frac{\frac{dp}{dt}(x)}{p(x)}.$$

To find the value of φ'' at the maximum, it is necessary to take $x(p)$ for x. Then, we obtain $p[x(p)] = p$, so that

$$\left(\frac{d^2\varphi}{dx^2}\right)_{\max} = 2\mu\frac{\frac{dp}{dt}(p)}{p}.$$

Thus, the expansion of $\varphi(x)$ in the neighborhood of the maximum has the form

$$\varphi(x) = \int^{x(p)} \sqrt{2\mu(E-U)}\,dx - px(p) + \mu\frac{\frac{dp}{dt}(p)}{p}[x - x(p)]^2.$$

Substituting this expression into $\tilde{G}(p)$ and placing the slowly changing factor $\frac{1}{\sqrt{|p(x)|}}$ at the maximum $x = x(p)$ outside the integral sign, we obtain:

$$\tilde{G}(p) =$$

$$= \frac{c_1}{\sqrt{|p|\,2\pi\hbar}}\, e^{\frac{i}{\hbar}\left[\int^{x(p)}\sqrt{2\mu(E-U)}\,dx - px(p)\right]} \int dx\, e^{\frac{i\mu}{\hbar}\frac{\frac{dp}{dt}(p)}{p}[x - x(p)]^2} =$$

$$= \frac{c_1}{\sqrt{2\pi\hbar|p|}}\, e^{\frac{i}{\hbar}\left[\int^{x(p)}\sqrt{2\mu(E-U)}\,dx - px(p)\right]} \sqrt{\frac{\hbar\pi}{i\mu}\frac{|p|}{\left|\frac{dp}{dt}\right|}} =$$

$$= \frac{c_1}{\sqrt{2\mu i}}\frac{1}{\sqrt{\left|\frac{dp}{dt}\right|}}\, e^{\frac{i}{\hbar}\left[\int^{x(p)}\sqrt{2\mu(E-U)}\,dx - px(p)\right]}.$$

We shall now show that the expression in brackets can be represented in the form $-\int x(p)\,dp$.

For this, we find the derivative with respect to p:

$$\frac{d}{dp}\left\{\int^{x(p)} \sqrt{2\mu\,[E-U(x)]}\,dx - px(p)\right\} =$$

$$= \frac{dx}{dp}\sqrt{2\mu\,\{E-U\,[x(p)]\}} - p\frac{dx}{dp} - x(p).$$

From (9), the first two terms cancel each other out. Therefore,

$$\frac{d}{dp}\{\ldots\} = -x(p).$$

Hence,

$$\int^{x(p)} \sqrt{2\mu\,(E-U)}\,dx - px(p) = -\int x(p)\,dp.$$

Thus, the function $\tilde{G}$ has the form

$$\tilde{G}(p) = \frac{c_1}{\sqrt{2\mu i}}\,\frac{1}{\sqrt{\left|\frac{dp}{dt}\right|}}\,e^{-\frac{i}{\hbar}\int x(p)\,dp}$$

and consequently, except for a constant factor, it is identical with $G(p)$ [cf. (7)]:

$$\tilde{G}(p) = \text{const}\,G(p),$$

Q.E.D.

CHAPTER VIII

Spin. Identical Particles

1. Performing a cyclic permutation of the subscripts x, y, z in the well-known expressions for the Pauli matrices in the s_z-space, we obtain directly the desired operators in the s_x-space:

$$\hat{s}_x = \frac{1}{2}\begin{pmatrix} 1 & 0 \\ 0 & -1 \end{pmatrix}, \quad \hat{s}_y = \frac{1}{2}\begin{pmatrix} 0 & 1 \\ 1 & 0 \end{pmatrix}, \quad \hat{s}_z = \frac{1}{2}\begin{pmatrix} 0 & -i \\ i & 0 \end{pmatrix}.$$

2. In the given s_z-space, the Pauli matrices have the form

$$\hat{s}_x = \frac{1}{2}\begin{pmatrix} 0 & 1 \\ 1 & 0 \end{pmatrix}, \quad \hat{s}_y = \frac{1}{2}\begin{pmatrix} 0 & -i \\ i & 0 \end{pmatrix}, \quad \hat{s}_z = \frac{1}{2}\begin{pmatrix} 1 & 0 \\ 0 & -1 \end{pmatrix}.$$

In accordance with the two possible values $\left(\frac{1}{2} \text{ and } -\frac{1}{2}\right)$ of the argument of the spin functions $\chi(s_z)$, it is convenient to write these functions in the form of columns with two terms (i.e., in the form of two-dimensional vectors in spin space, which transform into one another when operated on by the Pauli matrices) of the type $\begin{pmatrix} c_1 \\ c_2 \end{pmatrix}$, where c_1 and c_2 are numbers.

Let us find the eigenfunctions and the eigenvalues of the operator $\hat{s}_x$ in the s_z-space.

The equation

$$\hat{s}_x \chi_{\sigma_x} = s_x \chi_{\sigma_x}$$

assumes the form

$$\frac{1}{2}\begin{pmatrix} 0 & 1 \\ 1 & 0 \end{pmatrix}\begin{pmatrix} c_1 \\ c_2 \end{pmatrix} = \begin{pmatrix} s_x c_1 \\ s_x c_2 \end{pmatrix}.$$

Multiplying the matrix by the column and equating the corresponding elements of the columns on the right and on the left, we obtain the following system of equations:

$$\left.\begin{aligned} \frac{1}{2} c_2 &= s_x c_1, \\ \frac{1}{2} c_1 &= s_x c_2, \end{aligned}\right\}$$

These give the two eigenvalues of the operator $\hat{s}_x$:

$$s_x = +\frac{1}{2} \text{ and } s_x = -\frac{1}{2}.$$

The first of these corresponds to the eigenfunction

$$\chi_{s_x=+\frac{1}{2}}(s_z) = \frac{1}{\sqrt{2}} e^{i\alpha}\begin{pmatrix}1\\1\end{pmatrix},$$

while the second corresponds to the eigenfunction

$$\chi_{s_x=-\frac{1}{2}}(s_z) = \frac{1}{\sqrt{2}} e^{i\beta}\begin{pmatrix}1\\-1\end{pmatrix},$$

where α, and β are arbitrary real phases. The functions χ are normalized to unity and are mutually orthogonal.

According to the definition of the s_z-space, the squared modulus of the upper element of the spin function $\chi_{s_x}(s_z)$ gives the probability of the component $s_z = +\frac{1}{2}$ in a state with a definite value of s_x, while the squared modulus of the lower element gives the probability of $s_z = -\frac{1}{2}$ in the same state. As we could expect on the basis of the perpendicularity of the z- and x-axes, these two probabilities are identical $\left(=\frac{1}{2}\right)$.

Quite analogously, we find

$$\chi_{s_y=+\frac{1}{2}}(s_z) = \frac{1}{\sqrt{2}} e^{i\alpha_1}\begin{pmatrix}1\\i\end{pmatrix}, \quad \chi_{s_y=-\frac{1}{2}}(s_z) = \frac{1}{\sqrt{2}} e^{i\beta_1}\begin{pmatrix}1\\-i\end{pmatrix},$$

$$\chi_{s_z=+\frac{1}{2}}(s_z) = e^{i\alpha_2}\begin{pmatrix}1\\0\end{pmatrix}, \quad \chi_{s_z=-\frac{1}{2}}(s_z) = e^{i\beta_2}\begin{pmatrix}0\\1\end{pmatrix}.$$

3. As distinguished from the actual components of the electron spin, the squares of these spin components can be measured simultaneously. (It can be said that the s_x-, s_y-, s_z-components of spin 1/2 are simultaneously determinable in regard to magnitude, but not in regard to sign.)

The point here is that the corresponding operators (the squares of the Pauli matrices) commute with one another. Indeed, using the anticommutativity of the Pauli matrices($\hat{s}_x\hat{s}_y = -\hat{s}_y\hat{s}_x$, etc.), we have

$$\hat{s}_x^2\hat{s}_y^2 = -\hat{s}_x\hat{s}_y\hat{s}_x\hat{s}_y = -\hat{s}_y\hat{s}_x\hat{s}_y\hat{s}_x = \hat{s}_y^2\hat{s}_x^2, \text{ i.e.,}$$

The operators in question have the form

$$\hat{s}_x^2 = \hat{s}_y^2 = \hat{s}_z^2 = \frac{1}{4}\begin{pmatrix}1 & 0\\0 & 1\end{pmatrix} \equiv \frac{1}{4}\cdot\hat{1}. \tag{1}$$

Since they are multiples of the unit matrix $\hat{1}$, they have form (1) in any space (since, in a transformation from one space to another, i.e., in a unitary transformation, the matrix $\hat{1}$ transforms into itself).

4. Denoting the ordinary vector by $\boldsymbol{a}$, and the spin vector 1/2 by $\hat{\boldsymbol{s}}$, we have

$$(\boldsymbol{a}\hat{\boldsymbol{s}})^2 = (a_x\hat{s}_x + a_y\hat{s}_y + a_z\hat{s}_z)(a_x\hat{s}_x + a_y\hat{s}_y + a_z\hat{s}_z). \qquad (1)$$

As a result of the multiplication in the right member of (1), all the off-diagonal terms yield zeros because of the anticommutivity of the Pauli matrices:

$$\hat{s}_x\hat{s}_y + \hat{s}_y\hat{s}_x = 0 \text{ , etc.}$$

Thus,

$$(\boldsymbol{a}\hat{\boldsymbol{s}})^2 = a_x^2\hat{s}_x^2 + a_y^2\hat{s}_y^2 + a_z^2\hat{s}_z^2.$$

Substituting $\hat{s}_x^2 = \hat{s}_y^2 = \hat{s}_z^2 = \frac{1}{4}\cdot\hat{1}$, where $\hat{1}$ is the unit matrix, we find finally

$$(\boldsymbol{a}\hat{\boldsymbol{s}})^2 = \frac{a^2}{4}\cdot\hat{1}, \quad \text{or, briefly,} \quad (\boldsymbol{a}\hat{\boldsymbol{s}})^2 = \frac{a^2}{4}.$$

5. We denote the spin-vector operators of subsystems 1 and 2 by $\hat{\boldsymbol{s}}_1$ and $\hat{\boldsymbol{s}}_2$, and the operator of the total spin of the system (1 + 2) by $\hat{\boldsymbol{S}}$ $(\boldsymbol{S} = \boldsymbol{s}_1 + \boldsymbol{s}_2)$.

We have

$$\hat{S}^2 = \hat{s}_1^2 + \hat{s}_2^2 + 2\hat{\boldsymbol{s}}_1\hat{\boldsymbol{s}}_2.$$

Hence,

$$\hat{\boldsymbol{s}}_1\hat{\boldsymbol{s}}_2 = \frac{\hat{S}^2 - \hat{s}_1^2 - \hat{s}_2^2}{2}. \qquad (1)$$

However, in the states of the spin system — whether triplet (parallel spins) or singlet (antiparallel spins) — all the quantities appearing in the right member of (1) have definite values: $S(S+1)$, $s_1(s_1+1)$, and $s_2(s_2+1)$ correspondingly $(s_1 = s_2 = \frac{1}{2}$; $S = 1$ in the triplet state and $S = 0$ in the singlet state). Consequently, the left member of (1) — the scalar product — also has a definite value in each of the spin states:

$$\boldsymbol{s}_1\boldsymbol{s}_2 = \frac{S(S+1) - s_1(s_1+1) - s_2(s_2+1)}{2} = \frac{S(S+1) - 2\cdot\frac{1}{2}\cdot\frac{3}{2}}{2}.$$

Thus, in the triplet states, we have

$$\boldsymbol{s}_1\boldsymbol{s}_2 = \frac{1\cdot 2 - \frac{3}{2}}{2} = \frac{1}{4},$$

while in the singlet state,

$$s_1 s_2 = \frac{0 \cdot 1 - \frac{3}{2}}{2} = -\frac{3}{4}.$$

6. The operators for the electron-spin components $\hat{s}_x$, $\hat{s}_y$, $\hat{s}_z$ form an axial matrix vector, which transforms as an ordinary polar vector in rotations of the coordinate system. Taking the plane of rotation of the axes to be the (z, x)-plane, and using the well-known equations for coordinate transformations

$$z' = z\cos\alpha + x\sin\alpha, \qquad x' = -z\sin\alpha + x\cos\alpha, \qquad y' = y,$$

we obtain

$$\hat{s}_{z'} = \cos\alpha\,\hat{s}_z + \sin\alpha\,\hat{s}_x,\ \hat{s}_{x'} = -\sin\alpha\,\hat{s}_z + \cos\alpha\,\hat{s}_x,\ \hat{s}_{y'} = \hat{s}_y. \tag{1}$$

For the given system of rotation of the axes, relations (1) are correct in any space. In particular, in the s_z-space, we find

$$\hat{s}_{z'} = \frac{1}{2}\left\{\cos\alpha\begin{pmatrix}1 & 0\\ 0 & -1\end{pmatrix} + \sin\alpha\begin{pmatrix}0 & 1\\ 1 & 0\end{pmatrix}\right\} = \frac{1}{2}\begin{pmatrix}\cos\alpha & \sin\alpha\\ \sin\alpha & -\cos\alpha\end{pmatrix}. \tag{2}$$

Reducing the operator $\hat{s}_{z'}$ to a diagonal form, we obtain its eigenvalues: $s_{z'} = +\frac{1}{2}$, $s_{z'} = -\frac{1}{2}$.

7. The problem can be solved by several methods. We shall give the two simplest methods.

1. Solution in the s_z-space.

The problem reduces to an expansion of the normalized eigenfunction of the operator $\hat{s}_z$, i.e.,

$$\chi_{s_z = +\frac{1}{2}}(s_z) = \begin{pmatrix}1\\ 0\end{pmatrix},$$

into normalized eigenfunctions of the operator $\hat{s}_z$, and to the squaring of the coefficients of this superposition.

Using equation (2) of the preceding problem, we find the eigenvalues of $\hat{s}_{z'}$:

$$\hat{s}_{z'}\chi_{s_{z'}}(s_z) = \frac{1}{2}\begin{pmatrix}\cos\alpha & \sin\alpha\\ \sin\alpha & -\cos\alpha\end{pmatrix}\begin{pmatrix}c_1\\ c_2\end{pmatrix} = s_{z'}\begin{pmatrix}c_1\\ c_2\end{pmatrix}.$$

By carrying out the matrix multiplication and equating the corresponding components of the spin functions, we easily find the eigenfunction of $\hat{s}_{z'}$ corresponding to the eigenvalue $s_{z'} = +\frac{1}{2}$:

$$\chi_{s_{z'} = +\frac{1}{2}}(s_z) = \begin{pmatrix}\cos\frac{\alpha}{2}\\ \sin\frac{\alpha}{2}\end{pmatrix},$$

and the eigenfunction of $s_{z'}$ corresponding to the eigenvalue $s_{z'}=-\frac{1}{2}$:

$$\chi_{s_{z'}=-\frac{1}{2}}(s_z)=\begin{pmatrix}-\sin\frac{\alpha}{2}\\ \cos\frac{\alpha}{2}\end{pmatrix}.$$

The above-mentioned expansion

$$\chi_{s_z=+\frac{1}{2}}(s_z)=a_1\chi_{s_{z'}=+\frac{1}{2}}(s_z)+a_2\chi_{s_{z'}=-\frac{1}{2}}(s_z)$$

assumes the form

$$\begin{pmatrix}1\\0\end{pmatrix}=a_1\begin{pmatrix}\cos\frac{\alpha}{2}\\ \sin\frac{\alpha}{2}\end{pmatrix}+a_2\begin{pmatrix}-\sin\frac{\alpha}{2}\\ \cos\frac{\alpha}{2}\end{pmatrix}.$$

Hence,

$$a_1=\cos\frac{\alpha}{2}, \quad a_2=-\sin\frac{\alpha}{2}.$$

The probabilities are

$$w\left(s_{z'}=+\frac{1}{2}\right)=|a_1|^2=\cos^2\frac{\alpha}{2},$$

$$w\left(s_{z'}=-\frac{1}{2}\right)=|a_2|^2=\sin^2\frac{\alpha}{2}.$$

As we would expect, the mean value

$$\overline{s_{z'}}=\left(+\frac{1}{2}\right)w\left(s_{z'}=+\frac{1}{2}\right)+\left(-\frac{1}{2}\right)w\left(s_{z'}=-\frac{1}{2}\right)=\frac{1}{2}\cos\alpha$$

is identical with the classical component of the spin vector $s\left(s=\frac{1}{2}\right)$, directed along the z-axis.

2. Solution in the $s_{z'}$-space.

Using equations (1) of the preceding problem, we find (for any space)

$$\hat{s}_z=\cos\alpha\,\hat{s}_{z'}-\sin\alpha\,\hat{s}_{x'}.$$

Thus, in the $s_{z'}$-space,

$$\hat{s}_z=\frac{1}{2}\cos\alpha\begin{pmatrix}1&0\\0&-1\end{pmatrix}-\frac{1}{2}\sin\alpha\begin{pmatrix}0&1\\1&0\end{pmatrix}=\frac{1}{2}\begin{pmatrix}\cos\alpha&-\sin\alpha\\-\sin\alpha&-\cos\alpha\end{pmatrix}. \qquad (1)$$

We now introduce the eigenfunction of the operator s_z corresponding to the eigenvalue $s_z = +\frac{1}{2}$ in the $s_{z'}$-space. Denoting it by $\chi_{s_z=+\frac{1}{2}}(s_{z'})$, we have by definition

$$\hat{s}_z \chi_{s_z=+\frac{1}{2}}(s_{z'}) = \left(+\frac{1}{2}\right) \cdot \chi_{s_z=+\frac{1}{2}}(s_{z'}).$$

Substituting $\hat{s}_z$ from (1), we find in the usual way

$$\chi_{s_z=+\frac{1}{2}}(s_{z'}) = \begin{pmatrix} \cos\frac{\alpha}{2} \\ -\sin\frac{\alpha}{2} \end{pmatrix}.$$

As we would expect, this spin function is identical with the pair of coefficients (a_1, a_2) in part 1 [see also equation (5′) of problem No. 24, Chapter III].

From the definition of the $s_{z'}$-space, the components of $\chi_{s_z=+\frac{1}{2}}(s_{z'})$ give the probabilities of the corresponding eigenvalues of $s_{z'}$:

$$w\left(s_{z'} = +\frac{1}{2}\right) = \cos^2\frac{\alpha}{2},$$
$$w\left(s_{z'} = -\frac{1}{2}\right) = \sin^2\frac{\alpha}{2}, \qquad \overline{s_{z'}} = \frac{1}{2}\cos\alpha,$$

in agreement with part 1.

8. As we know [1, 6], an operator $\hat{G}$ is transformed from one space to another by means of the corresponding unitary matrix $\hat{S}$ according to the equation

$$\hat{G}' = \hat{S}^{-1}\hat{G}\hat{S}. \tag{1}$$

We shall now carry out transformation (1) for the operator $\hat{\sigma}_z \equiv 2\hat{s}_z$,* taking as the "old" space the s_z-space and as the "new" space (indicated by a prime) the s_x-space. Then (see problem No. 1),

$$\hat{\sigma}_z' = \begin{pmatrix} 0 & -i \\ i & 0 \end{pmatrix}, \quad \hat{\sigma}_z = \begin{pmatrix} 1 & 0 \\ 0 & -1 \end{pmatrix}. \tag{2}$$

Operating from the left on both members of equation (1) with the matrix

---

*We are using the doubled spin operators $\hat{\sigma}_i$ simply to avoid using the letter s, which we use in another sense.

$$\hat{S} \equiv \begin{pmatrix} s_{11} & s_{12} \\ s_{21} & s_{22} \end{pmatrix}$$

and substituting $G \equiv \hat{\sigma}_z$ and $\hat{G}' \equiv \sigma'_z$, we have

$$\begin{pmatrix} s_{11} & s_{12} \\ s_{21} & s_{22} \end{pmatrix} \begin{pmatrix} 0 & -i \\ i & 0 \end{pmatrix} = \begin{pmatrix} 1 & 0 \\ 0 & -1 \end{pmatrix} \begin{pmatrix} s_{11} & s_{12} \\ s_{21} & s_{22} \end{pmatrix}.$$

Carrying out the matrix multiplication and equating separately the corresponding matrix elements appearing on the left and on the right, we arrive at the following system of equations for the elements s_{ik}:

$$s_{11} = is_{12}, \quad s_{12} = -is_{11}, \; s_{21} = -is_{22}, \quad s_{22} = is_{21}. \tag{3}$$

Of these equations, only two are independent.

Let us now use the unitarity conditions of the matrix $\hat{S}$:

$$\hat{S}\hat{S}^{+} = \hat{1},$$

or

$$\begin{pmatrix} s_{11} & s_{12} \\ s_{21} & s_{22} \end{pmatrix} \begin{pmatrix} \overset{*}{s}_{11} & \overset{*}{s}_{21} \\ \overset{*}{s}_{12} & \overset{*}{s}_{22} \end{pmatrix} = \begin{pmatrix} 1 & 0 \\ 0 & 1 \end{pmatrix}.$$

Carrying out the matrix multiplication and equating the corresponding elements of the matrices, we obtain the equations

$$\left. \begin{aligned} |s_{11}|^2 + |s_{12}|^2 = 1, \qquad s_{11}\overset{*}{s}_{21} + s_{12}\overset{*}{s}_{22} = 0; \\ s_{21}\overset{*}{s}_{11} + s_{22}\overset{*}{s}_{12} = 0, \qquad |s_{21}|^2 + |s_{22}|^2 = 1. \end{aligned} \right\} \tag{4}$$

Two of these equations are identical with one another and are, moreover, a consequence of equations (3).

Thus, as a result, we have the system of equations

$$\left. \begin{aligned} s_{12} = -is_{11}, \quad s_{21} = -is_{22}, \\ |s_{11}|^2 + |s_{12}|^2 = 1, \quad |s_{21}|^2 + |s_{22}|^2 = 1. \end{aligned} \right\} \tag{5}$$

Solving this system, we find

$$\left. \begin{aligned} s_{11} = \frac{1}{\sqrt{2}} e^{i\alpha}, \qquad s_{12} = -\frac{i}{\sqrt{2}} e^{i\alpha}, \\ s_{21} = -\frac{i}{\sqrt{2}} e^{i\beta}, \qquad s_{22} = \frac{1}{\sqrt{2}} e^{i\beta}, \end{aligned} \right\} \tag{6}$$

where α and β are arbitrary phases, whose values cannot be determined from system (5). Thus, the matrix $\hat{S}$ has the form

$$\hat{S} = e^{i\alpha}\begin{pmatrix} \frac{1}{\sqrt{2}} & -\frac{i}{\sqrt{2}} \\ -\frac{i}{\sqrt{2}}e^{i(\beta-\alpha)} & \frac{1}{\sqrt{2}}e^{i(\beta-\alpha)} \end{pmatrix}. \tag{7}$$

This matrix contains two arbitrary phases α and β. One of them appears in the phase factor $e^{i\alpha}$ standing in front of the entire matrix. Since this factor does not operate on the spin variables, it drops out in the transformation of the operators to the new space [see (1)], and the form of the new operators will not depend on α. In the transformation of the ψ-function to the new space according to the formula

$$\psi' = \hat{S}^{-1}\psi \tag{8}$$

this factor appears as a phase factor in front of ψ. Consequently, the existence of this factor results only in a change of the phase of the ψ-function by a constant amount, and this, as we know, is not important. Therefore, we shall omit this factor by setting α equal to zero:

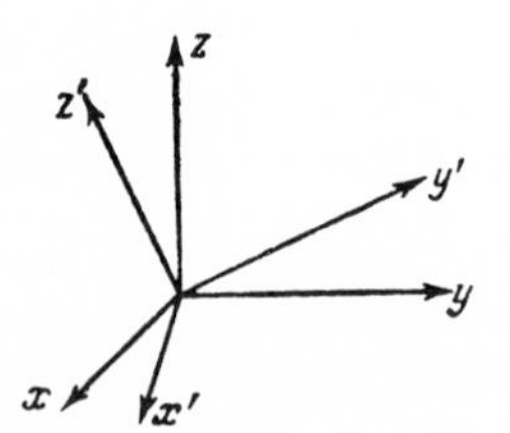

$$\hat{S} = \begin{pmatrix} \frac{1}{\sqrt{2}} & -\frac{i}{\sqrt{2}} \\ -\frac{i}{\sqrt{2}}e^{i\beta} & \frac{1}{\sqrt{2}}e^{i\beta} \end{pmatrix}. \tag{7'}$$

The value of the second arbitrary constant β affects the form of the matrix essentially. Thus, the initial requirement for the transformation of $\hat{\sigma}_z$ into $\hat{\sigma}'_z$ is not sufficient for a single-valued determination of $\hat{S}$. This result can be explained in the following way. With each direction in three-dimensional space, let us associate a definite spin matrix which is the operator for the component of spin in this direction. Then, each new space of the operators $\hat{\sigma}_x$, $\hat{\sigma}_y$ and $\hat{\sigma}_z$ will correspond to a new system of axes x', y', and z'. A transformation to a new space will consist of a rotation of the coordinate system in our space. The initially given condition reduces to the requirement [cf. (2)] that the z'-axis of the new coordinate system coincide with the y-axis $(\hat{\sigma}'_z \equiv \sigma_y)$; However, this does not define single-valuedly the position of all the axes of the new coordinate system. For such a single-valued definition, it is also necessary to give the position of still another axis or else the form of still another operator. According to the definition of the new space (the s_x-space), it is necessary to require that the operator $\hat{s}'_x$ be diagonal, i.e., that

$$\hat{\sigma}'_x \equiv 2s'_x = \begin{pmatrix} 1 & 0 \\ 0 & -1 \end{pmatrix}. \tag{9}$$

By means of this requirement, we superpose the x'-axis of the new coordinate system on the z-axis. Likewise, the y'-axis is superposed on the x-axis, and our entire transformation amounts to a rotation of 120° about the main diagonal of the first octant.

From condition (9), proceding in the same way as in the derivation of equation (3), we find

$$s_{11} = s_{21}, \qquad s_{22} = -s_{12}. \tag{10}$$

By placing these conditions on matrix (7′), we obtain $\beta = \frac{\pi}{2}$. Thus, the matrix for our unitary transformation finally assumes the form

$$\hat{S} = \frac{1}{\sqrt{2}}\begin{pmatrix} 1 & -i \\ 1 & i \end{pmatrix}.$$

9. Because of the weakness of the interaction of the spins, the spin functions which we must determine can be represented in the form of linear combinations of the products of the eigenfunctions of the operators $\hat{s}_1^2$ and $\hat{s}_2^2$.

Each of these operators has two eigenfunctions corresponding to the two possible values of the spin component 1/2 along an arbitrary axis.

Let us select the z-axis as this "axis of quantization." Then, the common eigenfunctions of the operators $\hat{s}_1^2$ and $\hat{s}_{1z}$ (in the s_{1z}-space) can be written in the form

$$\chi_\alpha(s_{1z}) \equiv \chi_\alpha(1) = \begin{pmatrix} 1 \\ 0 \end{pmatrix}, \qquad \chi_\beta(s_{1z}) \equiv \chi_\beta(1) = \begin{pmatrix} 0 \\ 1 \end{pmatrix}. \tag{1}$$

The common eigenfunctions of the operators s_2^2 and s_{2z} have the same form (in the s_{2z}-space) — $\chi_\alpha(2)$ and $\chi_\beta(2)$.

The function χ_α (1) belongs to the eigenvalues $s_1^2 \to s_1(s_1+1) = \frac{3}{4}$ and $s_{1z} = +\frac{1}{2}$; the function χ_β (1) corresponds to the values $s_1^2 = \frac{3}{4}$ and $s_{1z} = -\frac{1}{2}$; and similarly for the functions $\chi_\alpha(2)$ and $\chi_\beta(2)$. At the same time, the functions $\chi_\alpha(i)$ and $\chi_\beta(i)$ $(i = 1, 2)$ are mutually orthogonal and normalized.

For the subsequent discussion, it is convenient to introduce the operator $\hat{\sigma} \equiv 2\hat{s}$. As we know, in the s_z-space, the matrices for its components and its square have the form

$$\left.\begin{aligned} &\hat{\sigma}_x = \begin{pmatrix} 0 & 1 \\ 1 & 0 \end{pmatrix}, \quad \hat{\sigma}_y = \begin{pmatrix} 0 & -i \\ i & 0 \end{pmatrix}, \quad \hat{\sigma}_z = \begin{pmatrix} 1 & 0 \\ 0 & -1 \end{pmatrix}; \\ &\hat{\sigma}^2 = \hat{\sigma}_x^2 + \hat{\sigma}_y^2 + \hat{\sigma}_z^2 = 3\begin{pmatrix} 1 & 0 \\ 0 & 1 \end{pmatrix} \equiv 3 \cdot \hat{1}, \end{aligned}\right\} \tag{2}$$

where $\hat{1}$ is the unit matrix (the operator for multiplication by unity).

Applying these operators to functions (1), we have

$$\hat{\sigma}_x\chi_\alpha = \begin{pmatrix} 0 & 1 \\ 1 & 0 \end{pmatrix}\begin{pmatrix} 1 \\ 0 \end{pmatrix} = \begin{pmatrix} 0 \\ 1 \end{pmatrix} = \chi_\beta\,, \text{ i.e.,}$$

Let us write out the results of these elementary operations:

$$\left.\begin{array}{llll} \hat{\sigma}_x\chi_\alpha = \chi_\beta, & \hat{\sigma}_y\chi_\alpha = i\chi_\beta, & \hat{\sigma}_z\chi_\alpha = \chi_\alpha, & \hat{\sigma}^2\chi_\alpha = 3\chi_\alpha; \\ \hat{\sigma}_x\chi_\beta = \chi_\alpha, & \hat{\sigma}_y\chi_\beta = -i\chi_\alpha, & \hat{\sigma}_z\chi_\beta = -\chi_\beta, & \hat{\sigma}^2\chi_\beta = 3\chi_\beta. \end{array}\right\} \quad (3)$$

It is somewhat more convenient to carry out the subsequent computations with the combinations of operators $\hat{\sigma}_x \pm i\hat{\sigma}_y$ rather than with $\hat{\sigma}_x$, $\hat{\sigma}_y$.

From (3), we find directly

$$\left.\begin{array}{l} (\hat{\sigma}_x + i\hat{\sigma}_y)\,\chi_\alpha = \hat{\sigma}_x\chi_\alpha + i\hat{\sigma}_y\chi_\alpha = \chi_\beta + i\,(i\chi_\beta) = 0, \\ (\hat{\sigma}_x - i\hat{\sigma}_y)\,\chi_\alpha = 2\chi_\beta, \\ (\hat{\sigma}_x + i\hat{\sigma}_y)\,\chi_\beta = 2\chi_\alpha, \\ (\hat{\sigma}_x - i\hat{\sigma}_y)\,\chi_\beta = 0. \end{array}\right\} \quad (4)$$

We emphasize that equations (3) and (4), as well as all the subsequent calculations and results, are in no way connected with the choice of a specific space (for instance, the σ_z-space). Thus, equations (3) and (4) are special cases of the "unitary invariant" equation (i.e., equations independent of the space) obtained in problem No. 9, Chapter IV, for $L = \frac{1}{2}$.

According to the conditions specified in the problem, we are required to find the common eigenfunctions of the operators

$$\hat{S}^2 = (\hat{s}_1 + \hat{s}_2)^2 = \hat{s}_1^2 + \hat{s}_2^2 + 2\hat{s}_1\hat{s}_2 = \frac{1}{4}\left(\hat{\sigma}_1^2 + \hat{\sigma}_2^2 + 2\hat{\sigma}_1\hat{\sigma}_2\right) \quad (5)$$

and

$$\hat{S}_z = \hat{s}_{1z} + \hat{s}_{2z} = \frac{1}{2}(\hat{\sigma}_{1z} + \hat{\sigma}_{2z}). \quad (6)$$

According to the above discussion, the most general form of such a function is

$$\begin{aligned} \Psi(1;\ 2) = a\chi_\alpha(1)\,\chi_\alpha(2) + b\chi_\beta(1)\,\chi_\beta(2) + \\ + c\chi_\alpha(1)\,\chi_\beta(2) + d\chi_\alpha(2)\,\chi_\beta(1), \end{aligned} \quad (7)$$

where a, b, c, and d are constants which must be determined.

We shall require first of all that Ψ be an eigenfunction of $\hat{S}_z$:

$$\hat{S}_z \Psi = S_z \Psi. \tag{8}$$

Since each of the operators $\hat{\sigma}_{1z}$ and $\hat{\sigma}_{2z}$ acts only on the spin variables of "its own" subsystem 1 or 2 as the case may be, by using (6), (7) and (3), we can reduce this equation to the form

$$a\chi_\alpha(1)\chi_\alpha(2) - b\chi_\beta(1)\chi_\beta(2) = S_z [a\chi_\alpha(1)\chi_\alpha(2) + \\ + b\chi_\beta(1)\chi_\beta(2) + c\chi_\alpha(1)\chi_\beta(2) + d\chi_\alpha(2)\chi_\beta(1)].$$

Equating the coefficients of the linearly independent functions such as $\{\chi_\alpha(1)\ \chi_\alpha(2)\}$ in the two members of this equation, we conclude that, if $S_z \neq 0$, then $c = d = 0$, $a = S_z a$, $-b = S_z b$. Hence, either $S_z = +1$, $b = 0$, or $S_z = -1$, $a = 0$. If, on the other hand, $S_z = 0$, then $a = b = 0$.

Thus, from all the functions of the type of (7), condition (8) selects only the following ones:

$$\Psi = a\chi_\alpha(1)\chi_\alpha(2) \quad \text{(the eigenvalue} \quad S_z = +1), \tag{9}$$

$$\Psi = b\chi_\beta(1)\chi_\beta(2) \quad \text{(the eigenvalue} \quad S_z = -1), \tag{10}$$

$$\Psi = c\chi_\alpha(1)\chi_\beta(2) + d\chi_\alpha(2)\chi_\beta(1) \quad \text{(the eigenvalue} \quad S_z = 0) \tag{11}$$

At the same time, functions (9) and (10) are also eigenfunctions of $\hat{S}^2$, corresponding to the value $S=1$. Indeed, if, using (9), (10) and (5), we expand $\hat{\boldsymbol{\sigma}}_1 \hat{\boldsymbol{\sigma}}_2$ according to the formula

$$\hat{\boldsymbol{\sigma}}_1 \hat{\boldsymbol{\sigma}}_2 = \frac{1}{2}(\hat{\sigma}_{1x} + i\hat{\sigma}_{1y})(\hat{\sigma}_{2x} - i\hat{\sigma}_{2y}) + \\ + \frac{1}{2}(\hat{\sigma}_{1x} - i\hat{\sigma}_{1y})(\hat{\sigma}_{2x} + i\hat{\sigma}_{2y}) + \hat{\sigma}_{1z}\hat{\sigma}_{2z} \tag{12}$$

and if we consider (3) and (4), we obtain

$$\hat{S}^2 [a\chi_\alpha(1)\chi_\alpha(2)] = 2[a\chi_\alpha(1)\chi_\alpha(2)],$$

$$\hat{S}^2 [b\chi_\beta(1)\chi_\beta(2)] = 2[b\chi_\beta(1)\chi_\beta(2)].$$

Hence, $S(S+1) = 2$, i.e., $S = 1$.

From the condition that the spin functions (9) and (10) are normalized to unity, we find, moreover,

$$a = 1, \qquad b = 1. \tag{13}$$

Indeed, if we consider the normalization of the functions $\chi_\alpha(i)$ ($i = 1, 2$) and if we compute the normalization sum in the (s_{1z}, s_{2z})-space (to select a specific case), we obtain

$$\sum_{s_{1z}}\sum_{s_{2z}}\Psi^*(s_{1z},\ s_{2z})\,\Psi(s_{1z},\ s_{2z}) =$$
$$= \sum_{s_{1z}}\sum_{s_{2z}}[a\chi_\alpha(s_{1z})\chi_\alpha(s_{2z})]^*\,[a\chi_\alpha(s_{1z})\chi_\alpha(s_{2z})] =$$
$$= |a|^2\left[\sum_{s_{1z}}\overset{*}{\chi_\alpha}(s_{1z})\,\chi_\alpha(s_{1z})\right]\left[\sum_{s_{2z}}\overset{*}{\chi_\alpha}(s_{2z})\,\chi_\alpha(s_{2z})\right] = |a|^2$$

and likewise for function (10).

After equating these quantities to unity, we obtain

$$|a| = 1, \quad |b| = 1.$$

This is equivalent to (13) because of the arbitrariness of the phase of the wave function.

As regards spin functions of the type of (11), these are eigenfunctions of $\hat{S}^2$ only for definite relations between the coefficients c and d. To determine these relations, we substitute (11) into the equation for the eigenfunctions of the operator S^2:

$$\hat{S}^2\Psi = S(S+1)\Psi,$$

After we have performed some simple calculations using (5), (12), (3), and (4), this equation assumes the form

$$(c+d)[\chi_\alpha(1)\chi_\beta(2) + \chi_\beta(1)\chi_\alpha(2)] =$$
$$= S(S+1)[c\chi_\alpha(1)\chi_\beta(2) + d\chi_\alpha(2)\chi_\beta(1)].$$

Equating the coefficients of the linearly independent functions in the two members of this equation, we obtain the following system of equations for c and d:

$$\left.\begin{aligned} [S(S+1)-1]\,c \qquad\qquad\qquad -d &= 0, \\ c - [S(S+1)-1]\,d &= 0. \end{aligned}\right\} \tag{14}$$

This system has nontrivial solutions only in the case where its determinant is equal to zero:

$$[S(S+1)-1]^2 - 1 = 0, \quad \text{or} \quad S(S+1) - 1 = \pm 1.$$

Hence, we find the two possible values S: $S = 0$ and $S = 1$.*

According to (14), the first of these values corresponds to the relation $d = -c$, i.e., to the eigenfunction

$$\Psi_a = c\,[\chi_\alpha(1)\,\chi_\beta(2) - \chi_\alpha(2)\,\chi_\beta(1)]. \tag{15}$$

---

*Since we are dealing with the addition of two spins $\frac{1}{2}$, these values of S are of course evident beforehand.

The second value corresponds to the relation $d = c$, i.e., to the function

$$\Psi_s = c\,[\chi_\alpha(1)\chi_\beta(2) + \chi_\alpha(2)\chi_\beta(1)], \tag{16}$$

Here, the subscripts s and a denote "symmetric" and "antisymmetric" respectively (see below).

The value of c can be derived from the normalization condition. Thus, considering the orthonormal nature of the functions χ_α and χ_β, we obtain for (15):

$$\sum_{s_{1z}}\sum_{s_{2z}} \Psi_a^*(s_{1z}, s_{2z})\Psi_a(s_{1z}, s_{2z}) =$$

$$= |c|^2 \sum_{s_{1z}}\sum_{s_{2z}} [\chi_\alpha(s_{1z})\chi_\beta(s_{2z}) - \chi_\alpha(s_{2z})\chi_\beta(s_{1z})]^* \times$$

$$\times [\chi_\alpha(s_{1z})\chi_\beta(s_{2z}) - \chi_\alpha(s_{2z})\chi_\beta(s_{1z})] =$$

$$= |c|^2 \left\{ \left[\sum_{s_{1z}} \chi_\alpha^*(s_{1z})\chi_\alpha(s_{1z})\right]\left[\sum_{s_{2z}} \chi_\beta^*(s_{2z})\chi_\beta(s_{2z})\right] + \right.$$

$$+ \left[\sum_{s_{1z}} \chi_\beta^*(s_{1z})\chi_\beta(s_{1z})\right]\left[\sum_{s_{2z}} \chi_\alpha^*(s_{2z})\chi_\alpha(s_{2z})\right] -$$

$$- \left[\sum_{s_{1z}} \chi_\alpha^*(s_{1z})\chi_\beta(s_{1z})\right]\left[\sum_{s_{2z}} \chi_\beta^*(s_{2z})\chi_\alpha(s_{2z})\right] -$$

$$\left. - \left[\sum_{s_{1z}} \chi_\beta^*(s_{1z})\chi_\alpha(s_{1z})\right]\left[\sum_{s_{2z}} \chi_\alpha^*(s_{2z})\chi_\beta(s_{2z})\right] \right\} =$$

$$= |c|^2 \{1\cdot 1 + 1\cdot 1 - 0\cdot 0 - 0\cdot 0\} = 2|c|^2.$$

By equating this quantity to unity, we find, except for an unessential phase factor,

$$c = \frac{1}{\sqrt{2}}. \tag{17}$$

The same value of c is obviously obtained for (16).

Below we give a table of the eigenvalues and eigenfunctions of the total spin $S = s_1 + s_2$ of a system of two particles of spin $\frac{1}{2}$, compiled on the basis of (9), (10), (13), (15), (16) and (17). This table shows the type of symmetry of the spin functions with respect to interchange of the two spins of 1 and 2.

We emphasize that we have not conducted any operations of symmetrization or antisymmetrization of the spin functions which we have obtained. The common eigenfunctions of the operators $\hat{S}^2$ and $\hat{S}_z$ turned out automatically to have a definite symmetry with respect to interchange (cf. problem No. 11).

'he first three functions, corresponding to $S = 1$, form a so-
:d spin triplet ($2S + 1 = 3$), while the fourth function represents the state of a spin singlet ($2S + 1 = 1$).

Spin function	Eigenvalue			Symmetry with respect to spins of 1 and 2
	S	$S(S+1)$	S_z	
$\chi_\alpha(1)\chi_\alpha(2)$	1	2	1	Symmetric
$\frac{1}{\sqrt{2}}[\chi_\alpha(1)\chi_\beta(2)+\chi_\beta(1)\chi_\alpha(2)]$			0	
$\chi_\beta(1)\chi_\beta(2)$			−1	
$\frac{1}{\sqrt{2}}[\chi_\alpha(1)\chi_\beta(2)-\chi_\beta(1)\chi_\alpha(2)]$	0	0	0	Antisymmetric

It is easily verified that a set of triplet functions is in all respects equivalent to a three-component or "vector" spin function for a single particle with spin 1: not only are the corresponding eigenvalues of the operators $\hat{S}^2$ and $\hat{S}_z$ identical (cf. table), but also the results of the application of the operators $\hat{S}_x$ or $\hat{S}_y$ to the set of triplet functions are identical with the results of the application of the corresponding matrices of spin 1 (see next problem) to the above mentioned three-component function.

Likewise, the singlet function is completely equivalent to the scalar wave function of a particle with spin 0.

This situtation characterizes a sort of "fusion" of the spins of the two subsystems $\left(\frac{1}{2}\right)$ in their addition into the total spin of the system (1 or 0).

10. By setting $s = 1$ in the general formulas for the matrices of the angular momentum (spin) 1 in the (s, s_z)-space* (and consequently $s_z = +1, 0, -1$), we obtain the following third-order matrices for the required operators:

$$\hat{s}_x = \frac{1}{\sqrt{2}}\begin{pmatrix} 0 & 1 & 0 \\ 1 & 0 & 1 \\ 0 & 1 & 0 \end{pmatrix}, \quad \hat{s}_y = \frac{1}{\sqrt{2}}\begin{pmatrix} 0 & -i & 0 \\ i & 0 & -i \\ 0 & i & 0 \end{pmatrix}, \quad \hat{s}_z = \begin{pmatrix} 1 & 0 & 0 \\ 0 & 0 & 0 \\ 0 & 0 & -1 \end{pmatrix}. \tag{1}$$

Hence,

---

*See [1], p. 223, equations (54.2a), where $\sigma \equiv s_z$.

$$\hat{s}^2 = \hat{s}_x^2 + \hat{s}_y^2 + \hat{s}_z^2 = 2\begin{pmatrix}1 & 0 & 0\\ 0 & 1 & 0\\ 0 & 0 & 1\end{pmatrix} \equiv 2 \cdot \hat{1}, \tag{2}$$

where $\hat{1}$ is the unit matrix.

We note that the matrices $\hat{s}_x$, $\hat{s}_y$, $\hat{s}_z$ can be obtained formally, except for a constant factor, by termwise addition of two corresponding Pauli matrices "superimposed" on one another in the way indicated in the figure. This symbolic rule obviously reflects the addition of two spins $\frac{1}{2}$ into a spin 1.

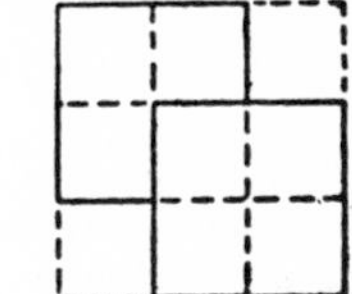

In accordance with the possible spin components s_z, an arbitrary wave function of a particle (system) with spin $s = 1$ has three components $(2s + 1 = 3)$:

$$\Psi(x, y, z, s_z) = \begin{pmatrix}\Psi_{+1}(x, y, z)\\ \Psi_0(x, y, z)\\ \Psi_{-1}(x, y, z)\end{pmatrix},$$

where $|\Psi_{+1}(x, y, z)|^2$ gives the probability distribution of the position of the particle in the state $s_z = +1$, while $\int\int\int |\Psi_{+1}|^2\, dx\, dy\, dz$ gives the total probability that the particle will have $s_z = +1$, and likewise for the other components of the Ψ-function.

If we ignore the position-dependence of the Ψ-function, which is permissible in particular for a negligibly small spin-orbit interaction,* we can consider the spin function alone. We represent this spin function in the form of a column (a vector)

$$\begin{pmatrix}c_{+1}\\ c_0\\ c_{-1}\end{pmatrix}, \tag{3}$$

where $|c_{+1}|^2$, $|c_0|^2$, and $|c_{-1}|^2$ give the probability that the particle will have $s_z = +1$, 0, and -1 respectively.

---

*In this case, the spatial degrees of freedom are independent of the spin's degree of freedom, since in this case all three functions $\Psi_{+1}(x, y, z)$, $\Psi_0(x, y, z)$ and $\Psi_{-1}(x, y, z)$ are identical with one another, except for constant factors, and accordingly the total Ψ-function can be represented in the form of the product

$$\Psi(x, y, z, s_z) = \Psi_0(x, y, z) \cdot \begin{pmatrix}c_{+1}\\ c_0\\ c_{-1}\end{pmatrix},$$

where c_{+1}, c_0, c_{-1} are numbers.

Accordingly, the spin functions of states with definite values of s_z have the form

$$\chi_{+1}(s_z) \equiv \chi_\alpha = \begin{pmatrix} 1 \\ 0 \\ 0 \end{pmatrix}, \quad \chi_0(s_z) \equiv \chi_\beta = \begin{pmatrix} 0 \\ 1 \\ 0 \end{pmatrix},$$
$$\chi_{-1}(s_z) \equiv \chi_\gamma = \begin{pmatrix} 0 \\ 0 \\ 1 \end{pmatrix}, \tag{4}$$

where the variable s_z indicates the selected space (i.e., the quantity whose probability is expressed directly, by definition, by the wave function), while the subscripts indicate the corresponding eigenvalues of s_z.

Functions (4) are eigenfunctions not only of the operator $\hat{s}_z$, but also of the operator $\hat{s}^2$ [since, according to (2), the latter is simply the operator for multiplication by two] corresponding to the eigenvalue $s(s+1) = 2$. These functions are normalized to unity (in each of them, the sum of the squares of the components is equal to unity) and are mutually orthogonal:

$$\sum_{s_z} \chi_\alpha^*(s_z)\chi_\beta(s_z) = \overset{+}{\chi_\alpha}\chi_\beta = (1\ 0\ 0)\cdot\begin{pmatrix} 0 \\ 1 \\ 0 \end{pmatrix} = 0 \quad \text{, etc.}$$

Applying the operators $\hat{s}_x, \hat{s}_y$ [see (1)] to functions (4), we obtain*:

$$\left.\begin{aligned} \hat{s}_x\chi_\alpha &= \frac{1}{\sqrt{2}}\chi_\beta, & \hat{s}_y\chi_\alpha &= \frac{i}{\sqrt{2}}\chi_\beta; \\ \hat{s}_x\chi_\beta &= \frac{1}{\sqrt{2}}(\chi_\alpha + \chi_\gamma), & \hat{s}_y\chi_\beta &= \frac{i}{\sqrt{2}}(\chi_\gamma - \chi_\alpha), \\ \hat{s}_x\chi_\gamma &= \frac{1}{\sqrt{2}}\chi_\beta, & \hat{s}_y\chi_\gamma &= -\frac{i}{\sqrt{2}}\chi_\beta. \end{aligned}\right\} \tag{5}$$

Hence, we have directly (for completeness, we also write out the results of the application of the operator $\hat{s}_z$):

$$\left.\begin{aligned} &(\hat{s}_x + i\hat{s}_y)\chi_\alpha = 0, & &(\hat{s}_x - i\hat{s}_y)\chi_\alpha = \sqrt{2}\chi_\beta, & &\hat{s}_z\chi_\alpha = \chi_\alpha; \\ &(\hat{s}_x + i\hat{s}_y)\chi_\beta = \sqrt{2}\chi_\alpha, & &(\hat{s}_x - i\hat{s}_y)\chi_\beta = \sqrt{2}\chi_\gamma, & &\hat{s}_z\chi_\beta = 0; \\ &(\hat{s}_x + i\hat{s}_y)\chi_\gamma = \sqrt{2}\chi_\beta, & &(\hat{s}_x - i\hat{s}_y)_\gamma\chi = 0, & &\hat{s}_z\chi_\gamma = -\chi_\gamma. \end{aligned}\right\} \tag{6}$$

Finally, according to (2),

$$\hat{s}^2\chi_{\alpha,\beta,\gamma} = 2\chi_{\alpha,\beta,\gamma}. \tag{7}$$

---

*Compare with [1], equation (54.2), or problem No. 9, Chapter IV.

11. The complete set of spin operators $\hat{s}_1^2$, $\hat{s}_2^2$, $\hat{s}_{1z}$, $\hat{s}_2$ obviously has the following $(2s+1)^2 = 3^2 = 9$ eigenfunctions (see the preceding problem):

$$\begin{array}{ccc} \chi_\alpha(1)\chi_\alpha(2), & \chi_\alpha(1)\chi_\beta(2), & \chi_\alpha(1)\chi_\gamma(2), \\ \chi_\beta(1)\chi_\alpha(2), & \chi_\beta(1)\chi_\beta(2), & \chi_\beta(1)\chi_\gamma(2), \\ \chi_\gamma(1)\chi_\alpha(2), & \chi_\gamma(1)\chi_\beta(2), & \chi_\gamma(1)\chi_\gamma(2), \end{array}$$

where the arguments 1 and 2 indicate the spin components of $\boldsymbol{s}_1$ and $\boldsymbol{s}_2$ which have been selected as variables of the space, for instance, s_{1z} and s_{2z}.

All these functions, which are products of the eigenfunctions of the operators $\hat{s}_{1z}$ and $\hat{s}_{2z}$, are consequently eigenfunctions of the sum of these operators $\hat{S}_z$ as well.* However, generally speaking, they are not eigenfunctions of $\hat{S}^2$. The eigenfunctions of this operator will be definite linear combinations of these functions, the most general form for which is

$$\begin{aligned} \Psi(1;\ 2) = {} & a_1\chi_\alpha(1)\chi_\alpha(2) + a_2\chi_\beta(1)\chi_\beta(2) + a_3\chi_\gamma(1)\chi_\gamma(2) + \\ & + a_4\chi_\alpha(1)\chi_\beta(2) + a_5\chi_\alpha(1)\chi_\gamma(2) + a_6\chi_\beta(1)\chi_\gamma(2) + \\ & + a_7\chi_\beta(1)\chi_\alpha(2) + a_8\chi_\gamma(1)\chi_\alpha(2) + a_9\chi_\gamma(1)\chi_\beta(2), \end{aligned} \tag{1}$$

where $a_1, a_2, \ldots, a_9$ are constants which must be determined.

First of all, we note that the simple requirement that $\Psi(1;\ 2)$ be an eigenfunction of $\hat{S}_z$ leads to a considerable simplification of the possible combinations (1). Indeed, using equation (1) and equations (6) of the preceding problem, this requirement can be written in the form

$$\begin{aligned} \hat{S}_z\Psi(1;\ 2) = (\hat{s}_{1z} + \hat{s}_{2z})\Psi(1;\ 2) = 2a_1\chi_\alpha(1)\chi_\alpha(2) - \\ - 2a_3\chi_\gamma(1)\chi_\gamma(2) + a_4\chi_\alpha(1)\chi_\beta(2) - a_6\chi_\beta(1)\chi_\gamma(2) + \\ + a_7\chi_\beta(1)\chi_\alpha(2) - a_9\chi_\gamma(1)\chi_\beta(2) = S_z\Psi(1;\ 2). \end{aligned}$$

Substituting (1) into the right member and equating corresponding coefficients in front of the linearly independent equations, we obtain the following system of equations for the coefficients $a_1, \ldots, a_9$:

$$\left.\begin{aligned} S_z \cdot a_1 = 2a_1,\ S_z \cdot a_2 = 0,\ S_z \cdot a_3 = -2a_3,\ S_z \cdot a_4 = a_4; \\ S_z \cdot a_5 = 0,\quad S_z \cdot a_6 = -a_6,\ S_z \cdot a_7 = a_7,\ S_z \cdot a_8 = 0, \\ S_z \cdot a_9 = -a_9. \end{aligned}\right\} \tag{2}$$

*Of course, they are also eigenfunctions of $\hat{s}_1^2$ and $\hat{s}_2^2$. In effect, the result of the solution should be expressions for the eigenfunctions of the set $(\hat{s}_1^2,\ \hat{s}_2^2,\ \hat{S}^2,\ \hat{S}_z)$ in terms of the eigenfunctions of the set $(\hat{s}_1^2,\ \hat{s}_2^2,\ \hat{s}_{1z},\ \hat{s}_{2z})$.

From the individual equations of this system, we obtain the possible eigenvalues of S_z (which were obvious beforehand):

$$S_z = 0, \quad \pm 1, \quad \pm 2.$$

For each of these S_z, the consistency of the system of equations (2) requires that most of the coefficients a_i. equal zero. Without giving the corresponding, purely elementary arguments, we write out a table of the nonzero coefficients* for each S_z:

S_z	Coefficients $\neq 0$
0	a_2; a_5; a_8
+1	a_4; a_7
−1	a_6; a_9
+2	a_1
−2	a_3

Following this table, the possible eigenfunctions of $\hat{S}_z$ have the form

$$S_z = 0: \quad \Psi(1;\ 2) = a_2\chi_\beta(1)\chi_\beta(2) + a_5\chi_\alpha(1)\chi_\gamma(2) + a_8\chi_\gamma(1)\chi_\alpha(2), \tag{3}$$

$$S_z = +1: \ \Psi(1;\ 2) = a_4\chi_\alpha(1)\chi_\beta(2) + a_7\chi_\beta(1)\chi_\alpha(2), \tag{4}$$

$$S_z = -1: \ \Psi(1;\ 2) = a_6\chi_\beta(1)\chi_\gamma(2) + a_9\chi_\gamma(1)\chi_\beta(2), \tag{5}$$

$$S_z = +2: \ \Psi(1;\ 2) = a_1\chi_\alpha(1)\chi_\alpha(2), \tag{6}$$

$$S_z = -2: \ \Psi(1;\ 2) = a_3\chi_\gamma(1)\chi_\gamma(2). \tag{7}$$

We shall now require that for the spin functions (3)-(7), the equation

$$\hat{S}^2\Psi(1;\ 2) = S(S+1)\Psi(1;\ 2) \tag{8}$$

be satisfied.

---

*More accurately, coefficients which can be other than zero (see below: $a_2 = 0$ for $S_z = 0$, $S = 1$).

We substitute $\Psi(1;\,2)$ from (3), (4), etc., expand the left member of (8) by means of the operator identity

$$\hat{S}^2 = (\hat{s}_1 + \hat{s}_2)^2 \equiv$$
$$\equiv \hat{s}_1^2 + \hat{s}_2^2 + 2\hat{s}_{1z}\hat{s}_{2z} + (\hat{s}_{1x} + i\hat{s}_{1y})(\hat{s}_{2x} - i\hat{s}_{2y}) +$$
$$+ (\hat{s}_{1x} - i\hat{s}_{1y})(\hat{s}_{2x} + i\hat{s}_{2y})$$

and equations (6) and (7) of the preceding problem, and equate corresponding coefficients of the linearly independent functions in the two members of (8). As a result, we obtain a system of linear homogeneous equations, the number of which is equal to the number of unknown coefficients a_i. The condition for a nontrivial solution of this system (the requirement that the determinant of this system be equal to zero) yields the possible values of $S(S+1)$ for a given S_z. By substituting these values back into the system of equations, we obtain the coefficients a_i (except for a common constant factor, which can be determined subsequently from the condition that the Ψ-function is normalized).

For (3)-(7), we obtain in succession the values of S and a_i given below.

$S_z = 0$. In this case,

$$\hat{S}^2\Psi(1;\,2) = (4a_2 + 2a_5 + 2a_8)\chi_\beta(1)\chi_\beta(2) +$$
$$+ (2a_5 + 2a_2)\chi_\alpha(1)\chi_\gamma(2) + (2a_8 + 2a_2)\chi_\gamma(1)\chi_\alpha(2) =$$
$$= S(S+1)[a_2\chi_\beta(1)\chi_\beta(2) + a_5\chi_\alpha(1)\chi_\gamma(2) + a_8\chi_\gamma(1)\chi_\alpha(2)].$$

Hence,

$$\left.\begin{aligned} [4 - S(S+1)]\,a_2 + 2a_5 + 2a_8 &= 0, \\ 2a_2 + [2 - S(S+1)]\,a_5 &= 0, \\ 2a_2 + [2 - S(S+1)]\,a_8 &= 0. \end{aligned}\right\} \qquad (9)$$

The determinant of this system of equations is

$$S(S+1)[2 - S(S+1)][S(S+1) - 6].$$

Equating it to zero, we obtain three values of S: 0, 1, 2 (all obvious beforehand). Substituting them successively into (9), we find

$$\left.\begin{aligned} S = 0&: \quad a_5 = a_8 = -a_2, \\ S = 1&: \quad a_2 = 0,\ a_8 = -a_5, \\ S = 2&: \quad a_5 = a_8 = \frac{1}{2}a_2. \end{aligned}\right\} \qquad (10)$$

$S_z = +1$. Here,

$$\hat{S}^2\Psi(1;\,2) = (4a_4 + 2a_7)\chi_\alpha(1)\chi_\beta(2) + (4a_7 + 2a_4)\chi_\beta(1)\chi_\alpha(2) =$$
$$= S(S+1)[a_4\chi_\alpha(1)\chi_\beta(2) + a_7\chi_\beta(1)\chi_\alpha(2)].$$

Hence,

$$\left.\begin{aligned}[4-S(S+1)]\,a_4+2a_7=0,\\ 2a_4+[4-S(S+1)]\,a_7=0.\end{aligned}\right\} \tag{11}$$

The requirement that the determinant of the system be equal to zero yields, as we would expect, $S = 1$ and $S = 2$. Then, from (11), we find

$$\left.\begin{aligned}S=1:\quad a_7=-a_4,\\ S=2:\quad a_7=a_4.\end{aligned}\right\} \tag{12}$$

$S_z = -1$. The same procedure as for $S_z = +1$ yields

$$\left.\begin{aligned}S=1:\quad a_9=-a_6,\\ S=2:\quad a_9=a_6.\end{aligned}\right\} \tag{13}$$

$S_z = \pm 2$. In this case, we have

$$\hat{S}^2\Psi = 6\Psi = S(S+1)\Psi.$$

Hence,

$$S = 2.$$

We now compare (3)-(7) with (10), (12) and (13), collect spin functions with the same value of S, and compute the one remaining undetermined coefficient of each coefficient from the requirement that Ψ (1; 2) is normalized to unity. Thus, we finally find:

$$S=2\left\{\begin{aligned}&S_z=2: && \Psi(1;\,2)=\chi_\alpha(1)\chi_\alpha(2),\\ &S_z=1: && \Psi(1;\,2)=\frac{1}{\sqrt{2}}\{\chi_\alpha(1)\chi_\beta(2)+\\ &&&\qquad+\chi_\beta(1)\chi_\alpha(2)\},\\ &S_z=0: && \Psi(1;\,2)=\sqrt{\frac{2}{3}}\Big\{\chi_\beta(1)\chi_\beta(2)+\\ &&&\qquad+\frac{1}{2}\chi_\alpha(1)\chi_\gamma(2)+\frac{1}{2}\chi_\gamma(1)\chi_\alpha(2)\Big\},\\ &S_z=-1: && \Psi(1;\,2)=\frac{1}{\sqrt{2}}\{\chi_\beta(1)\chi_\gamma(2)+\\ &&&\qquad+\chi_\gamma(1)\chi_\beta(2)\},\\ &S_z=-2: && \Psi(1;\,2)=\chi_\gamma(1)\chi_\gamma(2);\end{aligned}\right. \tag{14}$$

$$S=1\left\{\begin{array}{ll} S_z=1: & \Psi(1;\ 2)=\frac{1}{\sqrt{2}}\{\chi_\alpha(1)\chi_\beta(2)- \\ & \qquad -\chi_\beta(1)\chi_\alpha(2)\}, \\ S_z=0: & \Psi(1;\ 2)=\frac{1}{\sqrt{2}}\{\chi_\alpha(1)\chi_\gamma(2)- \\ & \qquad -\chi_\gamma(1)\chi_\alpha(2)\}, \\ S_z=-1: & \Psi(1;\ 2)=\frac{1}{\sqrt{2}}\{\chi_\beta(1)\chi_\gamma(2)- \\ & \qquad -\chi_\gamma(1)\chi_\beta(2)\}; \end{array}\right\} \qquad (15)$$

$$\left.\begin{array}{c} S=0,\ S_z=0: \\ \Psi(1;\ 2)=\frac{1}{\sqrt{3}}\{\chi_\beta(1)\chi_\beta(2)-\chi_\alpha(1)\chi_\gamma(2)-\chi_\gamma(1)\chi_\alpha(2)\}. \end{array}\right\} \qquad (16)$$

The five functions (14) form a spin quintet ($2S+1=5$). The three functions (15) form a spin triplet ($2S+1=3$). Finally, function (16) represents a spin singlet ($2S+1=1$). The total number of spin functions is of course equal to nine, as formerly.

It is important to note that (as in the problem on the addition of two spins $\frac{1}{2}$) the simultaneous eigenfunctions of the operators $\hat{S}^2$ and $\hat{S}_z$ (14), (15), and (16) have automatically turned out to be symmetric and antisymmetric with respect to interchange of the spins of 1 and 2. All the functions corresponding to even S (the quintet $S=2$ and the singlet $S=0$) are symmetric with respect to the spins of 1 and 2, while all the functions with odd S (the triplet $S=1$) are antisymmetric with respect to the spins.

This situation is a special case of the single-valued relation between the symmetry of the spin function and the total spin of the system ([1], p. 244).

The ratio of the total number of symmetric spin functions (six) to the number of antisymmetric functions (three) is even, as it should be: $\frac{s+1}{s}=2$ [cf. problem No. 12].

In conclusion, let us explain how the normalization constants in (14), (15), and (16) are obtained.

The result of the summation (double) of $|\Psi(1;\ 2)|^2$ over the entire space of the spin variables of 1 and 2 (each of which assumes three values: 1, 0, - 1) must be equal to unity. As can be seen from (14)-(16), the quantity $|\Psi(1;\ 2)|^2$ contains terms of two types: the squared moduli of the terms appearing in the braces, and the "cross" products of these terms. Since, from the specified conditions, the functions χ_α, χ_β, χ_γ are mutually orthogonal and normalized to unity (in each of the spin subspaces 1 and 2), each term of the first type (except terms with coefficients 1/2) gives unity when it is added over all spin space (1; 2). Each term of the second type gives zero. Accordingly, the normalization sum $\sum_1\sum_2 |\Psi(1;\,2)|^2$ is simply equal to the product of the square of the normalization constant and the number N of terms in Ψ (1; 2). Consequently, the normalization constant must be equal to $\frac{1}{\sqrt{N}}$. Thus, we obtain the coefficients $\frac{1}{\sqrt{3}}$, $\frac{1}{\sqrt{2}}$ and 1 in equations (14)-(16).

For the function corresponding to $S = 2$, $S_z = 0$, we obviously have $\sum_1\sum_2 |\Psi\;(1;\;2)|^2 = 1 = (\text{coefficient})^2 \cdot \left(1+\frac{1}{4}+\frac{1}{4}\right)$. Hence, the coefficient $\sqrt{\frac{2}{3}}$ is obtained.

12. Since $(2I+1)$ orientations of the spin are possible for each of the particles, the total number of independent spin functions for a system of two particles A and B is equal to $(2I+1)^2$.

These functions (which have not been symmetrized with respect to the spins) have the form $\chi_i^{(A)}\chi_k^{(B)}$, where $i,\,k = -I,\,-I+1,\,\ldots,\,I-1,\,I$. Symmetrizing the functions, we obtain:

for $i = k$ $(2I+1)$ functions of the form $\chi_i^{(A)}\chi_i^{(B)}$ (symmetric);

for $i \neq k$, a remainder of $(2I+1)^2 - (2I+1) = 2I(2I+1)$ functions, of which half, i.e., $I(2I+1)$ functions, are of the form $\chi_i^{(A)}\chi_k^{(B)} + \chi_k^{(A)}\chi_i^{(B)}$ (symmetric), and half, i.e., $I(2I+1)$ functions, are of the form $\chi_i^{(A)}\chi_k^{(B)} - \chi_k^{(A)}\chi_i^{(B)}$ (antisymmetric).

Thus, a total of $(I+1)\,(2I+1)$ functions symmetric with respect to interchange of the spins of particles A and B is obtained, and a total of $I(2I+1)$ antisymmetric functions. This leads to the required ratio $\frac{1+I}{I}$.

13. We denote the set of coordinates of the i-th particle, including the spin component (for particles with nonzero spin), by ξ_i $(i = 1,\,2,\,3)$, and the complete set of quantum numbers characterizing the k-th given "one-particle" state $(k = 1,\,2,\,3)$ by p_k. This set consists of three or four quantum numbers, depending on whether or not the particles have spin.

Since, from the specified conditions, the interaction* of the particles is small, the Ψ-function of the system will appear as a linear combination of products of "one-particle" wave functions $\psi_{p_k}(\xi_i)$. At the same time, since we are dealing with Bose particles, the complete wave function $\Psi\,(\xi_1,\,\xi_2,\,\xi_3)$ will have to be symmetric with respect to interchange of any two particles. Thus, this linear combination must form a sum of products of the type

$$\psi_{p_1}(\xi_1)\,\psi_{p_2}(\xi_2)\,\psi_{p_3}(\xi_3)$$

with every possible permutation of the nonidentical subscripts p_k.

*We are speaking about the ordinary (nonexchange) interaction.

The functions $\psi_{p_k}(\xi_i)$ are assumed to be mutually orthogonal and normalized:

$$\int \psi^*_{p_k}(\xi_i)\,\psi_{p_l}(\xi_i)\,d\xi_i = \delta_{kl}. \tag{1}$$

In the general case, the integration with respect to $d\xi$ implies summation over the spin indices, in addition to the usual integration with respect to the coordinates. The δ_{kl} represents the production of the corresponding number (in the general case, four) of δ-symbols.

The normalization of the complete Ψ-function will differ, depending on whether or not the occupied states p_1, p_2, p_3 are identical with one another. Here, three cases should be distinguished.

1. All three occupied states are different, that is, symbolically,

$$p_1 \neq p_2 \neq p_3.$$

The wave function of the system, normalized to unity, is

$$\begin{aligned}\Psi_{p_1, p_2, p_3}(\xi_1, \xi_2, \xi_3) = \frac{1}{\sqrt{3!}}\{&\psi_{p_1}(\xi_1)\psi_{p_2}(\xi_2)\psi_{p_3}(\xi_3) + \\ &+ \psi_{p_1}(\xi_1)\psi_{p_3}(\xi_2)\psi_{p_2}(\xi_3) + \psi_{p_3}(\xi_1)\psi_{p_2}(\xi_2)\psi_{p_1}(\xi_3) + \\ &+ \psi_{p_3}(\xi_1)\psi_{p_1}(\xi_2)\psi_{p_2}(\xi_3) + \psi_{p_2}(\xi_1)\psi_{p_1}(\xi_2)\psi_{p_3}(\xi_3) + \\ &+ \psi_{p_2}(\xi_1)\psi_{p_3}(\xi_2)\psi_{p_1}(\xi_3)\}.\end{aligned} \tag{2}$$

Indeed, in the integration of $|\Psi(\xi_1, \xi_2, \xi_3)|^2$ over the variables ξ_1, ξ_2, ξ_3, all the "cross" terms of the type

$$\frac{1}{3!}\int\int\int \psi^*_{p_1}(\xi_1)\,\psi^*_{p_2}(\xi_2)\,\psi^*_{p_3}(\xi_3)\,\psi_{p_1}(\xi_1)\,\psi_{p_3}(\xi_2)\,\psi_{p_2}(\xi_3)\,d\xi_1 d\xi_2 d\xi_3$$

become zero because of (1). Thus, out of the total of $6 \cdot 6 = 36$ terms appearing in $|\Psi|^2$, only the six integrals of the squared moduli of each of the terms in sum (2) remain, these integrals being of the type

$$\frac{1}{3!}\int\int\int |\psi_{p_1}(\xi_1)|^2\,|\psi_{p_2}(\xi_2)|^2\,|\psi_{p_3}(\xi_3)|^2\,d\xi_1 d\xi_2 d\xi_3.$$

Because of (1), each of these 6 terms is equal to $\frac{1}{3!} \cdot 1 = \frac{1}{6}$. Therefore, it is true that

$$\int\int\int |\Psi_{p_1, p_2, p_3}(\xi_1, \xi_2, \xi_3)|^2\,d\xi_1\,d\xi_2\,d\xi_3 = 1.$$

2. Two of the occupied states are identical. Thus, for instance,

$$p_1 \neq p_2 = p_3.$$

The normalized Ψ-function of the three Bose particles is

$$\Psi_{p_1, p_2, p_2}(\xi_1, \xi_2, \xi_3) = \sqrt{\frac{2!}{3!}} \{\psi_{p_1}(\xi_1)\psi_{p_2}(\xi_2)\psi_{p_2}(\xi_3) + \\ + \psi_{p_2}(\xi_1)\psi_{p_1}(\xi_2)\psi_{p_2}(\xi_3) + \psi_{p_2}(\xi_1)\psi_{p_2}(\xi_2)\psi_{p_1}(\xi_3)\}.$$

Indeed, analogously to case 1, only 3 of the $3 \cdot 3 = 9$ terms are different from zero in the normalization integral $\int\int\int |\Psi|^2 d\xi_1 d\xi_2 d\xi_3$. Each of these three terms is equal to $\left(\sqrt{\frac{2!}{3!}}\right)^2 \cdot 1 = \frac{1}{3}$, and thus the normalization integral is equal to unity.

3. All three particles are in the same state, that is,

$$p_1 = p_2 = p_3.$$

The Ψ-function of the system, normalized to unity, is obviously

$$\Psi_{p_1, p_1, p_1}(\xi_1, \xi_2, \xi_3) = \psi_{p_1}(\xi_1)\psi_{p_1}(\xi_2)\psi_{p_1}(\xi_3).$$

CHAPTER IX

Atoms and Molecules

1. The problem deals with the configuration (nd). Since $l = 2$ for each electron, we have five possible values of m: 2, 1, 0, - 1, - 2. Moreover, two orientations of the spin are possible, $s_z = \pm\frac{1}{2}$. Consequently, the following ten one-electron states can occur (the first number gives m, the second s_z):

$$\left.\begin{array}{l} 2,\ \frac{1}{2};\quad 1,\ \frac{1}{2};\quad 0,\ \frac{1}{2};\quad -1,\ \frac{1}{2};\quad -2,\ \frac{1}{2}; \\ 2,\ -\frac{1}{2};\quad 1,\ -\frac{1}{2};\quad 0,\ -\frac{1}{2};\quad -1,\ -\frac{1}{2};\quad -2,\ -\frac{1}{2}. \end{array}\right\} \qquad (1)$$

According to Pauli's principle, only one electron can occur in each of these states. Hence, we conclude that the number of possible states of a two-electron system* is equal to the number of permutations of the ten states taken two at a time, i.e., $\frac{10\cdot 9}{1\cdot 2} = 45$.

By forming all the possible combinations of pairs of states (1), we obtain the possible states of the entire atom (the first number gives $M = m_1 + m_2$, the second, $S_z = s_{z_1} + s_{z_2}$):

one state each:	(4, 0); (—4, 0); (3, 1); (3, —1); (—3, —1); (—3, 1); (2, 1); (2, —1); (—2, 1); (—2, —1).
two states each:	(3, 0); (—3, 0); (1, 1); (1, —1); (—1, 1); (—1, —1); (0, 1); (0, —1).
three states each:	(2, 0); (—2, 0).
four states each:	(1, 0); (—1, 0).
five states:	(0, 0).

The existence of the states (± 4, 0) implies the existence of the term with $L = 4, S = 0$, i.e., the term ^1G. This term also corresponds to the states (± 3, 0), (± 2, 0), (± 1, 0), (0, 0) (one of each state).

*And consequently of the entire atom, since it is assumed that, in addition to the given configuration, there are only filled shells giving a term ^1S.

Thus, it corresponds to nine states in all [as we would expect, since for this term $(2L+1)(2S+1) = 9$].

Moreover, the existence of the states $(\pm 3, \pm 1)$ implies the existence of the term with $L = 3$, $S = 1$, i.e., the term ^3F. This term also corresponds to the remaining states of $(\pm 3, 0)$, the states $(\pm 2, \pm 1)$, and one each of the states $(\pm 2, 0)$, $(\pm 1, \pm 1)$, $(\pm 1, 0)$, $(0, \pm 1)$, $(0, 0)$. Consequently, this term corresponds to 21 states in all [as we would expect, since $(2L+1)(2S+1) = 7 \cdot 3 = 21$].

The existence of the last remaining states of $(\pm 2, 0)$ implies the existence of the term with $L = 2$, $S = 0$, i.e., the term ^1D. This term also corresponds to the states $(\pm 1, 0)$ and $(0, 0)$, and thus to five states in all, as we would expect.

Moreover, the remaining states of $(\pm 1, \pm 1)$ require that there be a term ^3P. This term also corresponds to the last remaining states of $(\pm 1, 0)$ and $(0, \pm 1)$, and to one state of $(0, 0)$ — a total of nine states, as we would expect for $L = S = 1$.

Finally, the last remaining state of $(0, 0)$ implies the existence of the term ^1S.

Thus, all the $9 + 21 + 5 + 9 + 1 = 45$ states of the atom are distributed among the following terms:

$$^1S,\ ^1D,\ ^1G \text{ (singlets) and } ^3P,\ ^3F \text{ (triplets)}.$$

2. Let us determine which of the terms we have found is the normal term, or the term with lowest energy. According to Hund's rule ([1], p. 264), this term is the one with the greatest value of the total spin S and the greatest value (which is possible for this S) of the total orbital angular momentum L. Consequently, in the case we are considering, the normal term is ^3F.

As regards the value of the total angular momentum of the electronic shell J $(\mathbf{J} = \mathbf{L} + \mathbf{S})$, its value for the normal term can be determined from another empirical rule, given, for instance, in [1], p. 269. This rule states that, for a shell less than half filled (which is the situation in our case, since the greatest number of equivalent d-electrons is equal to 10), $J = |L - S|$ in the normal state of the atom. Consequently, in our example $J = 3 - 1 = 2$. Thus, finally, the normal term for a configuration of two equivalent d-electrons is the term $^3F_2$.

We note that we have considered a real case, since the configuration $(nd)^2$ occurs in atoms which have besides it only an internal closed shell of inert gas and the configuration $(n+1, s)^2$, which produces the "spherically symmetric" shell $^1S_0$. Therefore, in these atoms (titanium, $Z = 22$; zirconium, $Z = 40$; hafnium, $Z = 72$), the normal term is indeed $^3F_2$.

2. In the ground electronic state, the rotational wave function of a molecule is determined only by the motion of the nuclei. Since the nuclei of the molecule D_2 (deuterons) are Bose particles (their spins are equal to unity), the complete Ψ-function for the system of two deuterons must be symmetric with respect to interchange.

Consequently, the position function and the spin function of this system must have the same interchange symmetry. Since, moreover, the interchange of the coordinates of two identical particles is equivalent to the operation of inversion relative to their center of mass, while the parity of a rotational state with an orbital angular momentum L is $(-1)^L$, we conclude that the even and odd rotational states are respectively identical with states with a symmetric position function and with states with an antisymmetric position function (and consequently states with the corresponding spin function!).

It follows directly from the results of problem No. 11, Chapter VIII, that the functions symmetric in the spins of the two deuterons correspond to even values of the total spin S, namely, the spin quintet ($S=2$) and the spin singlet ($S=0$) — 6 functions in all — while the functions antisymmetric in the spins correspond to the odd value $S=1$, namely the three functions of the spin triplet.

Thus, the ratio of the number of possible symmetric spin functions to the number of possible antisymmetric spin functions, and consequently the ratio of the number of possible even rotational states to the number of odd rotational states, is $\frac{6}{3}=2$.

3. The electrons and the nucleus form a system of particles moving in a finite region of space and interacting through Coulomb forces. Applying the virial theorem (see problem No. 3, Chapter IV) to this system, we have

$$\overline{U}=-2\overline{T},$$

where $\overline{U}$ and $\overline{T}$ are the average potential interaction energy and the average kinetic energy of all the particles of the system.

Let us consider an atom with an atomic number Z. As we know, its average "Thomas-Fermi" radius $\overline{a}$ is of the order of $Z^{-1/3}$ atomic units. Obviously $|\overline{U}|\sim\frac{Z\cdot Z}{\overline{a}}\sim Z^{7/3}$ atomic units. On the other hand, $\overline{T}\approx Z\frac{\overline{v^2}}{2}\sim Z\frac{(\overline{v})^2}{2}$ atomic units (we are entitled to set $\overline{v^2}\sim(\overline{v})^2$, since $v>0$ is the absolute value of the velocity).

By equating the orders of magnitude of the quantities $|\overline{U}|$ and $2\overline{T}$ to one another, we obtain the required result

$$\overline{v}\sim Z^{2/3}\,\text{atomic units}=Z^{2/3}\frac{e^2}{\hbar}.$$

4. The energy levels of s-electrons are determined from the quantization obtained in problem No. 6, Chapter VII,

$$\int_0^{r_{max}}\sqrt{2[E+\varphi(r)]}\,dr=\pi n$$

[we are using atomic units; $U(r)=-\varphi(r)$].

From the definition of the Thomas-Fermi distribution (one electron in each state), the number of s-electrons is obviously equal to twice the number of values of n (in consideration of the spin) for which $E \leqslant E_{\max}$, where $E_{\max}$ is the maximum value of the total energy of a Thomas-Fermi electron. For a neutral atom, this value is equal to zero, and thus $r_{\max} = \infty$. Therefore, the maximum n is determined from the equation

$$n_{\max} = \frac{1}{\pi} \int_0^\infty \sqrt{2\varphi(r)}\, dr.$$

Transforming to Thomas-Fermi units ([1], p. 276)

$$r = xbZ^{-1/3} \qquad (b = 0.885),$$
$$\varphi(r) = \frac{Z}{r} \chi\left(\frac{rZ^{1/3}}{b}\right) = \frac{Z^{4/3}}{b} \frac{\chi(x)}{x},$$

we obtain

$$n_{\max} = \frac{1}{\pi} \frac{Z^{2/3}}{\sqrt{b}} bZ^{-1/3} \int_0^\infty \sqrt{2\frac{\chi(x)}{x}}\, dx = \text{const}\, Z^{1/3}.$$

Thus, the number of electrons in s-states is proportional to $Z^{1/3}$.

5. In the case where the applied electric field is of the order of the Thomas-Fermi field (i.e., the electric field of the atom in the region where the Thomas-Fermi electrons are chiefly distributed), the relative change in the distribution will be of the order of unity. Consequently, in this case, the dipole moment of the atom will be of the order of the Thomas-Fermi (T.-F.) quantities: the Thomas-Fermi radius for one electron, and $Zr_{\text{T.-F.}}$ for the entire atom.

Considering the linear dependence of the dipole moment on the applied field, we can now write for arbitrary (but small) $\mathscr{E}$:

$$d = Zr_{\text{T.F.}} \frac{\mathscr{E}}{\mathscr{E}_{\text{T.-Ф.}}},$$

where $\mathscr{E}_{\text{T.-F.}}$ is the intensity of the Thomas-Fermi electric field. We evaluate its order of magnitude:

$$|\mathscr{E}_{\text{T.-Ф.}}| = \left|\frac{d\varphi(r)}{dr}\right|_{r \sim r_{\text{T.-Ф.}}} = \frac{Z^{1/3} Z^{4/3}}{b\; b} \left|\frac{d}{dx}\left\{\frac{\chi(x)}{x}\right\}\right|_{x \sim 1}$$

Here, we have transformed to Thomas-Fermi units and have expressed the potential in terms of the universal function $\chi(x)$ ([1], p. 276). The derivative $\frac{d}{dx}\left\{\frac{\chi(x)}{x}\right\}$ for $x \sim 1$ is also of the order of unity. Therefore, $\mathscr{E}_{\text{T.-F.}} \sim Z^{5/3}$. The Thomas-Fermi radius is of the order of $Z^{-1/3}$. Consequently,

$$d \sim Z \cdot Z^{-1/3} \frac{\mathcal{E}}{Z^{5/3}} = \frac{\mathcal{E}}{Z}.$$

Hence,

$$\frac{d}{\mathcal{E}} \sim \frac{1}{Z}.$$

In ordinary units,

$$\frac{d}{\mathcal{E}} \sim \frac{\hbar^6}{Z\mu^3 e^6} = \left(\frac{\hbar^2}{Z^{1/3}\mu e^2}\right)^3,$$

Thus, the polarizability is of the order of magnitude of the cube of the Thomas-Fermi radius of the atom.*

In conclusion, we note that for a valence electron this same quantity, the polarizability, is of the order of unity in atomic units, since a valence electron moves in a field $U(r) \approx -\frac{e^2}{r}$. Consequently (since $Z \gg 1$), the polarizability is determined by valence electrons rather than Thomas-Fermi electrons.

6. The basic physical factor in the quantum mechanics of the molecule is the extremely large magnitude of the ratio $\frac{M}{m}$, where M is the mass of the nuclei and m is the mass of the electrons. The mere existence of this large dimensionless parameter (of the order of 10^3 to 10^4) is the cause of the considerable differences in the orders of magnitude of the quantities listed in the problem.

Let us denote by a the order of magnitude of the linear dimensions of a diatomic molecule. It is obvious that the distance between the nuclei must be of the same order of magnitude. Indeed, by definition this distance cannot be greater than a, while it cannot be very much smaller than a because of the mutual electrostatic repulsion of the nuclei.**

1. First of all, let us evaluate the order of magnitude of the energy of the valence electrons and thus the order of magnitude of the intervals between the electron levels of the molecule. Since the valence electrons move in a region of space of linear dimensions $\sim a$ (as distinguished from the electrons of the "unshared" inner shells of each of the nuclei), the corresponding uncertainty in the

---

*This result is completely analogous to that obtained in the classical theory of the electron for the polarizability of different models of the atom (the Thomson model, the conducting-sphere model, and others) [21].

**By means of similar arguments, it is easy to arrive at the conclusion that a must be of the order of magnitude of the linear dimensions of the atom. However, this specification of the order of magnitude of a does not play a role in the estimates with which we are concerned.

momentum Δp is of the order of $\hbar/a$. Thus, the "zero-point energy" of the electron (or the difference between the energies of adjacent electron levels) is of the order of magnitude of

$$E_{\mathrm{el}} \sim \frac{(\Delta p)^2}{m} \sim \frac{\hbar^2}{ma^2}. \tag{1}$$

We shall now consider the vibrations of the nuclei in the molecule. A model for these vibrations (at least for normal and weakly excited levels) is provided by the motion of a harmonic oscillator with a mass of the order of M (more accurately, with the reduced mass of the nuclei) and with an elastic constant K. This elastic constant can be estimated from the fact that a change of the internuclear distance by an amount of the order of a should cause a considerable distortion (of the order of unity) of the Ψ-function of an electron. Thus, the change in the internuclear distance should be connected with a change in the energy of the order of E_{el}:

$$Ka^2 \sim E_{\mathrm{el}}.$$

Hence, defining in the usual way the frequency of the oscillations of the nuclei in the molecule $\omega \sim \sqrt{\frac{K}{M}}$ and remembering (1), we obtain

$$E_{\mathrm{vib}} \approx \hbar\omega \sim \hbar\left(\frac{E_{\mathrm{el}}}{Ma^2}\right)^{1/2} \sim \frac{\hbar^2}{(mM)^{1/2}a^2} \sim \left(\frac{m}{M}\right)^{1/2} E_{\mathrm{el}} \tag{2}$$

for the intervals between the vibrational levels.

Finally, it is obviously possible to treat the rotational levels of the molecule as the levels of a rotator with a moment of inertia $I \sim Ma^2$. Thus, the intervals between the rotational levels are equal to

$$E_{\mathrm{rot}} \sim \frac{\hbar^2}{I} \sim \frac{\hbar^2}{Ma^2} \sim \frac{m}{M} E_{\mathrm{el}}. \tag{3}$$

It is apparent from (1), (2) and (3) that the orders of magnitude of E_{el}, E_{vib}, and E_{rot} form a geometric progression with a common ratio $\left(\frac{m}{M}\right)^{1/2} \sim 10^{-2}$.

2. Let us denote the amplitude of the zero-point oscillations of the nuclei in the molecule by b. This amplitude is of the order of magnitude of $\sqrt{\frac{\hbar}{M\omega}}$.* After substitution of ω from (2), this quantity becomes

*This estimate can be obtained in different ways, as by equating the order of magnitude of the energy of the oscillator ($\sim \hbar\omega$) to its potential energy when it is deflected through b ($\sim M\omega^2 b^2$).

$$b \sim \left(\frac{m}{M}\right)^{1/4} a. \tag{4}$$

Thus, the ratio of the amplitude of the oscillations of the nuclei b to the equilibrium internuclear distance a in the molecule is of the order of magnitude of $\left(\frac{m}{M}\right)^{1/4} \ll 1$. This quantity serves as a small parameter for expansions in the theory of molecules. From part 1, in terms of this parameter, E_{el} is a zeroth-order quantity, E_{vib} is a second-order quantity, and E_{rot} is a fourth order quantity.

3. The orders of magnitude of the period of the electronic motions and of the period of the nuclear oscillations in the nucleus are respectively

$$T_{\text{el}} \sim \frac{1}{\omega_{\text{el}}} \sim \frac{\hbar}{E_{\text{el}}} \sim \frac{ma^2}{\hbar}, \tag{5}$$

$$T_{\text{vib}} \sim \frac{1}{\omega_{\text{vib}}} \sim \frac{(mM)^{1/2} a^2}{\hbar}. \tag{6}$$

The corresponding characteristic velocities are obviously equal to

$$v_{\text{el}} \sim \frac{a}{T_{\text{el}}} \left(\text{or} \sim \sqrt{\frac{E_{\text{el}}}{m}}\right) \sim \frac{\hbar}{ma}, \tag{7}$$

$$v_{\text{vib}} \sim \frac{b}{T_{\text{vib}}} \left(\text{or} \sim \sqrt{\frac{E_{\text{vib}}}{M}}\right) \sim \frac{\hbar}{m^{1/4} M^{3/4} a}. \tag{8}$$

From (5), (6), (7), and (8), we obtain

$$\frac{T_{\text{vib}}}{T_{\text{el}}} \sim \left(\frac{M}{m}\right)^{1/2} \gg 1, \quad \frac{v_{\text{vib}}}{v_{\text{el}}} \sim \left(\frac{m}{M}\right)^{3/4} \ll 1. \tag{9}$$

These inequalities indicate that the motions of the nuclei are slow relative to the motions of the electrons in the molecule. This factor makes it possible to account for the motion of the nuclei in the adiabatic approximation.

7. We denote the mass of an electron by m, the coordinates of the nucleus in some fixed frame of reference by ξ_0, η_0, ζ_0, and the coordinates of the i-th electron by ξ_i, η_i, ζ_i ($i = 1, 2, \ldots, n$).

Using the center-of-mass coordinates of the atom

$$X = \frac{M\xi_0 + m\sum_{i=1}^{n} \xi_i}{M + nm} \quad \text{(and likewise for } Y \text{ and } Z\text{)} \tag{1}$$

and the relative coordinates ($i = 1, 2, \ldots, n$)

$$x_i = \xi_i - \xi_0 \quad \text{(and likewise for } y_i \text{ and } z_i\text{)}, \tag{2}$$

we have

$$\frac{\partial}{\partial\xi_i}=\frac{m}{M+nm}\frac{\partial}{\partial X}+\frac{\partial}{\partial x_i},\quad \frac{\partial}{\partial\xi_0}=\frac{M}{M+nm}\frac{\partial}{\partial X}-\sum_{i=1}^{n}\frac{\partial}{\partial x_i}. \tag{3}$$

The Hamiltonian of the atom (in a fixed coordinate system) has the form

$$\hat{H}=-\frac{\hbar^2}{2M}\left(\frac{\partial^2}{\partial\xi_0^2}+\frac{\partial^2}{\partial\eta_0^2}+\frac{\partial^2}{\partial\zeta_0^2}\right)-\frac{\hbar^2}{2m}\sum_{i=1}^{n}\left(\frac{\partial^2}{\partial\xi_i^2}+\frac{\partial^2}{\partial\eta_i^2}+\frac{\partial^2}{\partial\zeta_i^2}\right)+U, \tag{4}$$

where U is the potential energy of the atom, depending only on the relative coordinates (2).

If we perform the substitution of variables (1), (2), and (3) in (4), we obtain $\hat{H}$ in the form of two components, one of which depends only on coordinates (1), and the other only on coordinates (2). Accordingly, by separating (in the usual way) the free motion of the center of mass of the atom, which presents no interest, we obtain the following Schrödinger equation in the center-of-mass system:

$$\left\{-\frac{\hbar^2}{2m}\sum_{i=1}^{n}\Delta_i-\frac{\hbar^2}{2M}\sum_{i=1}^{n}\sum_{k=1}^{n}\left(\frac{\partial^2}{\partial x_i\,\partial x_k}+\frac{\partial^2}{\partial y_i\,\partial y_k}+\frac{\partial^2}{\partial z_i\,\partial z_k}\right)+U(x_1,\ \ldots,\ x_n)\right\}\Psi(x_1,\ \ldots,\ x_n)=E\Psi(x_1,\ \ldots,\ x_n). \tag{5}$$

The effect of the finiteness of M (in other words, the effect of "co-motion" of the nucleus) depends on the second term inside the braces. It is clear that this effect results in a small correction of the relative order of magnitude of $\frac{m}{M}$ on the atomic terms for $M=\infty$.

In (5), if we collect terms with $i=k$ and $i\neq k$, and if we use the reduced mass of the electron and of the nucleus

$$\mu=\frac{mM}{m+M}, \tag{6}$$

we obtain

$$\left\{-\frac{\hbar^2}{2\mu}\sum_{i}\Delta_i-\frac{\hbar^2}{M}\sum_{i<k}\sum\left(\frac{\partial^2}{\partial x_i\,\partial x_k}+\frac{\partial^2}{\partial y_i\,\partial y_k}+\frac{\partial^2}{\partial z_i\,\partial z_k}\right)+U(x_1,\ \ldots,\ x_n)\right\}\Psi(x_1,\ \ldots,\ x_n)=E\Psi(x_1,\ \ldots,\ x_n). \tag{7}$$

From the equation we have obtained, it is immediately apparent that the effect of the finiteness of the mass of the nucleus reduces, first of all, to the replacement of the electron mass m by the reduced mass μ in the Hamiltonian for $M = \infty$, and second to the addition of a perturbation term

$$\hat{H}' = -\frac{\hbar^2}{M}\sum_{i<k}\sum\left(\frac{\partial^2}{\partial x_i\,\partial x_k}+\frac{\partial^2}{\partial y_i\,\partial y_k}+\frac{\partial^2}{\partial z_i\,\partial z_k}\right). \tag{8}$$

The first of these alterations of the Schrödinger equation expresses the so-called "elementary" or "normal" effect of the co-motion of the nucleus. As is well known, this effect occurs already in the hydrogen atom. Obviously, the "normal" effect acts on all the terms of the atom in the same way, causing a reduction in the frequency of all the spectral lines of the atom to a value given by the ratio

$$\frac{\mu}{m} = \frac{M}{M+m} \approx 1 - \frac{m}{M}.$$

On the contrary, the second effect we have noted is significantly different for different states of the atom. Indeed, the first correction of perturbation theory* to an energy level of an atom is

$$\Delta E = \int \Psi^{(0)*}\hat{H}'\Psi^{(0)}\,d\tau, \tag{9}$$

where $\Psi^{(0)}$ is the wave function of the atom for $M = \infty$, and $d\tau = \prod_{i=1}^{n} d\tau_i = \prod_{i=1}^{n} dx_i\,dy_i\,dz_i$ is an element of volume of the configuration space of the atom.

We substitute (8) into (9), change the order of summation and integration, and integrate by parts, considering the fact that the Ψ-function becomes zero at infinity. As a result, we obtain

$$\Delta E = \frac{\hbar^2}{M}\sum_{i<k}\sum\int(\mathrm{grad}_i\,\Psi^{(0)*}\,\mathrm{grad}_k\,\Psi^{(0)})\,d\tau, \tag{10}$$

which of course depends considerably on the form of $\Psi^{(0)}$.

In particular, if the motions of the electrons were quite independent of one another, i.e., if the unperturbed wave function of the atom were simply the product of the wave functions φ_i for the individual electrons

$$\Psi^{(0)} = \prod_{i=1}^{n}\varphi_i(x_i,\ y_i,\ z_i), \tag{11}$$

*Perturbation theory is obviously applicable here, since $\frac{m}{M} \ll 1$.

the effect we are considering would not occur at all. Indeed, if we substitute (11) into (10) and consider that $\int \varphi_i^* \varphi_i \, d\tau_i = 1$, we obtain

$$\Delta E = \frac{\hbar^2}{M} \sum_{i<k} \sum \int \varphi_i \operatorname{grad} \varphi_i^* \, d\tau_i \int \varphi_k^* \operatorname{grad} \varphi_k \, d\tau_k = 0,$$

since all the integrals inside the double summation sign are equal to zero (see problem No. 4, Chapter IV).

In reality, the motions of the electrons in the atom are not independent of one another, and thus the effect we are discussing (which, to distinguish it from the "normal" effect, is called the "specific" effect of the finiteness of the mass of the nucleus, and which is characteristic for atoms with a number of electrons $n \geq 2$) is, generally speaking, not only different from zero, but even, in a number of cases, considerably more important than the "normal" effect.

The mutual correlation of the electron motions to which we have referred is the result both of the trivial fact of the electrostatic interaction of electrons and also (most important) of the identical nature of the electrons. This basic and characteristically quantum-mechanical part of the specific effect can therefore be called the "exchange" effect.

Indeed, the complete Ψ-function of an atom (the product of the position function and the spin function in the case where the spin-orbital interaction is ignored) must be antisymmetric with respect to interchange of any pair of electrons. Therefore, each value of the total spin S of an electronic shell (and consequently each type of interchange symmetry of the spin function) must correspond to a definite interchange symmetry of the position function of the shell. By using a crude classical analogy, we can characterize the above situation either as predominant motion of the electrons in the same direction (the case of a symmetric position function) or as predominant motion of the electrons in opposite directions (the case of an antisymmetric position function). Since the center of mass of the atom is at rest, it is clear that in the first case the co-motion of the nucleus will be stronger, and in the second case weaker, than in the case of independent motion of the electrons. In other words, in the first case, the specific effect (or, more accurately, the exchange effect) will "add" to the normal effect, while, in the second case, the effects will act in opposite directions.

We note that both of these effects play a crucial role in the so-called isotope displacement of the spectral lines of the lightest elements (since the mass M of the nucleus varies for different isotopes and this difference is greatest for light elements).

A qualitative examination of the exchange effect of the co-motion of the nucleus will be conducted in the next chapter for the example of a diatomic atom (or ion).

8. The ignoring of the electrostatic interaction of the electrons is equivalent to the selection of an unperturbed position function for a two-electron system in the form of a superposition of products of hydrogenlike functions. At the same time, from the requirement that the complete wave function be antisymmetric with respect to interchange of the electrons, it follows that this position function must have the form

$$\Psi^{(0)}(1;\ 2)=\frac{1}{\sqrt{2}}[\varphi_{100}(1)\,\varphi_{nlm}(2)\pm\varphi_{nlm}(1)\,\varphi_{100}(2)], \qquad (1)$$

where 1 and 2 represent the sets of spatial coordinates of the electrons; $\varphi_{100}\equiv u$ and $\varphi_{nlm}\equiv v$ are the hydrogenlike functions of an electron which belong to the given quantum numbers, the first function being taken for an effective charge of the nucleus Z_i, and the second function for an effective charge of the nucleus Z_e* (in the general case, $Z_e\neq Z_i$); and the factor $\frac{1}{\sqrt{2}}$ is introduced to normalize the Ψ-function to unity.

The upper sign in equation (1) obviously corresponds to states of a two-electron system which are antisymmetric in the spins (paraterms, $S = 0$), while the lower sign corresponds to states which are symmetric in the spins (orthoterms, $S = 1$).

By substituting function (1) into equation (10) of the preceding problem (with $i, k = 1,\ 2$), we obtain

$$\Delta E=\frac{\hbar^2}{M}\int\int v^*(2)\,\nabla u^*(1)\,[u(1)\,\nabla v(2)\pm v(1)\,\nabla u(2)]\,d\tau_1 d\tau_2.$$

The first term yields zero, since (see problem No. 4, Chapter IV) $\int v^*(i)\,\nabla v(i)\,d\tau_i=0$ [and likewise $u(i)$]. The second term yields

$$\Delta E=\pm\frac{\hbar^2}{M}\int v(1)\,\nabla u^*(1)\,d\tau_1\int v^*(2)\,\nabla u(2)\,d\tau_2= \\ =\pm\frac{\hbar^2}{M}\left|\int v(i)\,\nabla u^*(i)\,d\tau_i\right|^2. \qquad (2)$$

---

*The subscripts i and e refer to the "internal" and "external" electrons in accordance with the qualitative meaning of the functions φ_{100} and φ_{nlm}, which describe the normal and excited states of an electron in the atom.

This is the final general expression for the first-approximation exchange correction for the finiteness of the mass of the nucleus.

Let us determine the selection rules for quantity (2). From the foregoing discussion, the functions u and v satisfy the following equations (in atomic units)

$$\left(-\frac{1}{2}\Delta-\frac{Z_i}{r}\right)u=E_1u, \tag{3}$$

$$\left(-\frac{1}{2}\Delta-\frac{Z_e}{r}\right)v=E_nv, \tag{4}$$

where

$$E_n=-\frac{Z_e^2}{2n^2}, \quad E_1=-\frac{Z_i^2}{2}. \tag{5}$$

Let us multipy equation (3) by $\mathbf{r}v^*$ and subtract from it the complex conjugate of equation (4) multiplied by $\mathbf{r}u$. Then, integrating over all space, we have

$$\frac{1}{2}\int \mathbf{r}(u\,\Delta v^*-v^*\,\Delta u)\,d\tau=(Z_i-Z_e)\int\frac{\mathbf{r}}{r}\,uv^*\,d\tau+ \\ +(E_1-E_n)\int \mathbf{r}uv^*\,d\tau. \tag{6}$$

Transforming the left member of this equation, we obtain in succession

$$\frac{1}{2}\int \mathbf{r}(u\,\Delta v^*-v^*\,\Delta u)\,d\tau=\frac{1}{2}\int \mathbf{r}\,\mathrm{div}\,(u\,\nabla v^*-v^*\,\nabla u)\,d\tau= \\ =-\frac{1}{2}\int(u\,\nabla v^*-v^*\,\nabla u)\,d\tau=\int v^*\,\nabla u\,d\tau.$$

Here, we have used the identities*

$$\int \mathbf{r}\,\mathrm{div}\,\mathbf{A}\,d\tau=-\int \mathbf{A}\,d\tau \text{ and } \int \mathrm{grad}\,\chi\,d\tau=\oint\chi\,d\mathbf{S}.$$

Thus, equation (6) becomes**

$$\int v\,\nabla u^*\,d\tau=(Z_i-Z_e)\int\frac{\mathbf{r}}{r}\,u^*v\,d\tau+(E_1-E_n)\int \mathbf{r}u^*v\,d\tau. \tag{7}$$

---

*These identities are easily proved by multiplying both sides by a constant vector and integrating the resulting equations by parts with the use of the Gauss-Ostrogradskiy theorem.

**For $Z_i=Z_e$, i.e., when u and v are eigenfunctions of the same Hamiltonian, equation (7) transforms to equation (2) of problem No. 4, Chapter IV.

The selection rules for the two integrals in the right member are given by the well-known orthogonality relations of the spherical harmonics $Y_{lm}(\theta, \varphi)$ appearing in them. It is obvious that the two integrals are different from zero only when the well-known condition

$$l_u - l_v = \pm 1$$

is satisfied. Since, from the condition specified in the problem (always observed in practice), one of the electrons is in the $1s$ state (i.e., $l_u = 0$), we conclude that the left member of (7) and consequently the exchange correction (2) are different from zero only for $l_v = 1$ (i.e., for p-states of the second electron). In other words, the specific effect (more accurately, the exchange effect) of the comotion of the nucleus occurs only for P-terms of a two-electron atom or ion (He, Li^+, Be^{++}, etc.), at least in the first approximation in terms of $\frac{m}{M}$.

Regarding the sign of the specific effect, it is apparent from (2) that for paraterms $\Delta E > 0$, i.e., the specific effect has the same sign as the normal effect, whereas for orthoterms the signs of these effects are opposite. This is in complete agreement with the general qualitative statement made at the end of the preceding problem, since both electrons move, roughly speaking, predominantly in the same direction in para states, whereas they move predominantly in opposite directions in ortho states.

To find the numerical value of the specific effect, we shall use equations (2) and (7). From (7), it follows that

$$\begin{aligned} \left| \int v \nabla u^* d\tau \right|^2 = & \left| (Z_i - Z_e) \int \frac{x}{r} u^* v \, d\tau + (E_1 - E_n) \int x u^* v \, d\tau \right|^2 + \\ & + \left| (Z_i - Z_e) \int \frac{y}{r} u^* v \, d\tau + (E_1 - E_n) \int y u^* v \, d\tau \right|^2 + \\ & + \left| (Z_i - Z_e) \int \frac{z}{r} u^* v \, d\tau + (E_1 - E_n) \int z u^* v \, d\tau \right|^2 . \end{aligned} \tag{8}$$

The integrals appearing in this equation can be computed without difficulty. If we use the representation of the hydrogenlike functions of an electron in spherical coordinates ([1], p. 149) and if we transform from Coulomb units to atomic units,* we have

$$u \equiv \psi_{100}(r) = R_{10}(r) Y_{00}(\theta, \varphi), \tag{9}$$

$$v \equiv \psi_{nlm}(r) = R_{nl}(r) Y_{lm}(\theta, \varphi), \tag{10}$$

*It is easily seen that this transformation is accomplished by means of the substitution r (Coulomb units) = Zr (A. U.), R_{nl} (Coulomb units) = $Z^{-3/2} R_{nl}$ (A. U.).

where the Y_{lm} are normalized spherical harmonics, and the R_{nl} are normalized radial functions (in v, we set $l=1$ in accordance with the selection rules),

$$R_{n1}=Z_e^{3/2}\frac{2}{3!\,n^3}\sqrt{\frac{(n+1)!}{(n-2)!}}\,2Z_e r e^{-\frac{Z_e r}{n}}F\left(-n+2,\,4,\,\frac{2Z_e r}{n}\right)\ \text{(A. U.)}, \quad (11)$$

$$R_{10}=2Z_i^{3/2}e^{-Z_i r} \quad \text{(A. U.)}. \quad (12)$$

From (9) and (10), it is apparent that the integrals in (8) are equal to

$$\int\frac{x}{r}u^*v\,d\tau=\int\sin\theta\cos\varphi\,Y_{00}Y_{1m}\,d\Omega\int_0^\infty R_{10}R_{n1}r^2\,dr,$$

$$\int zu^*v\,d\tau=\int\cos\theta\,Y_{00}Y_{1m}\,d\Omega\int_0^\infty R_{10}R_{n1}r^3\,dr, \text{ etc.}$$

The integrals over the angles are computed in an elementary fashion from the fact that $Y_{00}=\frac{1}{\sqrt{4\pi}}$, $\sin\theta\cos\varphi=\frac{1}{2}\sqrt{\frac{8\pi}{3}}\,(Y_{11}+Y_{1,-1})$, etc., and from the orthonormal property of the spherical harmonics. To compute the radial integrals, which, according to (11) and (12), contain an exponential term, a power term, and a confluent hypergeometric function, we can use equations (f, 1) and (f, 4) given in [1], p. 564. In this way, we finally obtain the following value of the specific effect for the P-term (in ordinary units):

$$\Delta E=\pm\frac{64}{3}\frac{m}{M}(Z_iZ_e)^5\frac{(Z_in-Z_e)^{2n-4}}{(Z_in+Z_e)^{2n+4}}n^3(n^2-1)\frac{me^4}{\hbar^2},$$

where n is the total quantum number of the p-electron, and Z_i and Z_e are the effective charges of the nucleus for the $1s$-electron and the np-electron respectively. The last two quantities are usually determined by the variation method [14]. Thus, for the 2^3P-terms of the Li^+ ion, $Z_i=2.98$, $Z_e=2.16$.*

---

*These values of the effective charges are in fairly good agreement with those which could be expected on the basis of the following elementary considerations: a) the true charge of the Li nucleus is equal to 3; b) the dimensions of the orbit of the outer electron ($n=2$) are roughly speaking $2^2=4$ times greater than the dimensions of the inner electron; c) the outer electron has $l=1$ and consequently does not penetrate far inside the orbit of the s-electron. In other words, the inner electron screens the nucleus strongly from the outer electron, and thus we would expect $Z_i\approx3$, $Z_e\approx2$.

CHAPTER X

Motion in a Magnetic Field

1. Let us take the z-axis in the direction of the field $\mathcal{H}$ and denote by e and μ the charge and mass of the particle. The energy levels and wave functions of stationary states with a definite value of the generalized momentum component p_x were found in [1, Section 125] by separation of the variables in terms of Cartesian coordinates. We must obviously solve our problem by separating the variables in terms of cylindrical coordinates. Accordingly, we shall select a vector potential of the field in the form $\boldsymbol{A}=\frac{1}{2}\mathcal{H}\times\boldsymbol{r}$, so that $A_\rho=A_z=0,\ A_\varphi=\frac{1}{2}\mathcal{H}\rho$. Since div $\boldsymbol{A}=0$ for this choice of $\boldsymbol{A}$, the Hamiltonian of the particle has the form (see Problem No. 7, Chapter I)

$$\hat{H}=\frac{1}{2\mu}\hat{p}^2-\frac{e}{\mu c}\boldsymbol{A}\hat{\boldsymbol{p}}+\frac{e^2}{2\mu c^2}A^2, \tag{1}$$

or in cylindrical coordinates ρ, φ, z (substituting the components of $\boldsymbol{A}$)

$$\hat{H}=-\frac{\hbar^2}{2\mu}\left(\frac{\partial^2}{\partial\rho^2}+\frac{1}{\rho}\frac{\partial}{\partial\rho}+\frac{1}{\rho^2}\frac{\partial^2}{\partial\varphi^2}+\frac{\partial^2}{\partial z^2}\right)-\frac{\hbar}{2i}\frac{e\mathcal{H}}{\mu c}\frac{\partial}{\partial\varphi}+\frac{e^2\mathcal{H}^2}{8\mu c^2}\rho^2. \tag{2}$$

From form (2) of the Hamiltonian, it is clear that we can look for a solution to the Schrödinger equation $\hat{H}\Psi=E\Psi$ (E is the energy of the particle in the form

$$\Psi(\boldsymbol{r})=\text{const}\, e^{im\varphi+\frac{ip_z z}{\hbar}}f(\rho), \tag{3}$$

where m is an integer. Wave functions of form (3) describe states of the particle with definite values of the "longitudinal" components of the momentum p_z* and of the angular momentum $M_z=(\boldsymbol{r}\times\boldsymbol{p})_z$. The eigenvalues of p_z form the set of all real numbers, while the eigenvalues of M_z are equal to $m\hbar$.

---

*And also the velocity component $v_z=\frac{p_z}{\mu}$ (since $A_z=0$).

Substituting (3) into the Schrödinger equation, we obtain for the radial function $f(\rho)$ the equation

$$f'' + \frac{1}{\rho} f' + \left(k_t^2 + \frac{e}{|e|}\frac{m}{a^2} - \frac{m^2}{\rho^2} - \frac{\rho^2}{4a^4}\right) f = 0, \qquad (4)$$

where we have used the notation

$$k_t^2 = \frac{1}{\hbar^2}(2\mu E - p_z^2), \qquad (5)$$

$$a^2 = \frac{\hbar c}{|e|\mathscr{H}}. \qquad (6)$$

The length a is a characteristic parameter of the problem.

By defining the new independent variable $\xi = \frac{\rho^2}{2a^2}$, we can reduce equation (4) to the form

$$\frac{d^2 f}{d\xi^2} + \frac{1}{\xi}\frac{df}{d\xi} + \left(\frac{k_t^2 a^2}{2\xi} + \frac{e}{|e|}\frac{m}{2\xi} - \frac{m^2}{4\xi^2} - \frac{1}{4}\right) f = 0. \qquad (7)$$

As $\xi \to \infty$, we have approximately $f'' - \frac{1}{4} f = 0$. Hence $f \approx e^{\pm\frac{\xi}{2}}$; From the requirement that the Ψ-function be finite as $\rho \to \infty$, we retain only the asymptotic solution $e^{-\frac{\xi}{2}}$.

As $\xi \to 0$, let us look for a solution to equation (7) in the form $f = \xi^s$. Substituting this expression into (7) and retaining only the terms of the lowest order of magnitude, we obtain $s = \pm \frac{|m|}{2}$. From the requirement that the Ψ-function remain finite for $\rho = 0$, we retain only the solution $f = \xi^{\frac{|m|}{2}}$.

From the above discussion, it is clear that it is most convenient to look for a solution to equation (7) throughout the entire range of ξ in the form

$$f(\xi) = e^{-\frac{\xi}{2}} \xi^{\frac{|m|}{2}} w(\xi). \qquad (8)$$

Substituting (8) into (7), we arrive at the following equation for the function w:

$$\xi w'' + (|m| + 1 - \xi) w' - \frac{1}{2}\left(1 + |m| - \frac{e}{|e|} m - k_t^2 a^2\right) w = 0. \qquad (9)$$

A solution of this equation which satisfies the necessary condition [cf. (8)] of finiteness for $\xi = 0$ is the confluent hypergeometric function

$$w(\xi) = F\left[\frac{1}{2}\left(1 + |m| - \frac{e}{|e|} m - k_t^2 a^2\right), \ |m| + 1, \ \xi\right]. \qquad (10)$$

From the requirement that $f(\xi)$ be finite as $\xi \to \infty$ and from (8), it follows that at ∞ solution (10) must not increase more rapidly than a finite power of ξ; i.e., it must reduce to a polynomial. This will be the case only if the condition

$$\frac{1}{2}\left(1+|m|-\frac{e}{|e|}m-k_t^2a^2\right)=-r \quad (r=0,\ 1,\ 2,\ \ldots) \tag{11}$$

is satisfied. Hence, using the notation

$$2r+1+|m|-\frac{e}{|e|}m\equiv 2n+1, \tag{12}$$

and substituting (5) and (6), we obtain the condition for the quantization of the energy of the "transverse" motion E_t

$$E_t\equiv E-\frac{p_z^2}{2\mu}=\hbar\omega\left(n+\frac{1}{2}\right), \tag{13}$$

where we have introduced the angular frequency of the rotation (classical) of the particle in the field $\mathscr{H}$:

$$\omega\equiv\frac{|e|\mathscr{H}}{\mu c}. \tag{14}$$

Since $(|m|-\frac{e}{|e|}m)$ assumes the values of zero and $2|m|$, equation (12) defines the following values of n:

$$n=0,\ 1,\ 2,\ \ldots \tag{15}$$

Let us determine which values of m are possible for a given value of n, i.e., for a given energy E_t.

If the sign of m is the same as the sign of e, then $n=r$, and m will completely drop out from (12). Thus, any integral values of m compatible with the condition $em > 0$ will be permitted, namely, $m = 0, 1, 2, \ldots, \infty$ for $e > 0$, and $m = -\infty, \ldots, -1, 0$ for $e < 0$.

If the signs of m and e are opposite, we have from (12) $|m| = n - r$. Thus, for $e > 0$ (i.e., $m \le 0$), this becomes $m=r-n$, and consequently $m = -n, -n+1, \ldots, -1, 0$. For $e < 0$ (i.e., $m \ge 0$) $m=n-r$, and consequently $m = 0, 1, \ldots, n-1, n$.

As a result, we obtain the following values of m (which are possible for a given n):

$$\left.\begin{aligned}&\text{for } e>0:\ m=-n,\ -n+1,\ \ldots,-1,\ 0,\ 1,\ \ldots,\ +\infty,\\&\text{for } e<0:\ m=-\infty,\ \ldots,\ -1,\ 0,\ 1,\ \ldots,n-1,\ n.\end{aligned}\right\} \tag{16}$$

Thus, for a given energy, the possible values of $M_z = m\hbar$ are bound on one side (corresponding to the sign of the particle's charge).*

Using (3), (8), (10), and (11), and making the substitution $\xi = \frac{\rho^2}{2a^2}$, we obtain the following general expression for the wave functions (which is accurate except for the normalization constant):

$$\Psi_{n, m, p_z}(\rho, \varphi, z) = \\ = \exp\left(im\varphi + \frac{i}{\hbar} p_z z - \frac{\rho^2}{4a^2}\right)\left(\frac{\rho}{a}\right)^{|m|} F\left(-r, |m|+1, \frac{\rho^2}{2a^2}\right), \quad (17)$$

where r must be expressed in terms of n and m according to equation (12).

By repeating the argument preceding equation (16), we can specify the two last factors in the right member of (17) as follows (in all cases, the first factor remains the same):

$$\left.\begin{array}{ll} e>0 \begin{cases} m \geqslant 0: & \left(\frac{\rho}{a}\right)^{m} F\left(-n, m+1, \frac{\rho^2}{2a^2}\right), \\ m \leqslant 0: & \left(\frac{\rho}{a}\right)^{-m} F\left(-n-m, -m+1, \frac{\rho^2}{2a^2}\right); \end{cases} \\ e<0 \begin{cases} m \geqslant 0: & \left(\frac{\rho}{a}\right)^{m} F\left(-n+m, m+1, \frac{\rho^2}{2a^2}\right), \\ m \leqslant 0: & \left(\frac{\rho}{a}\right)^{-m} F\left(-n, -m+1, \frac{\rho^2}{2a^2}\right). \end{cases} \end{array}\right\} (17')$$

Each of the states described by the Ψ-functions (17), (17′) is characterized by definite values of the following three quantities: the energy of the motion in the plane perpendicular to the magnetic field (E_t); the momentum component in the direction of the magnetic field (p_z); and the component of the moment** of the generalized momentum in the same direction (M_z).

The stationary states (17) will be discussed further in the next problem.

---

*This result (16) has a simple classical analogue. Indeed, from the equations $\boldsymbol{M} = \boldsymbol{r} \times \boldsymbol{p}$, $\boldsymbol{p} = \mu \boldsymbol{v} + \frac{e}{c}\boldsymbol{A}$ and $\boldsymbol{A} = \frac{1}{2}(\mathcal{H} \times \boldsymbol{r})$ we have $M_z = \rho\left(\mu v_\varphi + \frac{e}{2c}\mathcal{H}\rho\right)$. Hence, it is clear that very large values of M_z correspond to large values of ρ, for which the second term in the parentheses is much larger than the first term. Thus, M_z has the same sign as e.

**We emphasize that we are speaking about the angular momentum relative to an arbitrarily selected origin of coordinates, as follows from the derivation.

2. 1. The Hamiltonian of the particle has the form

$$\hat{H}=\frac{1}{2\mu}\hat{\pi}^2=\frac{1}{2\mu}(\hat{\pi}_x^2+\hat{\pi}_y^2+\hat{\pi}_z^2)\equiv\hat{H}_t+\frac{\hat{\pi}_z^2}{2\mu}, \tag{1}$$

where*

$$\hat{\pi}=\hat{p}-\frac{e}{c}A. \tag{2}$$

It is easily verified that the components of π satisfy the commutation relations**

$$[\hat{\pi}_x, \hat{\pi}_y]=\frac{ie\hbar}{c}\mathscr{H}_z; \quad [\hat{\pi}_y, \hat{\pi}_z]=\frac{ie\hbar}{c}\mathscr{H}_x,$$

$$[\hat{\pi}_z, \hat{\pi}_x]=\frac{ie\hbar}{c}\mathscr{H}_y. \tag{3}$$

For our choice of coordinates, we have

$$[\hat{\pi}_x, \hat{\pi}_y]=\frac{ie\hbar}{c}\mathscr{H}, \quad [\hat{\pi}_y, \hat{\pi}_z]=[\hat{\pi}_z, \hat{\pi}_x]=0. \tag{3'}$$

Considering (1) and (3′), we have for the operators of the time derivatives

$$\dot{\hat{\pi}}_x=\frac{i}{\hbar}[\hat{H}, \hat{\pi}_x]=\frac{i}{2\mu\hbar}[\hat{\pi}_y^2, \hat{\pi}_x]=\frac{e\mathscr{H}}{\mu c}\hat{\pi}_y, \tag{4}$$

$$\dot{\hat{\pi}}_y=\frac{i}{\hbar}[\hat{H}, \hat{\pi}_y]=\frac{i}{2\mu\hbar}[\hat{\pi}_x^2, \hat{\pi}_y]=-\frac{e\mathscr{H}}{\mu c}\hat{\pi}_x, \tag{5}$$

$$\dot{\hat{\pi}}_z=\frac{i}{\hbar}[\hat{H}, \hat{\pi}_z]=0, \tag{6}$$

$$\hat{v}\equiv\dot{\hat{r}}=\frac{i}{\hbar}[\hat{H}, r]=$$

$$=\frac{i}{2\mu\hbar}(\boldsymbol{i}[\hat{\pi}_x^2, x]+\boldsymbol{j}[\hat{\pi}_y^2, y]+\boldsymbol{k}[\hat{\pi}_z^2, z])=\frac{\hat{\pi}}{\mu}. \tag{7}$$

---

*From now on, we shall not place operator symbols above r, A, $\mathscr{H}$, etc. This is equivalent to choosing the position space (which is most convenient in the given case).

**See Problem No. 8, Chapter I, or [1], p. 533. We note that it is necessary to reverse the sign in the right members of the commutators given in [1].

In deriving (7), we have made use of the commutation relations

$$[\hat{\pi}_i, x_k] = [\hat{p}_i, x_k] = -i\hbar\delta_{ik}, \tag{8}$$

which follow from (2).

Equation (6) implies that π_z is a constant of the motion, i.e., that there exist stationary states in which π_z has a definite value. In these states, the motion along the z-axis is the motion of a free particle. Let us assume, as in Problem No. 1, that $A = \frac{1}{2}(\mathcal{H} \times r)$. Then, $\pi_z = p_z$. Thus, the Ψ-functions of the above-mentioned stationary states depend on z through the factor $e^{\frac{ip_z z}{\hbar}}$, where p_z changes from $-\infty$ to $+\infty$.*

The constants of the "transverse" motion can be found by eliminating $\hat{\pi}_y$ from (4) and (7), and $\hat{\pi}_x$ from (5) and (7). This yields

$$\dot{\hat{\pi}}_x - \frac{e\mathcal{H}}{c}\dot{\hat{y}} = 0, \qquad \dot{\hat{\pi}}_y + \frac{e\mathcal{H}}{c}\dot{\hat{x}} = 0. \tag{9}$$

If we define the operators

$$\hat{y}_0 \equiv y - \frac{c}{e\mathcal{H}}\hat{\pi}_x, \qquad \hat{x}_0 \equiv x + \frac{c}{e\mathcal{H}}\hat{\pi}_y, \tag{10}$$

we can rewrite (9) in the form

$$\dot{\hat{y}}_0 = \frac{i}{\hbar}[\hat{H}, \hat{y}_0] = 0, \qquad \dot{\hat{x}}_0 = \frac{i}{\hbar}[\hat{H}, \hat{x}_0] = 0. \tag{9'}$$

These equations imply that the quantities x_0 and y_0, which are defined by equations (10), are constants of motion.

The operators $\hat{x}_0$ and $\hat{y}_0$ also commute with $\hat{\pi}_x$, $\hat{\pi}_y$, and $\hat{\pi}_z$, as can easily be shown by means of (10), (8), and (3'). However, they do not commute with one another. Indeed, using the same equations, we obtain

$$[\hat{x}_0, \hat{y}_0] = -\frac{c}{e\mathcal{H}}[x, \hat{\pi}_x] + \frac{c}{e\mathcal{H}}[\hat{\pi}_y, y] - \frac{c^2}{e^2\mathcal{H}^2}[\hat{\pi}_y, \hat{\pi}_x] = -i\frac{\hbar c}{e\mathcal{H}}. \tag{11}$$

---

*Of course, by no means does p_z have a definite value in every stationary state (cf. Problem No. 9, Chapter I). An example of stationary states of this second type is provided by states described by a superposition of Ψ-functions containing factors $e^{\frac{ip_z z}{\hbar}}$ and $e^{-\frac{ip_z z}{\hbar}}$.

By making use of the characteristic length $a = \sqrt{\frac{\hbar c}{|e|\mathcal{H}}}$, defined in Problem No. 1, we can rewrite (11) in the form

$$[\hat{x}_0, \hat{y}_0] = -i\frac{e}{|e|}a^2. \tag{11'}$$

Equations (4)-(7), (9) and (10) have the same for as the corresponding classical equations. In these classical equation, x_0 and y_0 stand for the coordinates of the fixed center of the circular orbit of the particle. Therefore, it is natural to regard the operators $\hat{x}_0$ and $\hat{y}_0$ as the quantum-mechanical generalization of the classical coordinates of the center of the orbit. Below we shall determine the extent to which the properties of the classical quantities x_0 and y_0 are preserved (or lose their strength) in the quantum-mechanical case.

First of all, we note that according to (11) the coordinates x_0 and y_0 cannot have definite values simultaneously. As in the classical case, the possible values of x_0 and y_0 coincide with the set of all real numbers.* As we would expect ([1], p. 43), the energy levels of the particle are degenerate because of the existence of mutually noncommuting constants of motion (in the given case, x_0 and y_0). This degeneracy is infinite in degree (see [1] and the preceding problem): each energy level corresponds to an infinite set of Ψ-functions which belong to different eigenvalues of x_0 or y_0 (or to some function of x_0 and y_0). The classical analogue of this is the independence of the energy of the particle from the position of the center of its orbit, as a result of which each given value of the energy corresponds to an infinite set of pairs of values of (x_0, y_0).

Moreover, in the classical theory the time averages of x and y are equal to x_0 and y_0 respectively. In the quantum-mechanical theory, the average values of x and y (over the Ψ-function) are equal to the average values of x_0 and y_0 respectively in this state (the average values of x_0 and y_0, since in any state at least one of the quantities x_0 and y_0 does not have a definite value). Indeed, from (10), (4), (1), and (3′), we successively obtain

$$\bar{x} - \bar{x}_0 = \overline{x - x_0} \sim \bar{\pi}_y \sim \overline{[H, \pi_x]} = \overline{[H_t, \pi_x]}.$$

But this last quantity represents the diagonal matrix element of the commutator $(\hat{H}_t\hat{\pi}_x - \hat{\pi}_x\hat{H}_t)$, which is obviously equal to zero. Thus, $\bar{x} = \bar{x}_0$. The equation $\bar{y} = \bar{y}_0$ is proved similarly.

---

*This is almost obvious from (10) in combination with (2), and follows absolutely rigorously from the identical form of the commutators (11) and $[\hat{p}_x, \hat{x}] = -i\hbar$, if it is considered that p_x and x have a continuous spectrum of eigenvalues from $-\infty$ to $+\infty$.

2. Let us define the operator

$$\hat{\rho}_0^2 = \hat{x}_0^2 + \hat{y}_0^2, \qquad (12)$$

which is the quantum-mechanical analogue of the square of the cylindrical radius vector of the center of the circular orbit. It follows from (9′) that the quantity ρ_0^2 is a constant of the motion. The spectrum of its eigenvalues is obtained directly from comparison of (12) and (11) with the corresponding pair of equations for a linear harmonic oscillator*

$$\hat{H} = \frac{1}{2\mu}\hat{p}^2 + \frac{1}{2}\mu\omega^2\hat{q}^2, \qquad [\hat{p}, \hat{q}] = -i\hbar, \qquad (13)$$

whose spectrum of eigenvalues has the form

$$E_n = \hbar\omega\left(n + \frac{1}{2}\right)\ldots \qquad (n = 0, 1, 2, \ldots). \qquad (14)$$

A comparison of (12) and (11) with (13) shows the complete formal correspondence of these two pairs of equations, the mutual analogues in them being the operators $\hat{\rho}_0^2$ and $\hat{H}$, $\hat{x}_0$ and $\frac{1}{\sqrt{2\mu}}\hat{p}$, $\hat{y}_0$ and $\sqrt{\frac{\mu}{2}}\,\omega\hat{q}$, and consequently $[\hat{x}_0, \hat{y}_0] = -i\frac{\hbar c}{e\mathscr{H}}$ and $\frac{\omega}{2}[\hat{p}, \hat{q}] = -i\hbar\frac{\omega}{2}$. Thus, the spectrum of eigenvalues of ρ_0^2 is obtained directly from (14) by replacing E by ρ_0^2 and $\hbar\omega$ by $2\frac{\hbar c}{|e|\mathscr{H}} = 2a^2$**:

$$(\rho_0^2)_l = 2\frac{\hbar c}{|e|\mathscr{H}}\left(l + \frac{1}{2}\right) = a^2(2l+1) \quad (l = 0, 1, 2, \ldots). \quad (15)$$

Thus, using classical terminology, we can say that the geometric locations of the possible "centers of the orbits" form a discrete family of concentric circles whose center lies at the origin of coordinates and whose radii are equal to $\sqrt{(\rho_0^2)_l} = a\sqrt{2l+1}$ (we emphasize that in the given case the origin of coordinates represents

---

*The method of determining the eigenvalues which we use below was introduced by L. Landau in his work on the diamagnetism of metals (1930), in which he obtained the energy levels E_l of a particle in a magnetic field in the same way [see equations (1) and (3′), and equation (13) of the preceding problem].

**The difference in the signs in front of i in commutators (11) and (13) which can occur for $e < 0$ of course plays no role, since the actual sign of the commutator depends only on the order of the corresponding operators, and these appear symmetrically both in ρ_0^2 and in $\hat{H}$.

a fixed "center of quantization" which is distinguished by the measurement, its position in space being of course quite arbitrary). From (11), we know that the positions of the actual "centers of the orbits" are not definite; the root-mean-square uncertainties in the coordinates x_0 and y_0 being connected by the relation

$$\Delta x_0 \Delta y_0 \geqslant \frac{1}{2} a^2 \tag{16}$$

[this follows directly from a comparison of (11′) and (13) and consideration of the uncertainty principle $\Delta p \Delta q \geq \frac{1}{2} h$].

3. Let us now introduce the operator

$$\hat{\rho}_L^2 = (x - \hat{x}_0)^2 + (y - \hat{y}_0)^2, \tag{17}$$

which is the quantum-mechanical analogue of the square of the radius of the Larmor orbit. According to (10) and (1), it reduces to the form

$$\hat{\rho}_L^2 = \frac{c^2}{e^2 \mathcal{H}^2} (\hat{\pi}_x^2 + \hat{\pi}_y^2) = \frac{2\mu c^2}{e^2 \mathcal{H}^2} \hat{H}_t. \tag{18}$$

Consequently, its eigenvalues occur automatically in states with a given value of E_t and are equal to [cf. (15)]

$$(\rho_L^2)_n = \frac{2\mu c^2}{e^2 \mathcal{H}^2} (E_t)_n = a^2 (2n + 1), \text{where } n = 0, 1, 2, \ldots \tag{19}$$

(we have used equations (13)—(15) of Problem No. 1). Equation (18) or (19) relating ρ_L^2 and E_t is exactly the same as in the classical theory. In all states with a given "transverse" energy, the value of ρ_L^2 is identical. Like E_t, ρ_L^2 is a constant of the motion. Moreover, $\hat{\rho}_L^2$ commutes with $\hat{\rho}_0^2$.

4. The operator for the component of the moment of the generalized momentum $\boldsymbol{M} = \boldsymbol{r} \times \boldsymbol{p}$ in the direction of $\mathcal{H}$ has the form

$$\hat{M}_z = x\hat{p}_y - y\hat{p}_x = x\hat{\pi}_y - y\hat{\pi}_x + \frac{e\mathcal{H}}{2c}(x^2 + y^2) \tag{20}$$

[where we have used equation (2) and $\boldsymbol{A} = \frac{1}{2}(\mathcal{H} \times \boldsymbol{r})$]. By substituting $\hat{\pi}_x$ and $\hat{\pi}_y$ from (10) and using (12) and (17), after a simple transformation, we obtain

$$\hat{M}_z = \frac{e\mathcal{H}}{2c} (\hat{\rho}_0^2 - \hat{\rho}_L^2). \tag{21}$$

Thus, M_z is a constant of motion like the two quantities on the right side of this equation (of course, we could have known this beforehand, since $\hat{M}_z = -i\hbar \frac{\partial}{\partial\varphi}$ in cylindrical coordinates, and the Hamiltonian does not depend on φ; cf. Problem No. 1). According to (15) and (19), the eigenvalues of M_z are

$$M_z = \frac{e\mathcal{H}}{2c} a^2 (2l - 2n) = \hbar \frac{e}{|e|}(l - n).$$

If we define the quantum number $m \equiv \frac{M_z}{\hbar}$, we can obtain from this the relationship between the quantum numbers of the transverse energy (n), the angular-momentum component (m), and the "center of the orbit" (l):

$$m = \frac{e}{|e|}(l - n). \tag{22}$$

Thus, only two of these three quantum numbers (and of the three constants of motion corresponding to them) are independent.

Since $l = 0, 1, \ldots, \infty$, equations (16) of Problem No. 1, which give the possible values of m for a given n (depending on the sign of the charge), follow directly from (22).

The Ψ-functions (17) and (17) of Problem No. 1 describe states with definite values of p_z, E_t, and M_z, as well as with definite values of ρ_0^2 equal to $a^2(2l+1)$, where, according to (22),

$$\left.\begin{aligned} &\text{for} \quad e > 0: \quad l = n + m; \\ &\text{for} \quad e < 0: \quad l = n - m. \end{aligned}\right\} \tag{22'}$$

Thus, a Ψ-function of the form of (17) describes a uniform distribution over φ and z of the circular orbits of radius $\sqrt{\overline{\rho_\perp^2}} = a\sqrt{2n+1}$, the centers of these orbits lying on a circle of radius $\sqrt{\rho_0^2} = a\sqrt{2l+1}$, whose own center lies at the origin of coordinates.*

3. According to (22′) (see Problem No. 2), for an electron ($e < 0$) we have $l = n - m$. Therefore, in the states with which we are concerned, $m = n \geqslant 0$. Accordingly, equations (17) and (17′) for the Ψ-functions of these states (see Problem No. 1) assume the form

$$\Psi_{n,n,p_z} = \exp\left(in\varphi + \frac{i}{\hbar} p_z z - \frac{\rho^2}{4a^2}\right)\left(\frac{\rho}{a}\right)^n F\left(0, n+1, \frac{\rho^2}{2a^2}\right). \tag{1}$$

The function F which appears here is obviously equal to unity. For our subsequent discussion, we need only to know $|\Psi|^2$, which is equal to

$$|\Psi_{n,n,p_z}|^2 = e^{-\frac{\rho^2}{2a^2}}\left(\frac{\rho}{a}\right)^{2n}. \tag{2}$$

---

*By contrast, the Ψ-function given in [1], p. 535, describes a uniform distribution over x and z of orbits with the same radius, but with centers lying on the straight line $y = y_0 = -\frac{cp_x}{e\mathcal{H}}$.

The average values of ρ and ρ^2 are

$$\bar{\rho} = \frac{\int_0^\infty \rho \,|\Psi|^2 2\pi\rho\, d\rho}{\int_0^\infty |\Psi|^2 2\pi\rho\, d\rho}, \qquad \overline{\rho^2} = \frac{\int_0^\infty \rho^2 |\Psi|^2 2\pi\rho\, d\rho}{\int_0^\infty |\Psi|^2 2\pi\rho\, d\rho}. \tag{3}$$

After we have substituted (2) into this equation and performed the transformation of variables $\frac{\rho^2}{2a^2} \equiv x$, these integrals reduce to Γ-functions, and we obtain*

$$\bar{\rho} = a\sqrt{2}\,\frac{\Gamma\left(n+\frac{3}{2}\right)}{\Gamma(n+1)} = a\sqrt{2\pi}\,\frac{(2n+1)!}{2^{2n+1}(n!)^2}, \tag{4}$$

$$\overline{\rho^2} = 2a^2(n+1). \tag{5}$$

The most probable value of ρ, i.e., the value $\rho = \tilde{\rho}$ corresponding to the maximum of the function $|\Psi|^2\rho$ (the density of the probability distribution function of ρ) is

$$\tilde{\rho} = a\sqrt{2n+1}. \tag{6}$$

Moreover, the eigenvalues ρ_0^2 and ρ_L^2 (see Problem No. 2) are

$$\rho_0^2 = a^2(2l+1) = a^2 = \frac{\hbar c}{|e|\mathscr{H}}, \tag{7}$$

$$\rho_Л^2 = a^2(2n+1) = (\tilde{\rho})^2. \tag{8}$$

In the quasi-classical limit ($n \gg 1$), if we simplify (4) by means of Stirling's formula

$$\Gamma(n+1) \approx \sqrt{2\pi n}\left(\frac{n}{e}\right)^n,$$

$$\Gamma\left(n+\frac{3}{2}\right) \approx \sqrt{2\pi\left(n+\frac{1}{2}\right)}\left(\frac{n+\frac{1}{2}}{e}\right)^{n+\frac{1}{2}},$$

*In transforming $\bar{\rho}$, we have used the "double-variable identity" [13]

$$\Gamma(2x) = \frac{1}{\sqrt{\pi}}\,2^{2x-1}\Gamma(x)\,\Gamma\left(x+\frac{1}{2}\right).$$

and if we replace $\left(n+\frac{1}{2}\right)^n$ by $n^n e^{1/2}$, we obtain

$$\bar{\rho} \approx a\sqrt{2n}. \qquad (4')$$

According to (4′), (5), (6), and (8), for $n \gg 1$, all the characteristic radii are approximately the same

$$\bar{\rho} \approx \sqrt{\overline{\rho^2}} \approx \tilde{\rho} = \sqrt{\rho_{\text{л}}^2} \approx a\sqrt{2n}, \qquad (9)$$

in complete agreement with the fact that in this case the radial distribution function $|\Psi|^2 \cdot \rho$ [cf. (2)] has a narrow maximum. The standard deviation of the radius is

$$\Delta\rho = \sqrt{\overline{\rho^2} - (\bar{\rho})^2} \approx a\sqrt{2} \ll \bar{\rho}. \qquad (10)$$

From what we have said, it is clear that the probability of finding the electron is different from zero only in a narrow ring-shaped region of radius $a\sqrt{2n}$ whose center lies at the origin of coordinates. This obviously corresponds to the limiting transition to the classical circular orbit of the electron (as it should for $n \gg 1$).

According to (7), the center of the quasi-classical orbit coincides with the origin of coordinates only with an accuracy within a. However, this does not contradict our previous statements, since the actual position of the orbit is determined only with an accuracy of the same order of magnitude [i.e., the effective "spread" $\Delta\rho \sim a$; see (10)].

Since $a = \sqrt{\frac{\hbar c}{|e|\mathcal{H}}}$, both of these uncertainties disappear completely only in the formal limiting transition $\hbar \to 0$.

From equation (9) and equations (18) and (19) of the preceding problem, it follows directly that the radius of the quasi-classical orbit of the electron is connected with its transverse energy in exactly the same way as in the classical theory.

We note that the condition $n \gg 1$ (a "quasi-classical energy") automatically implies the condition $m \gg 1$ (a "quasi-classical angular momentum") since $m = n$.

The quasi-classical condition $n \gg 1$ is equivalent (see Problem No. 1) to the inequality

$$E_t \equiv \frac{\mu v_t^2}{2} \gg \hbar\omega, \qquad (11)$$

where $\omega = \frac{|e|\mathcal{H}}{\mu c}$. It is also possible to obtain inequality (11) by requiring that the quantum-mechanical uncertainty in the momentum of the electron $(\Delta p)_q \sim \frac{\hbar}{\Delta\rho} \sim \frac{\hbar}{a}$ be small relative to the classical change in its momentum during the time of a rotation through an angle ~1, $(\Delta p_{cl})_q \sim \mu v t$, or from the requirement that the uncertainty in the position of the center of the orbit and of the actual orbit ($\sim a$) be small relative to the radius of the orbit.

Moreover, for $n \gg 1$, if we substitute $m = \frac{M_z}{\hbar}$ and $n \approx \frac{E_t}{\hbar\omega}$ into the exact equality $m = n$, which is correct for the states of the electron which we are considering, we can transform this equality into the classical equation connecting the angular momentum relative to the center of the orbit and the energy*:

$$E_t = \omega M_z = -\frac{e\mathcal{H}}{\mu c} M_z. \tag{12}$$

4. This problem is solved with the preceding problem as a model. According to (22′) (Problem No. 2), for $e < 0$ and $n = 0$, we have $m = -l \leq 0$. Therefore, the Ψ-function of the electron in the states we are considering has the form [see (17) and (17′) of Problem No. 1]

$$\Psi_{0,\,-l,\,p_z} = \exp\left(-il\varphi + \frac{i}{\hbar} p_z z - \frac{\rho^2}{4a^2}\right)\left(\frac{\rho}{a}\right)^l F\left(0,\ l+1,\ \frac{\rho^2}{2a^2}\right). \tag{1}$$

Thus, the function F becomes unity and $|\Psi|^2$ becomes

$$|\Psi_{0,\,-l,\,p_z}|^2 = e^{-\frac{\rho^2}{2a^2}}\left(\frac{\rho}{a}\right)^{2l} \tag{2}$$

The eigenvalues ρ_0^2 and ρ_L^2 are

$$\rho_0^2 = a^2(2l+1), \tag{3}$$

$$\rho_L^2 = a^2(2n+1) = a^2 = \frac{\hbar c}{|e|\mathcal{H}}. \tag{4}$$

Since equation (2) differs from the corresponding equation of Problem No. 3 only to the extent that n is replaced by l, we can write the values of $\bar{\rho}$, $\overline{\rho^2}$, and $\tilde{\rho}$ directly by analogy with equations (4)–(6)

---

*Equation (12) is obtained from the expression for the angular-momentum component relative to an arbitrary origin (see the second footnote to Problem No. 1), $M_z = \rho\left(\mu v_\varphi + \frac{e}{2c}\mathcal{H}\rho\right)$, by substituting the radius of the orbit $\frac{c\mu v_t}{|e|\mathcal{H}}$ for ρ (the cylindrical radius vector of the electron), and the total velocity of the electron's motion v_t for v_φ (the azimuthal component of its velocity).

of Problem No. 3:

$$\bar{\rho} = a\sqrt{2}\,\frac{\Gamma\left(l+\frac{3}{2}\right)}{\Gamma(l+1)} = a\sqrt{2\pi}\,\frac{(2l+1)!}{2^{2l+1}(l!)^2}, \tag{5}$$

$$\overline{\rho^2} = 2a^2(l+1), \tag{6}$$

$$\tilde{\rho} = a\sqrt{2l+1} = \sqrt{\rho_0^2}. \tag{7}$$

In the states with which we are concerned, the "transverse" energy E_t has its minimum possible value (for a given $\mathscr{H}$), being equal to $\frac{1}{2}\hbar\omega = \frac{\hbar|e|\mathscr{H}}{2\mu c}$. However, by contrast with the case in Problem No. 3, the component of the moment of the generalized momentum is not connected with the energy, and its absolute value can be arbitrarily large: $M_z = m\hbar = -l\hbar \leq 0$.

Since $n = 0$, in the states with which we are concerned, they are fundamentally "anti-classical," and they cannot be described in the language used for classical orbits. Nevertheless, it is instructive to consider the limiting case $l \gg 1$, when *

$$\bar{\rho} \approx \sqrt{\overline{\rho^2}} \approx \tilde{\rho} = \sqrt{\rho_0^2} \approx a\sqrt{2l}, \tag{8}$$

and the radial probability distribution function $|\Psi|^2 \cdot \rho$ [cf. (2)] has a narrow maximum [with a standard deviation $\Delta\rho = \sqrt{\overline{\rho^2} - (\bar{\rho})^2} \approx a\sqrt{2}$]. If we consider (4), it becomes clear that a state with $n = 0$ and some definite $l \gg 1$ can be roughly compared with a uniform distribution of the "orbits" of minimum "radius" a in a narrow ring-shaped region of radius $a\sqrt{2l} \gg a$, whose center lies at the origin of coordinates. Obviously, the implications of this picture are distinctly opposed to the quasi-classical picture considered at the end of the preceding problem.

The above statements do not contradict the fact that the probability distribution functions (2) have the same nature in both problems (for identical values of n and 1). The point here is that these probability distribution functions do not describe at all completely the corresponding states of the electrons, and the complete sets of constants of the motion which do characterize these states are entirely different in the given case of identical values of 1 and n (the value of the energy, the sign of the angular-momentum component, the existence or lack of a relation between the energy and the angular momentum). In the Ψ-functions (1), this difference is expressed

---

*Compare with equation (9) of Problem No. 3. Both series of equations are in part extremely similar, but they differ essentially in the replacement of $\sqrt{\rho_\pi^2}$ by $\sqrt{\rho_0^2}$. This is the cause for the sharp difference in the qualitative interpretations of the corresponding states of the electron (see below).

in particular by the factors $e^{in\varphi}$ and $e^{-il\varphi}$. It is easily seen that this difference is also taken into account qualitatively in our descriptive pictures.

5. Let us use a system of polar coordinates ρ, φ with its origin at the point of equilibrium of the oscillator. The Hamiltonian for this two-dimensional system has the form (cf. Problem No. 1)

$$\hat{H} = -\frac{\hbar^2}{2\mu}\left(\frac{\partial^2}{\partial\rho^2} + \frac{1}{\rho}\frac{\partial}{\partial\rho} + \frac{1}{\rho^2}\frac{\partial^2}{\partial\varphi^2}\right) - \\ -\frac{\hbar}{2i}\frac{e\mathscr{H}}{\mu c}\frac{\partial}{\partial\varphi} + \frac{e^2\mathscr{H}^2}{8\mu c^2}\rho^2 + \frac{1}{2}\mu\omega_0^2\rho^2, \tag{1}$$

where ω_0 is the natural cyclic frequency of the oscillator (all the other symbols are the same as in Problem No. 1).

In the Schrödinger equation $\hat{H}\Psi = E\Psi$, the variables separate:

$$\Psi(\rho, \varphi) = \text{const}\, e^{im\varphi} f(\rho) \qquad (m = 0, \pm 1, \pm 2, \ldots). \tag{2}$$

For the function f, we obtain the equation

$$f'' + \frac{1}{\rho}f' + \left[k^2 + m\frac{e\mathscr{H}}{\hbar c} - \frac{m^2}{\rho^2} - \left(\frac{e^2\mathscr{H}^2}{4\hbar^2c^2} + \frac{\mu^2\omega_0^2}{\hbar^2}\right)\rho^2\right] f = 0, \tag{3}$$

where $k^2 = \dfrac{2\mu E}{\hbar^2}$.

Using the characteristic lengths

$$a = \sqrt{\frac{\hbar c}{|e|\mathscr{H}}}, \qquad b = \left(\frac{e^2\mathscr{H}^2}{4\hbar^2c^2} + \frac{\mu^2\omega_0^2}{\hbar^2}\right)^{-1/4} \tag{4}$$

and performing the transformation of variables $\xi = \dfrac{\rho^2}{b^2}$, we can reduce (3) to the form

$$f''(\xi) + \frac{1}{\xi}f'(\xi) + \left(\frac{k^2b^2}{4\xi} + m\frac{e}{|e|}\frac{b^2}{a^2}\frac{1}{4\xi} - \frac{m^2}{4\xi^2} - \frac{1}{4}\right)f(\xi) = 0. \tag{5}$$

This equation differs from equation (7) of Problem No. 1 only in the substitution

$$\frac{k_t^2a^2}{2} + \frac{e}{|e|}\frac{m}{2} \to \frac{k^2b^2}{4} + \frac{e}{|e|}\frac{m}{4}\frac{b^2}{a^2}. \tag{6}$$

Therefore, its solution can be written out directly on the basis of the equation of Problem No. 1, namely, equations (8), (10) and (11). In this way, we obtain

$$\frac{1+|m|}{2}-\frac{e}{|e|}\frac{m}{4}\frac{b^2}{a^2}-\frac{k^2b^2}{4}=-n \qquad (n=0,\ 1,\ 2,\ \ldots), \tag{7}$$

$$f(\xi)=e^{-\frac{\xi}{2}}\xi^{\frac{|m|}{2}}F(-n,\ |m|+1,\ \xi). \tag{8}$$

According to (2) and (8), the wave equations of the stationary states (except for the normalization constant) have the form

$$\Psi_{nm}=e^{im\varphi-\frac{\rho^2}{2b^2}}\left(\frac{\rho}{b}\right)^{|m|}F\left(-n,\ |m|+1,\ \frac{\rho^2}{b^2}\right).$$

From (7), substituting for a^2, b^2, and k^2, we obtain the following equation for the energy spectrum of the system:

$$E_{nm}=(2n+|m|+1)\hbar\sqrt{\omega_0^2+\omega_L^2}-\frac{e}{|e|}m\hbar\omega_L, \tag{9}$$

where we have used the angular velocity of Larmor precession [5, 21]*

$$\omega_L=\frac{|e|\mathcal{H}}{2\mu c}. \tag{10}$$

Considering that $\frac{e}{|e|}$ and m can have either sign, it is convenient to replace n and m in (9) by two new (non-negative) quantum numbers n_1 and n_2 by writing

$$E_{n_1n_2}=(n_1+n_2+1)\hbar\sqrt{\omega_0^2+\omega_L^2}+(n_1-n_2)\hbar\omega_L$$
$$(n_1,\ n_2=0,\ 1,\ 2,\ \ldots). \tag{9'}$$

For $\omega_L \ll \omega_0$, if we confine ourselves to terms which are linear with respect to ω_L, we have

$$E_{n_1n_2}\approx n_1\hbar(\omega_0+\omega_L)+n_2\hbar(\omega_0-\omega_L)+\hbar\omega_0, \tag{11}$$

This represents the quantum-mechanical analogue of Larmor's theorem for the given system (indeed, we remember that Larmor's theorem holds only for a weak magnetic field, when $\omega_L \ll \omega_0$).

In the limiting case where $\omega_L=0$ (i.e., $\mathcal{H}=0$), equations (9′) or (11) transform to the usual expression for the energy levels of a plane isotropic oscillator

---

*The Larmor frequency is equal to half the frequency of rotation of a "free" particle in the field $\mathcal{H}$ (see Problem No. 1).

$$E_{n_1 n_2} = (n_1 + n_2 + 1)\hbar\omega_0,$$

where $\hbar\omega_0 = 2\frac{\hbar\omega_0}{2}$ is the zero-point energy of the oscillator.

In the opposite limiting case where $\omega_0 = 0$, we have, according to (9′) and (10),

$$E_{n_1} = \left(n_1 + \frac{1}{2}\right)\hbar\frac{|e|\mathscr{H}}{\mu c}.$$

As we would expect, this represents the expression for the energy levels of a "free" particle in a magnetic field (Problems No. 1 and No. 2).

6. The spin state of the proton and the electron in the hydrogen atom can be considered apart from the spatial motion of the particles. The reason for this is that the spatial motion is more rapid and, as a consequence, the magnetic interaction, which depends on the position of the two particles, can be averaged over this motion. The energy of the magnetic interaction of the proton and the electron can be written in the form

$$-\mu_p\hat{\sigma}_p\hat{\mathscr{H}}_e,$$

where $\mu_p = 2.78\frac{e\hbar}{2Mc}$, and $\hat{\mathscr{H}}_e$ is the magnetic field of the electron at the position of the proton. This magnetic field is equal to ([1], p. 548)

$$\hat{\mathscr{H}}_e = \frac{8\pi}{3}\mu_e|\psi(0)|^2\hat{\sigma}_e.$$

For the ground state of an electron in the hydrogen atom, $|\psi(0)|^2 = \frac{1}{\pi a^3}$ (where a is the Bohr radius). Hence,

$$\hat{\mathscr{H}}_e = \frac{8\mu_e}{3a^3}\hat{\sigma}_e,$$

and the interaction energy is

$$-\frac{8}{3}\frac{\mu_p\mu_e}{a^3}\hat{\sigma}_p\hat{\sigma}_e.$$

After adding the terms giving the interaction of the magnetic moments with the external field $\mathscr{H}$, we obtain the following Hamiltonian for the determination of the spin function:

$$\hat{H} = \mu_e\hat{\sigma}_e\mathscr{H} - \mu_p\hat{\sigma}_p\mathscr{H} - \frac{8}{3}\frac{\mu_e\mu_p}{a^3}\hat{\sigma}_p\hat{\sigma}_e.$$

If we define $\epsilon = \frac{8}{3}\frac{\mu_e\mu_p}{a^3}$ and take the z-axis in the direction of $\mathcal{H}$, we can write the Schrödinger equation in the form

$$(\mu_e \mathscr{H} \hat{\sigma}_{ez} - \mu_p \mathscr{H} \hat{\sigma}_{pz} - \varepsilon \hat{\boldsymbol{\sigma}}_e \hat{\boldsymbol{\sigma}}_p)\Psi = E\Psi.$$

There are four solutions to this equation. The first two solutions are functions corresponding to a total angular momentum 1 and to angular-momentum components 1 and -1:

$$\Psi_{1,1} = \chi_{\frac{1}{2}}(e)\chi_{\frac{1}{2}}(p),$$

$$\Psi_{1,-1} = \chi_{-\frac{1}{2}}(e)\chi_{-\frac{1}{2}}(p).$$

These correspond to the energies

$$E_{1,1} = (\mu_e - \mu_p)\mathscr{H} - \varepsilon,$$

$$E_{1,-1} = -(\mu_e - \mu_p)\mathscr{H} - \varepsilon.$$

Each of the two remaining states represents a superposition of functions with a total angular momentum of 0 and 1 and angular-momentum components 0:

$$\Psi_1^0 = \alpha_1^0\psi_{1,0} + \beta_1^0\psi_{0,0},$$

$$\Psi_0^0 = \alpha_0^0\psi_{1,0} + \beta_0^0\psi_{0,0},$$

where

$$\psi_{1,0} = \frac{1}{\sqrt{2}}\left\{\chi_{\frac{1}{2}}(e)\chi_{-\frac{1}{2}}(p) + \chi_{-\frac{1}{2}}(e)\chi_{\frac{1}{2}}(p)\right\},$$

$$\psi_{0,0} = \frac{1}{\sqrt{2}}\left\{\chi_{\frac{1}{2}}(e)\chi_{-\frac{1}{2}}(p) - \chi_{-\frac{1}{2}}(e)\chi_{\frac{1}{2}}(p)\right\}$$

are the functions corresponding to the angular-momentum component 0 and to the angular momenta 0 and 1. The coefficients α_1^0, β_1^0 and α_0^0, β_0^0 are easily found from the Schrödinger equation. They turn out to be

$$\alpha_1^0 = \frac{(\mu_e + \mu_p)\mathscr{H}}{\sqrt{(\mu_e + \mu_p)^2\mathscr{H}^2 + (\varepsilon + E_1^0)^2}},$$

$$\beta_1^0 = \frac{\varepsilon + E_1^0}{\sqrt{(\mu_e + \mu_p)^2\mathscr{H}^2 + (\varepsilon + E_1^0)^2}},$$

$$\alpha_0^0 = \frac{(\mu_e + \mu_p)\mathcal{H}}{\sqrt{(\mu_e + \mu_p)^2 \mathcal{H}^2 + (\varepsilon + E_0^0)^2}},$$

$$\beta_0^0 = \frac{\varepsilon + E_0^0}{\sqrt{(\mu_e + \mu_p)^2 \mathcal{H}^2 + (\varepsilon + E_0^0)^2}},$$

where E_1^0 and E_0^0 are the energies of the states Ψ_1^0 and Ψ_0^0, being equal to

$$E_1^0 = \varepsilon - \sqrt{4\varepsilon^2 + (\mu_e + \mu_p)^2 \mathcal{H}^2},$$

$$E_0^0 = \varepsilon + \sqrt{4\varepsilon^2 + (\mu_e + \mu_p)^2 \mathcal{H}^2}.$$

It is convenient to express Ψ_1^0 and Ψ_0^0, and the energies of these states, in terms of the quantity

$$x = \frac{(\mu_e + \mu_p)\mathcal{H}}{2\varepsilon} = \frac{\mathcal{H}_{\text{Gauss}}}{500}.$$

Then,

$$\alpha_1^0 = \frac{x}{\sqrt{x^2 + (1 - \sqrt{1 + x^2})^2}}, \qquad \beta_1^0 = \frac{1 - \sqrt{1 + x^2}}{\sqrt{x^2 + (1 - \sqrt{1 + x^2})^2}},$$

$$\alpha_0^0 = \frac{x}{\sqrt{x^2 + (1 + \sqrt{1 + x^2})^2}}, \qquad \beta_0^0 = \frac{1 + \sqrt{1 + x^2}}{\sqrt{x^2 + (1 + \sqrt{1 + x^2})^2}},$$

$$E_1^0 = 2\varepsilon\left(\frac{1}{2} - \sqrt{1 + x^2}\right),$$

$$E_0^0 = 2\varepsilon\left(\frac{1}{2} + \sqrt{1 + x^2}\right).$$

For weak magnetic fields ($x \ll 1$), we obtain

$$\Psi_1^0 \approx \psi_{1,0}, \qquad E_1^0 \approx -\varepsilon,$$

$$\Psi_0^0 \approx \psi_{0,0}, \qquad E_0^0 \approx 3\varepsilon,$$

i.e., the same wave functions and energy of the interacting spins as in the absence of a magnetic field (cf. Problem No. 5, Ch. VIII).

For a strong magnetic field ($x \gg 1$), we have

$$\Psi_1^0 \approx \chi_{-\frac{1}{2}}(e)\,\chi_{\frac{1}{2}}(p), \qquad E_1^0 \approx -(\mu_e + \mu_p)\mathcal{H},$$

$$\Psi_0^0 \approx \chi_{\frac{1}{2}}(e)\,\chi_{-\frac{1}{2}}(p), \qquad E_0^0 \approx (\mu_e + \mu_p)\mathcal{H},$$

i.e., wave functions and spin energies which are quantized independently in the external field.

CHAPTER XI

Theory of Collisions

1. It is known that the solution of the problem of elastic scattering by a potential $U(r)$ in the Born approximation leads to the following expression for the wave function:

$$\psi \approx \psi^{(0)} + \psi^{(1)}, \tag{1}$$

where

$$\left.\begin{aligned} \psi^{(0)}(r) &= e^{ikr}; \\ \psi^{(1)}(r) &= -\frac{m}{2\pi\hbar^2}\int U(r')\,\psi^{(0)}(r')\,\frac{e^{ik|r-r'|}}{|r-r'|}\,dr', \end{aligned}\right\} \tag{2}$$

Therefore, the asymptotic expression is

$$\psi^{(1)}_{r\to\infty}(r) \approx \left[-\frac{m}{2\pi\hbar^2}\int U(r')\,e^{iqr'}\,dr'\right]\frac{e^{ikr}}{r} \equiv f(\theta)\,\frac{e^{ikr}}{r}, \tag{2'}$$

where $q = k - k'$ is the change of the propagation vector of the particle in scattering, and θ is the scattering angle.

The differential effective cross section of scattering inside the solid-angle element $d\Omega$ at an angle θ to the direction of incidence of k is

$$d\sigma = |f(\theta)|^2\,d\Omega = \frac{m^2}{4\pi^2\hbar^4}\left|\int U(r')\,e^{iqr'}\,dr'\right|^2 d\Omega. \tag{3}$$

Let us compute the integral in (3). If we point the polar axis of a system of spherical coordinates along the vector q, and if we substitute for $U(r')$, we find

$$\int e^{-\varkappa r' + iqr'}\frac{dr'}{r'} = 2\pi\int_0^\infty e^{-\varkappa r'}\,r'\,dr'\int_{-1}^{1} e^{iqr'x}\,dx = \frac{4\pi}{\varkappa^2 + q^2}.$$

Hence, finally,

$$d\sigma = \left(\frac{2Am}{\hbar^2}\right)^2\frac{d\Omega}{(\varkappa^2 + q^2)^2}, \tag{4}$$

$$q = 2k\sin\frac{\theta}{2}.$$

By integrating (4) over the angles, we find the total scattering cross section

$$\sigma = \frac{4\pi}{\varkappa^2 + 4k^2}\left(\frac{2Am}{\varkappa\hbar^2}\right)^2 \tag{5}$$

Let us examine the limiting expressions for equation (4).

1) $k \ll \varkappa$, and consequently $q \ll \varkappa$:

$$d\sigma \approx \left(\frac{2Am}{\hbar^2\varkappa^2}\right)^2 d\Omega. \tag{4'}$$

Thus, here, in complete agreement with the general theory of the scattering of slow particles, the cross section does not depend on the scattering angle or on the energy of the particles.

2) $k \gg \varkappa$ (rapid particles).

Here, there are two characteristic regions of scattering angles:

a) $\theta \ll \frac{\varkappa}{k}$, and consequently $q \ll \varkappa$;

b) $\theta \gg \frac{\varkappa}{k}$, and consequently $q \gg \varkappa$ (large scattering angles).

In the region of scattering angles (small) of case (a), the cross section tends toward the constant limit (4′) as $\theta \to 0$.

In case (b), using the energy of the particles $E = \frac{\hbar^2k^2}{2m}$, we have

$$d\sigma \approx \left(\frac{A}{4E}\right)^2 \frac{d\Omega}{\sin^4\frac{\theta}{2}}. \tag{4''}$$

This is a formula of the Rutherford type, as we would expect, since in the significant region of distances $r \sim \frac{1}{q}$ the field is practically a Coulomb field.

The condition that Born's formulas (3) and (4) be valid is that the correction term $\psi^{(1)}$, describing the effect of the scattering field, be small relative to the main term $\psi^{(0)}$ [see (1)]. The smallness of this correction term is in any event assured if $|\psi^{(1)}|_{r=0} \ll |\psi^{(0)}| = 1$.*).

We have

$$\begin{aligned}\psi^{(1)}\big|_{r=0} &= -\frac{mA}{2\pi\hbar^2}\int e^{ikr'}\frac{e^{-\varkappa r'+ikr'}}{r'^2}dr' = \\ &= -\frac{2mA}{\hbar^2}\int_0^\infty e^{-\varkappa r'+ikr'}\frac{\sin kr'}{kr'}dr'.\end{aligned} \tag{2''}$$

---

*This condition for validity is sufficient. However, it may turn out to be too rigorous, especially in the case of small scattering angles.

In the case of slow particles ($k \lesssim \varkappa$), the significant region is $r' \sim \frac{1}{\varkappa}$, in which $e^{ikr'}\frac{\sin kr'}{kr'} \sim 1$. Thus, the order of magnitude of the integral is $\frac{1}{\varkappa}$, and the condition for the range of validity of formula (4) has the form

$$\frac{|A|m}{\varkappa\hbar^2} \ll 1. \qquad (6')$$

In the case of rapid particles ($k \gg \varkappa$) as a result of the rapidly oscillation function ($e^{ikr'}\sin kr'$), the significant region in the integral in $r' \sim \frac{1}{k}$. Thus, the integral is of the order of $\frac{1}{k}$ and the condition for the validity of Born's approximation will be

$$\frac{|A|}{\hbar v} \ll 1 \qquad (6'')$$

(where we have used the velocity of the particle $v = \frac{\hbar k}{m}$).

The meaning of inequalities (6′) and (6″) will be entirely clear if they are considered together with the corresponding limiting expressions of equation (5) for the total cross section. Then, after dropping the numerical coefficients, we see that these two inequalities are equivalent to the condition

$$\sigma \ll \frac{1}{\varkappa^2} \quad \left(\text{or } \sqrt{\sigma} \ll \frac{1}{\varkappa}\right).$$

Thus, the condition for the validity of the Born approximation is that the scattering cross section be small relative to the square of the effective dimensions of the scattering field, or equivalently, that the scattering amplitude $\sqrt{\sigma}$ be small relative to the effective dimensions of the field $\frac{1}{\varkappa}$ (cf. the note to problem No. 3).

On the basis of the results of this problem, it is possible to consider in particular the scattering of an electron by a neutral atom (in other words, by a screened Coulomb field). For this purpose, in all the relations, it is necessary to replace A by $(-Ze^2)$ and $\frac{1}{\varkappa}$ by the Thomas-Fermi radius of the atom, equal to $\frac{\hbar^2}{Z^{1/3}me^2}$ (as an order of magnitude).

2. From the problem, the scattering potential (actually, the potential energy) has the form

$$U(r) = B\delta(r), \qquad (1)$$

where the origin of coordinates is taken at the center of force. The constant B obviously represent the space integral of the potential energy:

$$B = \int U(r)\, dV = \text{const.} \tag{2}$$

The differential effective cross section of elastic scattering per unit solid angle (in the center-of-mass system) is

$$\frac{d\sigma}{do} = \frac{\mu^2}{4\pi^2\hbar^4}\left| \int U(r)\, e^{iqr}\, dV \right|^2, \tag{3}$$

where μ is the reduced mass of the colliding particles, and $\hbar \boldsymbol{q} = \boldsymbol{p} - \boldsymbol{p}'$ is the change in the momentum of their relative motion.

Substituting (1) into (3) and using the definition of $\delta(\boldsymbol{r})$, we obtain

$$\frac{d\sigma}{do} = \frac{\mu^2 B^2}{4\pi^2\hbar^4}. \tag{4}$$

Thus, the scattering by a δ-function potential is isotropic and does not depend on velocity. As we know, the scattering of sufficiently slow particles by a potential well of finite dimensions has the same properties. The connection of these facts will be shown below.

The total scattering cross section is

$$\sigma = 4\pi \frac{d\sigma}{do} = \frac{\mu^2 B^2}{\pi\hbar^4}. \tag{5}$$

Remembering the definition of the contant $B\left(B = \int U\, dV\right)$, we can convince ourselves that equations (4) and (5) are obtained from the general Born relation (3) in all cases where $e^{iqr_{\text{eff}}} \approx 1$, i.e., $|qr_{\text{eff}}| \ll 1$. For this to hold for all scattering angles, it is necessary that (since $q_{\max} \sim k$) the inequalities $kr_{\text{eff}} \ll 1$ or $r_{\text{eff}} \ll \lambdabar$ be satisfied, where r_{eff} is the size of the region in which $U(r)$ is significantly different from zero (the "radius of the forces of interaction").

Thus, the δ-function potential which we have considered is an idealization of a potential of forces of interaction with a very small "radius," or, more precisely, a radius much smaller than the de Broglie wavelength of the relative motion of the colliding particles. Accordingly, a δ-function potential can be used, for instance, in a formal description of the interaction of sufficiently slow neutrons with protons or heavier nuclei [1, 22].

In these cases, the formal use of the Born approximation yields the correct result, despite the fact that perturbation theory is essentially inapplicable to a δ-function potential of the above type. Indeed, according to [1], Section 45, the condition that perturbation theory be valid for slow particles ($ka \lesssim 1$) has the form

$$|U| \ll \frac{\hbar^2}{\mu a^2}.$$

If we rewrite this condition in the form $|U|a^3 \ll \frac{\hbar^2}{\mu} a$ and remember that, for the δ-function potential we have considered, this same $|U|a^3$ is a fixed finite quantity, we see that for sufficiently small a (and certainly for $a = 0$) perturbation theory and consequently Born's formula are inapplicable.

From the equations (4) and (5) which we have obtained, we see that the formal use of the Born approximation can also give a correct result in the case where the true effective cross section does not depend on the velocity. In this case, it is not, strictly speaking, necessary to compute the scattering cross section from the given potential, but rather to "reduce" the constants of the potential to the known value of the cross section ([1], Section 123).

3. This problem is solved with problem No. 1 as a model.

Using the same notation, we have the following expression for the diferential effective cross section of scattering througy an angle θ within the solid-angle element $d\Omega$:

$$d\sigma = \frac{m^2}{4\pi^2\hbar^4}\left|\int U(r)\, e^{iqr}\, dr\right|^2 d\Omega =$$

$$= \frac{m^2}{4\pi^2\hbar^4}\left|2\pi U_0 \int_0^a r^2\, dr \int_{-1}^{1} e^{iqrx}\, dx\right|^2 d\Omega =$$

$$= \left(\frac{2mU_0}{\hbar^2}\cdot\frac{\sin qa - qa\cos qa}{q^3}\right)^2 d\Omega,$$

where $q = 2k\sin\frac{\theta}{2}$.

If we define the dimensionless quantity $qa = 2ka\sin\frac{\theta}{2}$ as a convenient variable, we have finally

$$d\sigma = \frac{4m^2U_0^2a^6}{\hbar^4}\,\varphi\left(2ka\sin\frac{\theta}{2}\right)d\Omega. \tag{1}$$

Here,

$$\varphi(x) \equiv \frac{(\sin x - x\cos x)^2}{x^6} = \frac{\pi}{2x^3}\,[J_{3/2}(x)]^2, \tag{2}$$

where $J_{3/2}$ is a Bessel function (cf. problem No. 7, Chapter II).

The function $\varphi(x)$ which gives the angular distribution of the scattered particles has a maximum (equal to $\frac{1}{9}$) at $x = 0$, i.e., at $\theta = 0$. After this, it performs rapidly damped oscillations (about the curve $\frac{1}{x^4}$, for $x \gg 1$), becoming zero at the roots of the equation $x = \operatorname{tg} x$ (of which the first is near $\frac{3\pi}{2}$. The maximum nearest to $x \approx 6$ is negligibly small relative to the maximum at $x = 0$.

Let us consider the two limiting cases.

For $ka \ll 1$, $\varphi(x) \approx \text{const} = \frac{1}{9}$, and thus the scattering is isotropic and independent of the velocity, as should be the case for slow particles.

For $ka \gg 1$, on the contrary, the scattering takes place almost entirely within a narrow cone about $\theta = 0$. The angle of this cone is $(\Delta\theta)_{\text{eff}} \sim \frac{1}{ka} \ll 1$. This follows directly from the fact that the function $\varphi(x)$ is significantly different from zero only for $x \lesssim 1$.

The total scattering cross section σ is obtained by integrating (1) over the angles. Noting that

$$d\Omega = 2\pi \sin\theta \, d\theta = 8\pi \sin\frac{\theta}{2} \, d\left(\sin\frac{\theta}{2}\right) = \frac{8\pi}{(2ka)^2} x \, dx,$$

we can transform to an integral over $x = 2ka \sin\frac{\theta}{2}$. Using the formula

$$G(y) \equiv \frac{1}{y^2} \int_0^y \frac{(\sin x - x\cos x)^2}{x^5} dx = \frac{1}{4y^2}\left(1 - \frac{1}{y^2} + \frac{\sin 2y}{y^3} - \frac{\sin^2 y}{y^4}\right), \tag{3}$$

we arrive at the result

$$\sigma = \frac{32\pi m^2 U_0^2 a^6}{\hbar^4} G(2ka). \tag{4}$$

The function $G(y)$ decreases monotonically from a maximum at $y = 0$ (equal to $\frac{1}{18}$). In particular, for $y \gg 1$ $G(y) \approx \frac{1}{4y^2}$. Hence, we obtain the expressions for σ in the two limiting cases:

$$\sigma \approx \frac{16\pi m^2 U_0^2 a^6}{9\hbar^4} \qquad (ka \ll 1), \tag{4'}$$

$$\sigma \approx \frac{2\pi m^2 U_0^2 a^4}{\hbar^4 k^2} = \frac{\pi m U_0^2 a^4}{\hbar^2 E} \qquad (ka \gg 1), \tag{4''}$$

where $E = \frac{\hbar^2 k^2}{2m}$ is the energy of the particle. For fast particles, $\sigma \sim \frac{1}{E}$, as should be the case.

The condition for the Born approximation to be valid is that the scattered wave $\psi^{(1)}$ be small relative to the incident wave $\psi^{(0)}$ near the scattering center.* If we replace $\left(A\frac{e^{-\varkappa r}}{r}\right)$ by $-U_0$, in equation (2″) of problem No. 1, we obtain the inequality

$$|\psi^{(1)}|_{r=0}=\frac{2mU_0}{\hbar^2 k}\left|\int_0^a e^{ikr'}\sin kr'\,dr'\right|=\frac{mU_0}{\hbar^2 k^2}\left|\int_0^{ka}(e^{2ix}-1)\,dx\right|\ll 1$$

or

$$\frac{mU_0}{\hbar^2 k^2}\sqrt{\sin^2 ka+(ka)^2-ka\sin 2ka}\ll 1. \tag{5}$$

For $ka\ll 1$, the range of validity will consequently be

$$\frac{mU_0 a^2}{\hbar^2}\ll 1, \tag{5'}$$

while for $ka\gg 1$

$$\frac{mU_0 a}{\hbar^2 k}=\frac{U_0 a}{\hbar v}\ll 1, \tag{5''}$$

where $v=\frac{\hbar k}{m}$ is the velocity of the particle.

If there is a level for the scattered particle in the well, which, as we know, is the case for $U_0\gtrsim\frac{\hbar^2}{ma^2}$(1 , Section 33), condition (5′) will certainly be violated, and thus the Born approximation is valid only for sufficiently rapid particles.

Comparing (4′) with (5′), and (4″) with (5″), we see (cf. problem No. 1) that it is always possible to formulate the range of validity of Born's approximation by the condition that the scattering amplitude $\sqrt{\sigma}$ be small relative to the width of the potential well a.

Obviously, the condition $\sqrt{\sigma}\ll a$ can also be obtained from the asymptotic formula

$$\psi\approx e^{ikz}+\frac{f(\theta)}{r}e^{ikr},$$

if it is extrapolated to the edge of the well ($r\sim a$) (this is justified for sharply breaking-off potential wells), and if it is remembered

---

*This condition is sufficient, but it can be too rigorous. Thus, even if it is not satisifed, the scattering through small angles (the significant angles) will be "Bornlike," although this will not be the case for scattering through large angles.

that $|f| = \sqrt{\frac{\sigma}{4\pi}}$, as an order of magnitude, where σ is the total scattering cross section.

4. The effective cross section for scattering through an angle θ, expressed in terms of a unit solid angle, is, according to Born's approximation,

$$\frac{d\sigma}{do} = \frac{m^2}{4\pi^2\hbar^4}\left|\int U(\boldsymbol{r})\, e^{i\boldsymbol{qr}}\, dV\right|^2, \tag{1}$$

where $|\boldsymbol{q}| \equiv q = 2k \sin\frac{\theta}{2}$, while the potential energy of the electron $U(\boldsymbol{r}) = U(r)$ is that given analytically and graphically in problems No. 13, Chapter II, and No. 1, Chapter VI.

To compute the Fourier components of $U(\boldsymbol{r})$ appearing in (1), it is simplest to proceed as follows.

The function $U(\boldsymbol{r})$ is connected with the electrostatic potential of the nucleus $\varphi(\boldsymbol{r})$ by the relation $U(\boldsymbol{r}) = -e\varphi(\boldsymbol{r})$. The potential $\varphi(\boldsymbol{r})$ satisfies Poisson's equation

$$\Delta\varphi = -4\pi\rho, \tag{2}$$

where ρ is the space density of the charge.

Let us expand (2) into a Fourier integral

$$\Delta\varphi = \int (\Delta\varphi)_{\boldsymbol{q}}\, e^{-i\boldsymbol{qr}}\, d\boldsymbol{q} = -4\pi \int \rho_{\boldsymbol{q}} e^{-i\boldsymbol{qr}}\, d\boldsymbol{q}. \tag{3}$$

On the other hand, applying the Laplacian to the Fourier expansion of $\varphi(\boldsymbol{r})$, we have

$$\Delta\varphi = \Delta\left(\int \varphi_{\boldsymbol{q}} e^{-i\boldsymbol{qr}}\, d\boldsymbol{q}\right) = \int \varphi_{\boldsymbol{q}} \Delta(e^{-i\boldsymbol{qr}})\, d\boldsymbol{q} = -\int \varphi_{\boldsymbol{q}} q^2 e^{-i\boldsymbol{qr}}\, d\boldsymbol{q}. \tag{4}$$

Comparing (3) and (4), we obviously obtain

$$\varphi_{\boldsymbol{q}} q^2 = 4\pi\rho_{\boldsymbol{q}}.$$

Hence, substituting the expression for the Fourier components

$$\varphi_{\boldsymbol{q}} = \frac{1}{(2\pi)^3}\int \varphi(\boldsymbol{r})\, e^{i\boldsymbol{qr}}\, dV, \quad \rho_{\boldsymbol{q}} = \frac{1}{(2\pi)^3}\int \rho(\boldsymbol{r})\, e^{i\boldsymbol{qr}}\, dV,$$

we find

$$\int \varphi(\boldsymbol{r})\, e^{i\boldsymbol{qr}}\, dV = \frac{4\pi}{q^2}\int \rho(\boldsymbol{r})\, e^{i\boldsymbol{qr}}\, dV. \tag{5}$$

If we use the given condition that the charge density ρ is constant inside the nucleus and equal to zero outside of it, and if we express $\varphi(\boldsymbol{r})$ in terms of $U(\boldsymbol{r})$, we obtain

$$\int U(\boldsymbol{r})\, e^{i\boldsymbol{qr}}\, dV = -\frac{4\pi e\rho_0}{q^2}\int\limits_{r\leqslant R} e^{i\boldsymbol{qr}}\, dV, \tag{6}$$

where $\rho_0 = \frac{Ze}{\frac{4}{3}\pi R^3}$, and the integration is taken throughout the volume of the nucleus — a sphere of radius R (Ze is the charge of the nucleus).

We have already computed the integral appearing in (6) in problem No. 3:

$$\int_{r\leqslant R} e^{i\mathbf{qr}}\,dV = \frac{4\pi}{q^3}(\sin qR - qR\cos qR). \tag{7}$$

From (1), (6), and (7), after substitution of ρ_0, we finally obtain

$$\frac{d\sigma}{do} = \frac{36m^2}{\hbar^4}\cdot\frac{Z^2e^4}{q^4}\cdot\frac{(\sin qR - qR\cos qR)^2}{(qR)^6}. \tag{8}$$

The total scattering cross section which is obtained from (8) by integrating over $do = 2\pi\sin\theta\,d\theta = \frac{2\pi}{k^2}q\,dq$, is, of course, infinite. This is connected with the fact that, at distances $r > R$, the scattering is an ordinary Coulomb field.

The function

$$\varphi(x) = \frac{(\sin x - x\cos x)^2}{x^6} \qquad (x \equiv qR)$$

which appears in the angular distribution (8) of the scattered electrons is characterized in detail in problem No. 3. This function has the form of rapidly damped oscillations with a sharp, predominant first maximum $\varphi(0) = \frac{1}{9}$. In addition to this function, the angular distribution (8) contains a "Rutherford" factor $\frac{1}{q^4} \sim \frac{1}{\sin^4\frac{\theta}{2}}$, which approaches infinity rapidly as $\theta \to 0$. This factor is responsible for the divergence of the total scattering cross section.

The characteristic parameter of the distribution function (8) is the dimensionless quantity

$$qR = 2kR\sin\frac{\theta}{2}. \tag{9}$$

For $qR \ll 1$, the function $\varphi(qR)$ can be expanded into a series of powers of qR:

$$\varphi(qR) = \frac{1}{9} - \frac{1}{45}(qR)^2 + O[(qR)^4].$$

In this case, after substitution of $q = 2\,\frac{mv}{\hbar}\sin\frac{\theta}{2}$, expression (8) assumes the form

$$\frac{d\sigma}{do} = \left(\frac{Ze^2}{2mv^2}\right)^2 \frac{1}{\sin^4\frac{\theta}{2}}\left\{1 - \frac{1}{5}(qR)^2 + O\left[(qR)^4\right]\right\}. \tag{10}$$

The main term in (10) represents the Rutherford scattering cross section of electrons by a Coulomb point charge Ze. From (10), it is seen that, for $R = 0$, the Rutherford relation represents an exact solution of the given problem, as we would expect. For $R \neq 0$, the scattering cross section for any given angle θ is somewhat smaller than the Rutherford cross section (this is obviously connected with the decrease of the depth of the potential well in the transition from $R = 0$ to $R \neq 0$).

Let us study, moreover, the form of the angular distribution function (8) for a fixed $R \neq 0$ and different electron velocities. We shall consider two limiting cases.

1. $kR \ll 1$ (slow electrons).

In this case, according to (9), $qR \ll 1$ for all scattering angles θ. Therefore, the scattering cross section assumes a "quasi-Rutherford" form (10). The physical meaning of this result consists of the fact that, in the given case, the de Broglie wavelength of the electron $\lambda\!\!\!^{-} = \frac{1}{k} \gg R$, and thus by far the greater part of the wave packet corresponding to the electron is outside the nucleus, in the region of the ordinary Coulomb field.

2. $kR \gg 1$ (fast electrons).

When we consider that the function $\varphi(qR)$ is significantly different from zero only for $qR \lesssim 1$, we can conclude from (9) that the electrons are scattered chiefly forward, in a narrow cone about $\theta = 0$ forming an angle $(\Delta\theta)_{\text{eff}} \sim \frac{1}{kR} \ll 1$.

In particular, for the smallest angles $\theta \ll \frac{1}{kR}$, we have $qR \ll 1$. Therefore, in this region of angles, the scattering is described in the first approximation by Rutherford's formula.

In conclusion, we note that we could have indicated the region where Rutherford's formula is approximately correct without any computations, directly from the initial relation (1). Indeed, because of the oscillating factor e^{iqr} under the integral, the significant distances in this integral are

$$r_{\text{eff}} \lesssim \frac{1}{q}.$$

Obviously, the condition that Rutherford's relation be correct is the inequality

$$r_{\text{eff}} \gg R,$$

which is necessarily equivalent to the previous condition $qR \ll 1$.

5. A neutron interacts with the electric field $\mathcal{E}$, in which it is moving through its magnetic moment $\boldsymbol{\mu}$. Let us consider a frame of reference K associated with a heavy center (for instance, a heavy nucleus with a charge Ze), confining ourselves to the case of non-relativistic velocities of the neutrons, $v \ll c$. In this case, it follows from electrodynamics [5, 21] that a neutron has an electric moment $\boldsymbol{d} = \frac{1}{c}(\boldsymbol{v} \times \boldsymbol{\mu})$ in the frame of reference K relative to which it is moving with a velocity $\boldsymbol{v}$. Consequently, the classical potential energy of the interaction of the moving neutron with the Coulomb field, $U = -\boldsymbol{d}\mathcal{E}$, is

$$U = -\frac{1}{c}(\boldsymbol{v} \times \boldsymbol{\mu})\frac{Ze\boldsymbol{r}}{r^3} = -\frac{Ze}{Mc}\frac{(\boldsymbol{r} \times \boldsymbol{p})\boldsymbol{\mu}}{r^3}, \tag{1}$$

where $\boldsymbol{p}$ is the momentum of the neutron, M is its mass, and $\boldsymbol{r}$ is its radius vector relative to the center of the Coulomb field.

In quantum mechanics, all the quantities appearing in (1) must be replaced by the corresponding operators. We shall solve the problem in the space of the quantities $\boldsymbol{r}$ and s_z (s_z is the component of the spin of the neutron along some axis). Accordingly, we shall replace $\boldsymbol{p}$ by $\hat{\boldsymbol{p}}$, and $\boldsymbol{\mu}$ by the operator $\hat{\boldsymbol{\mu}}$, which is equal to $-\alpha_n \frac{e\hbar}{2Mc}\hat{\boldsymbol{\sigma}}$, where $\hat{\boldsymbol{\sigma}}$ is twice the Pauli spin vector, and $\alpha_n \approx 1.9$ is the absolute value of the magnetic moment of the neutron measured in nuclear magnetons $\frac{e\hbar}{2Mc}$. Thus, the operator for the energy of the interaction of the neutron with the Coulomb field has the form

$$\hat{U} = \alpha_n \frac{Ze^2\hbar}{2M^2c^2} \cdot \frac{\hat{\sigma}(\boldsymbol{r} \times \hat{\boldsymbol{p}})}{r^3}. \tag{2}$$

We note that this operator does not need to be symmetrized, since it is a product of commuting Hermitian operators* and is thus itself Hermitian.

It is easily seen that in our case, where the Ψ-function contains a spin factor and U is an operator, the formula for the scattering amplitude is still completely correct (see problem No. 7)

$$f(\boldsymbol{k}) = -\frac{M}{2\pi\hbar^2}\int e^{-i\boldsymbol{k}\boldsymbol{r}}\hat{U}\Psi\, dV, \tag{3}$$

---

*Indeed, the commutativity of the spin operator with the "position" operators is trivial, while the angular-momentum operator $(\boldsymbol{r} \times \hat{\boldsymbol{p}})$ acts only on the angular coordinates θ and φ, and therefore commutes with $\frac{1}{r^3}$.

where $\boldsymbol{k}$ is the propagation vector of the scattered neutron. In the Born approximation, we replace Ψ in the right member of (3) by the unperturbed wave function of the neutron $\Psi^{(0)}$:

$$\Psi \approx \Psi^{(0)} = e^{i\boldsymbol{k}_0\boldsymbol{r}}\chi, \tag{4}$$

where $\boldsymbol{k}_0$ is the propagation vector of the incident neutron, and χ is its spin function (containing two components).

Substituting (2) and (4) into (3), we have

$$f(\boldsymbol{k}) = -\frac{\alpha_n}{4\pi}\frac{Ze^2}{\hbar Mc^2}\int e^{-i\boldsymbol{k}\boldsymbol{r}}\frac{\boldsymbol{\sigma}}{r^3}(\boldsymbol{r}\times\hat{\boldsymbol{p}})\,e^{i\boldsymbol{k}_0\boldsymbol{r}}\chi\,dV. \tag{5}$$

By using the equation $\hat{\boldsymbol{p}}e^{i\boldsymbol{k}_0\boldsymbol{r}} = \hbar\boldsymbol{k}_0 e^{i\boldsymbol{k}_0\boldsymbol{r}}$ and the notation $\boldsymbol{q} \equiv \boldsymbol{k}_0 - \boldsymbol{k}$, we can reduce (5) to the form

$$f(\boldsymbol{k}) \equiv f(\boldsymbol{q}) = \frac{\alpha_n}{4\pi}\frac{Ze^2}{Mc^2}(\hat{\boldsymbol{\sigma}}\chi)\left(\boldsymbol{k}_0\times\int\frac{\boldsymbol{r}}{r^3}e^{i\boldsymbol{q}\boldsymbol{r}}\,dV\right). \tag{6}$$

The integral appearing in the vector product is a vector obviously directed along $\boldsymbol{q}$. Therefore,

$$\begin{aligned}\int\frac{\boldsymbol{r}}{r^3}e^{i\boldsymbol{q}\boldsymbol{r}}\,dV &= \frac{\boldsymbol{q}}{q}\int\frac{(\boldsymbol{q}\boldsymbol{r})}{q}e^{i\boldsymbol{q}\boldsymbol{r}}\frac{dV}{r^3} = 2\pi\frac{\boldsymbol{q}}{q}\int_0^\infty dr\int_{-1}^{1}xe^{iqrx}\,dx = \\ &= 2\pi\frac{\boldsymbol{q}}{q}\int_0^\infty\frac{d}{d(iqr)}\left(2\frac{\sin qr}{qr}\right)dr = 2\pi\frac{\boldsymbol{q}}{q}\frac{2i}{q} = 4\pi i\frac{\boldsymbol{q}}{q^2}.\end{aligned} \tag{7}$$

Substituting (7) into (6), we obtain

$$f(\boldsymbol{q}) = i\alpha_n\frac{Ze^2}{Mc^2}(\hat{\boldsymbol{\sigma}}\chi)\frac{[\boldsymbol{k}_0\times\boldsymbol{q}]}{q^2}. \tag{8}$$

If we consider that $\boldsymbol{k}_0\times\boldsymbol{q} = \boldsymbol{k}_0\times(\boldsymbol{k}_0 - \boldsymbol{k}) = \boldsymbol{k}\times\boldsymbol{k}_0$, or, using the unit vector $\boldsymbol{n}$ of the normal to the scattering plane,

$$\boldsymbol{k}\times\boldsymbol{k}_0 = \boldsymbol{n}k^2\sin\theta \tag{9}$$

(where $k = k_0$, and θ is the scattering angle), and if we substitute $q = 2k\sin\frac{\theta}{2}$, we can reduce (8) to the form

$$f(\boldsymbol{q}) = i\frac{\alpha_n}{2}\frac{Ze^2}{Mc^2}\operatorname{ctg}\frac{\theta}{2}\,\boldsymbol{n}\hat{\boldsymbol{\sigma}}\chi. \tag{10}$$

If the scattering amplitude $f(\boldsymbol{q})$ were scalar, then the scattering cross section per unit solid angle $\frac{d\sigma}{d\omega}$ would simply be equal to $|f|^2$, in view of the normalization of the function $\Psi^{(0)}$ which we have selected; see (4)]. Since in the given case $f(\boldsymbol{q})$ is a two-component quantity (a second-rank spinor), $\frac{d\sigma}{do}$ is equal to the scalar product f^+f, where the + sign indicates the Hermitian conjugate. Since $(\hat{\sigma}\chi)^+ = \chi^+(\hat{\sigma})^+ = \chi^+\hat{\sigma}$, we have

$$f^+(\boldsymbol{q}) = -i\frac{\alpha_n}{2}\frac{Ze^2}{Mc^2}\operatorname{ctg}\frac{\theta}{2}\chi^+\boldsymbol{n}\hat{\boldsymbol{\sigma}}. \tag{10'}$$

By forming the scalar product of the spinors (10) and (10′) and by remembering that $(\boldsymbol{n}\boldsymbol{\sigma})^2 = 4(\boldsymbol{n}\hat{\boldsymbol{s}})^2 = 1$ (see problem No. 4, Chapter VIII) and $\chi^+\chi = 1$ (the normalization), we obtain the scattering cross section for which we have been looking:

$$\frac{d\sigma}{do} = f^+f = \frac{\alpha_n^2}{4}\left(\frac{Ze^2}{Mc^2}\right)^2 \operatorname{ctg}^2\frac{\theta}{2}. \tag{11}$$

This cross section decreases monotonically as the scattering angle θ increases, becoming zero at $\theta = \pi$ and infinite at $\theta = 0$. The total cross section diverges logarithmically at small scattering angles.

We also note that the cross section (11) does not depend explicitly on the energy and does not contain the quantum-mechanical constant $\hbar$.

Let us determine the range of validity of the above relation for the case of the scattering of neutrons by a heavy atom. The scattering mechanism which we have considered must occur if the field is practically a Coulomb field at distances r_{eff} which are significant in the mechanism. In other words, for the mechanism to occur, it is necessary that the condition $R \ll r_{\text{eff}} \ll a$ hold, where R is the radius of the nucleus, and a is the Thomas-Fermi radius of the atom. It is seen from (6) that the order of magnitude of r_{eff} is given by the relationship $qr_{\text{eff}} \sim 1$. Accordingly, $r_{\text{eff}} \sim \frac{1}{q} \approx \frac{1}{k\theta}$. Hence, we obtain the condition for angles which are significant in the given scattering mechanism:

$$\frac{1}{ka} \ll \theta \ll \frac{1}{kR}. \tag{12}$$

After comparing (11) with (12), we conclude that the given scattering mechanism can play a significant role only for fairly fast neutrons, since only in this case does the interval (12) cover the small scattering angles (which are most significant).

Let us compute the contribution of collisions of the type we have considered to the total cross section. For $kR = \sqrt{\frac{2ME}{\hbar^2}}R \gtrsim 1$, which corresponds to a neutron energy $E \gtrsim 0.2$ Mev (for $Z \approx 80$-90), we have $\theta_{\text{eff}} \ll 1$. Therefore, according to (11) and (12),

$$\sigma = \frac{\alpha_n^2}{4}\left(\frac{Ze^2}{Mc^2}\right)^2 \int \operatorname{ctg}^2\frac{\theta}{2}\, do \approx$$

$$\approx \frac{\alpha_n^2}{4}\left(\frac{Ze^2}{Mc^2}\right)^2 8\pi \int\limits_{1/ka}^{1/kR} \frac{1}{\theta^2}\,\theta\, d\theta = 2\pi\alpha_n^2\left(\frac{Ze^2}{Mc^2}\right)^2 \ln\frac{a}{R}.$$

Assuming $R \approx 1.2\cdot 10^{-13}A^{1/3}$ cm, and $a \approx 0.5\cdot 10^{-8}Z^{-1/3}$ cm, and substituting $\alpha_n \approx 1.9$, $\frac{e^2}{Mc^2} = \frac{m}{M}\frac{e^2}{mc^2} = \frac{1}{1840}\cdot 2.8\times 10^{-13}$ cm, we obtain

$$\sigma \approx 5\cdot 10^{-31} Z^2 \ln\frac{4.5\cdot 10^4}{(AZ)^{1/3}}\ \text{cm}^2.$$

For lead ($Z = 82$), this yields $\sigma \approx 2.5\cdot 10^{-26}$ cm^2.

This quantity is small relative to the cross section of the nuclear scattering of neutrons, which is of the order of magnitude of 10^{-24} cm^2 for energies of the order of one Mev. Therefore, the validity of the Born approximation which we have used is limited by the nuclear scattering of neutrons: at distances $r_{\text{eff}} \sim \frac{1}{q}$, which play the significant role in the electrostatic scattering considered above, it is necessary that the distortion of the incident neutron wave by the nuclear forces be small. We shall not consider this in greater detail.*

6. As specified in the problem, the potential energy of the scattered particle in the scattering field has the form

$$U = \frac{\alpha}{r^n}, \tag{1}$$

where α and n are constants. Thus, this potential with the power factor contains only one dimensional constant.**

As a consequence, the cross section σ can be formed by combining all the quantities appearing in the problem, namely the mass of the particle m, its velocity v, the field constant a, and the quantum-mechanical constant $\hbar$. Let us express the dimensions of

---

*As regards the actual electromagnetic scattering, the condition that the scattered wave $\frac{f(q)}{r}e^{ikr}$ be small relative to the incident wave $e^{i\kappa_0 r}$ for $r \sim \frac{1}{q}$ reduces, according to (10), to the inequality

$$|f(q)\,q| \sim 2\frac{Ze^2}{Mc^2}k\cos\frac{\theta}{2} \approx 2\frac{Ze^2}{Mc^2}k \ll 1,$$

which is well satisfied in the region of energies which we are considering.

**As distinguished from a potential of the form $Ae^{-\varkappa r}$, the potential of a spherical "rectangular" well of radius α, etc., which contains two dimensional constants.

all these quantities in terms of M, L, and T — the dimensions of mass, length, and time:

$$[m] = M; \quad [v] = LT^{-1}, \quad [\hbar] = [\text{erg sec}] = ML^2T^{-1}; \quad [\alpha] = [\text{erg cm}^n] = ML^{n+2}T^{-2}. \tag{2}$$

From these, it is necessary to form a quantity with the dimensions of the cross section (L^2):

$$\sigma \sim m^{x_1} v^{x_2} \alpha^{x_3} \hbar^{x_4}, \tag{3}$$

where x_1, x_2, x_3, x_4 are numbers which must be determined on the basis of dimensional considerations.

According to (2), formula (3) corresponds to the following dimensional equation:

$$L^2 = M^{x_1+x_3+x_4} L^{x_2+(n+2)x_3+2x_4} T^{-x_2-2x_3-x_4}.$$

By equating the power indices of M, L, and T on the two sides of this equation to one another (we remember that the dimensions of M, L, and T are independent), we obtain the following equations for x_1, x_2, x_3, and x_4:

$$\left.\begin{aligned} x_1 + x_3 + x_4 &= 0, \\ x_2 + (n+2)x_3 + 2x_4 &= 2, \\ -x_2 - 2x_3 - x_4 &= 0. \end{aligned}\right\} \tag{4}$$

Thus, at first sight, it seems that we have three equations for four unknowns. However, since, according to the problem, we are to confine ourselves to the Born approximation, we can assert that the scattering cross section [which is proportional to the square of the matrix elements of a transition $\int U(r) e^{iqr} dV$] can contain α only in the form α^2 [cf. (1)]. Consequently, $x_3 = 2$.

If we substitute this value of x_3 into (4), and if we solve the resulting system of three equations with three unknowns, we find:

$$\left.\begin{aligned} x_1 &= 2(n-2), \\ x_2 &= 2(n-3), \\ x_4 &= 2(1-n). \end{aligned}\right\} \tag{5}$$

Thus, we finally obtain [see (3)]*:

$$\sigma \sim m^{2(n-2)} v^{2(n-3)} \alpha^2 \hbar^{2(1-n)}. \tag{6}$$

---

*For $n \leqslant 2$, when, as we know, the total scattering cross section σ does not exist ($=\infty$), we shall be speaking about the differential scattering cross section per unit solid angle $\frac{d\sigma}{d\Omega}$ (for scattering angles $\theta \sim 1$).

From relation (6), it is possible to draw some interesting conclusions for a number of special cases.

First of all, we note that for $n=1$ (a Coulomb field), the quantum-mechanical constant $\hbar$ drops from σ. To some extent, this explains the fact that the cross section for Coulomb scattering as computed in classical mechanics is exactly the same as that computed in quantum mechanics.* It is seen from formula (6) that no other such coincidence occurs for any other scattering potential (at least for potentials varying according to some power of the distance).

Moreover, it is seen from (6) that for $n=2$ the cross section does not depend on the mass of the particle. From the results of problem No. 9, it follows that this property is correct only in the Born approximation, and not for all velocities.

Finally, for $n=3$, the Born cross section is independent of velocity, according to relation (6) (see [1], problem No. 2 in Section 110, from which we see that in our dimensional estimate of the cross section, we have "missed" only the slowly changing logarithmic factor $\ln^2\frac{\text{const}}{q}$).

Of course, we could have obtained relation (6) directly from Born's relation

$$d\sigma=\frac{m^2}{4\pi^2\hbar^4}\left|\int U(r)\,e^{i\mathbf{q}\mathbf{r}}\,dV\right|^2 d\Omega \qquad \left(q\equiv\frac{2mv}{\hbar}\sin\frac{\theta}{2}\right)$$

by performing the change of variables $r\to qr$ under the integral sign. However, in our discussion, we have not used the explicit form of $d\sigma$.

7. The Schrödinger equation for our problem has the form

$$-\frac{\hbar^2}{2\mu}\Delta\psi+U\psi=E\psi.$$

Defining as usual $k^2=\frac{2\mu E}{\hbar^2}$, we reduce the equation to the form

$$\Delta\psi+k^2\psi=\frac{2\mu}{\hbar^2}U\psi. \tag{1}$$

---

*Since the scattering cross sections are identical in both limiting cases (the classical limit $\frac{\alpha}{\hbar v}\gg 1$, and the Born limit $\frac{\alpha}{\hbar v}\ll 1$), it is fairly natural that the same cross section would also be obtained as a result of exact quantum-mechanical computation.

We shall regard the right member as inhomogeneous. Then, we shall have to find the solution of an inhomogeneous equation satisfying the familiar boundary conditions

$$\psi_{r\to\infty} \approx e^{ik_0 r} + f\frac{e^{ikr}}{r}.$$

Using the expression for Green's function of equation (1)

$$G(r-r') = -\frac{1}{4\pi}\frac{e^{ik|r-r'|}}{|r-r'|},$$

we easily find the required solution

$$\psi = e^{ik_0 r} - \frac{\mu}{2\pi\hbar^2}\int U(r')\psi(r')\frac{e^{ik|r-r'|}}{|r-r'|}dV'.$$

For large r, we have

$$\frac{e^{ik|r-r'|}}{|r-r'|} \approx \frac{e^{ikr}}{r}\cdot e^{-ikr'} \qquad (r\to\infty),$$

where

$$k = k\frac{r}{r}.$$

Hence,

$$\psi \approx e^{ik_0 r} - \frac{\mu}{2\pi\hbar^2}\frac{e^{ikr}}{r}\int dV' e^{-ikr'}U(r')\psi(r'),$$

and therefore

$$f(k) = -\frac{\mu}{2\pi\hbar^2}\int dV e^{-ikr}U(r)\psi(r).$$

This equation is convenient for various approximate computations.

Thus, substituting $\psi(r) \approx e^{ik_0 r}$, we obtain the scattering amplitued in the first Born approximation.

8. A wave function describing a wave which falls on and is scattered by a center of force has an asymptotic form (the coordinates are selected in the usual fashion)

$$\psi_{r\to\infty}(r) = \psi(r, \theta) = e^{ikr\cos\theta} + \frac{f(\theta)}{r}e^{ikr}. \tag{1}$$

At the same time, as we know, the total scattering cross section σ_s is

$$\sigma_s = \int |f(\theta)|^2 d\Omega, \tag{2}$$

where the integration is taken over the entire solid angle $\int d\Omega = 4\pi$.

Let us take into consideration the vector of the probability current density

$$j = -\frac{i\hbar}{2m}(\psi^* \operatorname{grad}\psi - \psi \operatorname{grad}\psi^*)$$

and find the value of the resulting flux (per unit time) through the surface of a sphere with an extremely large but finite radius R surrounding the center of force. This value is equal to

$$\oint jn\, dS = R^2 \int [j_r]_{r=R}\, d\Omega, \tag{3}$$

where n is a unit vector of the outer normal to the area $dS = R^2\, d\Omega$ and j_r is the radial component of the probability current

$$j_r = -\frac{i\hbar}{2m}\left(\psi^* \frac{\partial\psi}{\partial r} - \psi \frac{\partial\psi^*}{\partial r}\right). \tag{4}$$

In the case of purely elastic scattering, when function (1) completely describes the state of the scattered particle, the current (3) is equal to zero. This expresses the conservation of the number of particles.

In the case where there is also inelastic scattering, function (1) describes only particles with the same (initial) values of k, i.e., particles with the initial energy $\frac{\hbar^2 k^2}{2m}$. Therefore, the total flux through a distant spherical surface computed from (4) and (3) will differ from zero. When this flux is taken with the opposite sign, it obviously gives the excess of the number of particles entering the sphere over the number of particles emerging from it with unchanged k; that is, it yields the number of inelastically scattered particles (including the number of captured particles).

In accordance with this and from the definition of the effective cross section σ_c, we thus have

$$\sigma_c = -\frac{\oint jn\, dS}{j_{\text{inc}}}, \tag{5}$$

where j_{inc} is the current density of the incident particles (normalized in the same way as j in the numerator). If we compute j_{inc} from the ψ-function (1), we have ($v = \frac{\hbar k}{m}$ is the velocity of the incident particles):

$$j_{\text{inc}} = v\,|\psi_{\text{inc}}|^2 = v\,|e^{ikr}|^2 = v.$$

The calculation of $[j_r]_{r=R}$ from (4) and (1) gives

$$[j_r]_{r=R} = v\cos\theta + \frac{v\,|f(\theta)|^2}{R^2} + \frac{v}{2R}(1+\cos\theta)[f(\theta)e^{ikR(1-\cos\theta)} + f^*(\theta)e^{-ikR(1-\cos\theta)}] + \frac{i\hbar}{2mR^2}[f(\theta)e^{ikR(1-\cos\theta)} - f^*(\theta)e^{-ikR(1-\cos\theta)}]. \tag{6}$$

To obtain σ_c, it is necessary to integrate expression (6) over $d\Omega = 2\pi \sin\theta \, d\theta = -2\pi d(\cos\theta)$ after multiplying it by $R^2 d\Omega$. The integral of the first term of (6) is obviously equal to zero, while the integral of the last term (enclosed in brackets) is proportional to $\frac{1}{R}$ and disappears as $R \to \infty$. According to (2), the integral of the second term is equal to $v\sigma_s$.

In the two remaining integrals, the functions $e^{\pm ikR(1-\cos\theta)}$ oscillate infinitely rapidly for all $\theta \neq 0$ as $R \to \infty$. Therefore, in these integrals, only the value $\theta = 0$ is important.

By carrying $f(\theta)$ and $f^*(\theta)$ outside the integral sign at this point, and performing the remaining elementary integration over $\cos\theta$ and taking the limit $R \to \infty$, we finally find

$$\sigma_c = -\sigma_s + \frac{2\pi}{ik}[f(0) - f^*(0)] = -\sigma_s + \frac{4\pi}{k}\,\mathrm{Im}\, f(0),$$

which is what we were required to prove.*

It is easily seen that this relation is also correct for the more general case where the scattering amplitude also depends on the azimuth φ (since we made no use of the spherical symmetry of the scattering potential in the proof).

9. The phase theory of scattering expresses the effective scattering cross section in terms of the phases $\delta_l(k)$ which appear in the asymptotic expressions for the radial parts $R_{kl}(r)$ of the wave functions of particles with a given value of the energy $E = \frac{\hbar^2 k^2}{2\mu}$ and all possible values of the square of the angular momentum $M^2 = \hbar^2 l(l+1)$.

Setting $\lambda \equiv \frac{2\mu\alpha}{\hbar^2}$, we can write the wave equation for $R_{kl}(r)$ in the given case in the form

$$R''_{kl} + \frac{2}{r} R'_{kl} + \left[k^2 - \frac{\lambda + l(l+1)}{r^2}\right] R_{kl} = 0. \tag{1}$$

We shall look for a solution to equation (1) in the form

$$R_{kl}(r) = r^s f_{kl}(r), \tag{2}$$

where s is a constant which shall remain arbitrary for the moment.

---

*This equation is easily obtained from the general formulas of the phase theory of inelastic scattering, given for instance in [1], Section 117. Our more direct proof (proposed by A. B. Migdal) shows more clearly that this equation requires no assumptions other than the conservation of the number of particles.

By substituting (2) into (1), we obtain the following equation for f_{kl}:

$$r^2 f''_{kl} + 2(s+1) r f'_{kl} + [k^2 r^2 - \lambda - l(l+1) + s(s+1)] f_{kl} = 0.$$

Let us now select the constant s in such a way that the above equation will reduce to an equation whose solution is known.

Obviously, if we set $s = -\frac{1}{2}$, it will reduce to Bessel's equation (temporarily, we introduce the variable $x = kr$):

$$x^2 f''_{kl} + x f'_{kl} + \left[x^2 - \lambda - \left(l + \frac{1}{2}\right)^2\right] f_{kl} = 0. \tag{3}$$

The general solution of equation (3) has the form

$$f_{kl}(r) = c_1 J_p(kr) + c_2 N_p(kr),$$

where J_p and N_p are Bessel functions of the first and second kinds,

$$p = \sqrt{\lambda + \left(l + \frac{1}{2}\right)^2},$$

the arithmetic value of the root being taken (we recall moreover that $\lambda > 0$ from the given condition).

The radial function $R_{kl}(r)$ thus has the form

$$R_{kl}(r) = c_1 r^{-1/2} J_p(kr) + c_2 r^{-1/2} N_p(kr). \tag{4}$$

From the requirement that $R_{kl}(r)$ be regular at $r = 0$, which corresponds to the conservation of the number of particles in elastic scattering ([1], Sections 33 and 105), it follows that c_2 must be equal to zero.

Using the asymptotic expression for the Bessel function J_p, we find

$$R_{kl}(r) \underset{r \to \infty}{\approx} \text{const} \cdot \frac{\sin\left(kr - p\frac{\pi}{2} + \frac{\pi}{4}\right)}{kr}. \tag{5}$$

Comparing (5) with the asymptotic form of $R_{kl}(r)$, which contains the definition of the phase δ_l,

$$R_{kl}(r) \underset{r \to \infty}{\approx} \text{const} \cdot \frac{\sin\left(kr - \frac{l\pi}{2} + \delta_l\right)}{kr},$$

we obtain the required scattering phases

$$\delta_l = \frac{\pi}{2}\left(l + \frac{1}{2} - p\right) = -\frac{\pi}{2}\left[\sqrt{\left(l + \frac{1}{2}\right)^2 + \lambda} - \left(l + \frac{1}{2}\right)\right] < 0. \tag{6}$$

The negative value of δ_l corresponds to repelling forces.* We note that in the given case δ_l does not depend on the velocity of the particle $v = \frac{\hbar k}{\mu}$. Therefore, the angular distribution of elastically scattered particles, which, as we know, is given by the relation

$$\frac{d\sigma(\theta)}{do} = \left| \frac{1}{2ik} \sum_{l=0}^{\infty} (2l+1)(e^{2i\delta_l} - 1) P_l(\cos\theta) \right|^2,$$

is identical for all particles, differing only by the "scale" factor $\frac{1}{k^2} \sim \frac{1}{E}$.

For a strongly scattering field ($\lambda \gg 1$), we have, according to (6):

for $l \ll \sqrt{\lambda}$:

$$\delta_l \approx -\frac{\pi\sqrt{\lambda}}{2} = \text{const}, \quad \text{where} \quad |\delta_l| \gg 1;$$

for $l \gg \sqrt{\lambda}$:

$$\delta_l \approx -\frac{\pi}{2} \cdot \frac{\lambda}{2l+1},$$

where $|\delta_l| \ll 1$ only for $l \gg \lambda$.

In a weak field ($\lambda \ll 1$),

$$\delta_l \approx -\frac{\pi}{2} \cdot \frac{\lambda}{2l+1}, \quad \text{i.e.,} \quad |\delta_l| \ll 1.$$

We note that in this case the cross section σ does not contain the mass μ (cf. problem No. 6).

Because of the slowness of the decrease of δ_l as $l \to \infty$, the total cross section $\int d\sigma$ becomes infinite.** Indeed,

$$\int d\sigma = \frac{4\pi}{k^2} \sum_{l=0}^{\infty} (2l+1) \sin^2 \delta_l.$$

In this sum, the largest contribution comes from the large l, when $|\delta_l| \ll 1$. Accordingly,

---

*From this, it is apparent that there is an error in the sign of δ_l in the solution of this problem in [9], Chapter II, Section 6.

**In complete agreement with the general result for potentials which do not decrease faster than $\frac{1}{r^2}$ at infinity.

$$\sum_{l=0}^{\infty}(2l+1)\sin^2\delta_l \approx \sum_{l>1}^{\infty}(2l+1)\delta_l^2 \sim \sum_{l>1}^{\infty}\frac{1}{2l+1},$$

and this series diverges (like the integral $\int^{\infty}\frac{dl}{l}$ which corresponds to it).

10. In the given case, the scattering potential has the form

$$U(r)=\begin{cases}\infty & (r\leqslant a),\\ 0 & (r\geqslant a).\end{cases} \tag{1}$$

The condition of impenetrability of the sphere which is equivalent to this can be formulated by the following boundary condition:

$$\psi(r)|_{r=a}=0, \tag{2}$$

where $\psi(r)$ is the wave function of scattered particles, which, according to (1), satisfies the equation

$$\Delta\psi+k^2\psi=0 \qquad \left(k^2\equiv\frac{2\mu E}{\hbar^2}\right) \tag{3}$$

for $r\geqslant a$, and equals zero for $r\leqslant a$.

In addition to condition (2), we must impose on the ψ-function the requirement that asymptotically (as $r\to\infty$) it represents a superposition of the incident plane wave and of the scattered spherical wave:

$$\psi|_{r\to\infty}\approx e^{ikz}+\frac{f(\theta)}{r}e^{ikr}. \tag{4}$$

Let us expand the exact ψ-function into a series of Legendre polynomials:

$$\psi(r)=\sum_{l=0}^{\infty}R_{kl}(r)P_l(\cos\theta). \tag{5}$$

After substituting (5) into (3), we obtain the following equation for $R_{kl}(r)$:

$$R''_{kl}+\frac{2}{r}R'_{kl}+\left[k^2-\frac{l(l+1)}{r^2}\right]R_{kl}=0.$$

The solution of this equation (for example, cf. problem No. 7), Chapter II) is a superposition of linearly independent functions $\frac{1}{\sqrt{r}}Z_{l+\frac{1}{2}}(kr)$, where Z is a cylindrical function. If we consider the familiar expansion of a plane wave into Legendre polynomials and the asymptotic behavior of different cylindrical functions, we can conclude that $Z_{l+\frac{1}{2}}$ must be a superposition of Bessel functions $J_{l+\frac{1}{2}}$ and of Hankel functions of the first type $H^{(1)}_{l+\frac{1}{2}}$. Consequently, the wave function has the form

$$\psi = \sum_{l=0}^{\infty} \{(2l+1)\, i^l J_{l+\frac{1}{2}}(kr) + c_l H^{(1)}_{l+\frac{1}{2}}(kr)\} \sqrt{\frac{\pi}{2kr}}\, P_l(\cos\theta), \qquad (6)$$

where the c_l are constants which must be determined. The coefficients in the first component are obviously selected to make the sum of the corresponding terms equal to e^{ikz}.

According to (2), expression (6) must become zero at $r = a$. In view of the linear independence of the Legendre polynomials, this means that the equation

$$(2l+1)\, i^l J_{l+\frac{1}{2}}(ka) + c_l H^{(1)}_{l+\frac{1}{2}}(ka) = 0$$

must be satisfied. If we solve this for c_l and substitute it into (6), and if we combine the first part of the sum into e^{ikz}, we obtain

$$\psi = e^{ikz} - \sum_{l=0}^{\infty} (2l+1)\, i^l \frac{J_{l+\frac{1}{2}}(ka)}{H^{(1)}_{l+\frac{1}{2}}(ka)} \sqrt{\frac{\pi}{2kr}}\, H^{(1)}_{l+\frac{1}{2}}(kr) P_l(\cos\theta). \qquad (7)$$

Using the asymptotic expression for the Hankel function

$$H^{(1)}_{l+\frac{1}{2}}(kr) \approx \sqrt{\frac{2}{\pi kr}}\, (-i)^{l+1} e^{ikr} \qquad (r \to \infty)$$

we obtain the asymptotic expression for the ψ-function (7)

$$\psi|_{r\to\infty} \approx e^{ikz} + \frac{i}{kr} e^{ikr} \sum_{l=0}^{\infty} (2l+1) \frac{J_{l+\frac{1}{2}}(ka)}{H^{(1)}_{l+\frac{1}{2}}(ka)} P_l(\cos\theta).$$

Comparing this expression with (4), we obtain the scattering amplitude

$$f(\theta) = \frac{i}{k} \sum_{l=0}^{\infty} (2l+1) \frac{J_{l+\frac{1}{2}}(ka)}{H^{(1)}_{l+\frac{1}{2}}(ka)} P_l(\cos\theta). \qquad (8)$$

The differential effective scattering cross section is

$$d\sigma(\theta) = |f(\theta)|^2 d\Omega = \frac{1}{k^2}\left|\sum_{l=0}^{\infty}(2l+1)\frac{J_{l+\frac{1}{2}}(ka)}{H^{(1)}_{l+\frac{1}{2}}(ka)}P_l(\cos\theta)\right|^2 d\Omega. \tag{9}$$

If we integrate (9) over $d\Omega = 2\pi\sin\theta\, d\theta$, using the orthonormal property of the Legendre polynomials

$$\int_0^{\pi} P_l(\cos\theta)P_{l'}(\cos\theta)\sin\theta\, d\theta = \frac{2}{2l+1}\delta_{ll'},$$

we obtain the total scattering cross section

$$\sigma = \int |f(\theta)|^2 d\Omega = \frac{4\pi}{k^2}\sum_{l=0}^{\infty}(2l+1)\left|\frac{J_{l+\frac{1}{2}}(ka)}{H^{(1)}_{l+\frac{1}{2}}(ka)}\right|^2. \tag{10}$$

Equations (8), (9), and (10) represent an exact solution to the problem of the scattering by an impenetrable sphere.

The characteristic dimensionless parameter of the problem is the ratio $\frac{a}{\lambda\!\!\!^{-}} = ka$ (where $\lambda\!\!\!^{-}$ is the de Broglie wavelength of the scattered particles). Accordingly, let us investigate equations (8)-(10) in the two limiting cases.

1) $ka \ll 1$ (slow particles).

In this case, we can use expansions of the cylindrical functions into series of increasing powers of the argument ka. If we confine ourselves to the main terms of the corresponding expansions, we have

$$J_{l+\frac{1}{2}}(ka) \approx \sqrt{\frac{2}{\pi}}\frac{2^l l!}{(2l+1)!}(ka)^{l+\frac{1}{2}}, \tag{11}$$

$$H^{(1)}_{l+\frac{1}{2}}(ka) \approx -i\sqrt{\frac{2}{\pi}}\frac{(2l)!}{l!2^l}(ka)^{-\left(l+\frac{1}{2}\right)}. \tag{12}$$

Since the ratio $\dfrac{J_{l+\frac{1}{2}}(ka)}{H^{(1)}_{l+\frac{1}{2}}(ka)}$ which appears in the sums (8), (9), and (10) is thus proportional to $(ka)^{2l+1}$ in particular, the values of the terms in these sums decrease rapidly with increasing l. If we retain only the principal term of the sum (corresponding to $l = 0$), we find

$$f(\theta) \approx \frac{i}{k} \frac{J_{1/2}(ka)}{H_{1/2}^{(1)}(ka)} \approx -a. \tag{13}$$

Hence,

$$\frac{d\sigma}{d\Omega} = |f(\theta)|^2 \approx a^2. \tag{14}$$

Thus, in complete agreement with the general properties of the scattering of slow particles, the differential cross section does not depend on the scattering angle or on the velocity of the particles.*

The total scattering cross section is

$$\sigma = \int |f(\theta)|^2 d\Omega \approx 4\pi a^2, \tag{15}$$

i.e., four times the classical scattering cross section of an impenetrable sphere.

It is easily verified that, if we consider the succeeding terms in the expansion into powers of ka, we obtain

$$\sigma = 4\pi a^2 \left[1 + \frac{1}{3}(ka)^4 + \ldots\right]. \tag{16}$$

Thus, as the velocity of the particles increases from zero, the scattering cross section grows at first from the value $4\pi a^2$ corresponding to $v = 0$.

2) $ka \gg 1$ (fast particles).

In this case, there are two different significant regions of values of l from the point of view of the value of the ratio $\dfrac{J_{l+\frac{1}{2}}(ka)}{H^{(1)}_{l+\frac{1}{2}}(ka)}$.

For $l + \frac{1}{2} > ka\,(\gg 1)$, we can use the asymptotic expansions of the cylindrical functions for large values of the index to compute this ratio approximately. For the case with which we are concerned (where the argument is smaller than the index), these expansions have the form ([13], p. 355)

$$J_p\left(\frac{p}{\operatorname{ch}\alpha}\right) \approx \frac{\exp(p \operatorname{th}\alpha - p\alpha)}{\sqrt{2\pi p \operatorname{th}\alpha}} \left\{1 + \frac{1}{p}\left(\frac{1}{8}\operatorname{cth}\alpha - \frac{5}{24}\operatorname{cth}^3\alpha\right) + \ldots\right\}, \tag{17}$$

*We recall [2] that in classical mechanics these properties of the scattering by an impenetrable sphere are not approximate, but accurate, and that $\frac{d\sigma}{d\Omega} = \frac{1}{4}a^2$, $\sigma = \pi a^2$; i.e., the scattering cross section is simply equal to the geometric cross section of the sphere.

$$N_p\left(\frac{p}{\operatorname{ch}\alpha}\right)\approx\frac{\exp(p\alpha-p\operatorname{th}\alpha)}{\sqrt{\frac{\pi}{2}p\operatorname{th}\alpha}}\left\{1-\frac{1}{p}\left(\frac{1}{8}\operatorname{cth}\alpha-\frac{5}{24}\operatorname{cth}^3\alpha\right)+\ldots\right\},\quad(18)$$

where N_p is Neumann's function.

In the given case, $p=l+\frac{1}{2}\approx l$, $\frac{p}{\operatorname{ch}\alpha}=ka$, i.e., $\operatorname{ch}\alpha=\frac{l+\frac{1}{2}}{ka}\approx\frac{l}{ka}$. For values of l which are not too close to ka [strictly speaking, these are the values for which expansions (17) and (18) are actually correct] $\operatorname{ch}\alpha$ is considerably larger than unity. Accordingly, $\operatorname{cth}\alpha\sim 1$, and the expressions inside the braces in (17) and (18) are approximately equal to unity. Moreover, under this same condition, the index of the exponential $p(\operatorname{th}\alpha-\alpha)$ will be fairly large in terms of its modulus (while its sign is always negative). If we correspondingly restrict ourselves to the main term in the asymptotic expansion of $H^{(1)}_{l+\frac{1}{2}}(ka)=J_{l+\frac{1}{2}}(ka)+iN_{l+\frac{1}{2}}(ka)$, computed from (17) and (18), we have

$$\frac{J_{l+\frac{1}{2}}(ka)}{H^{(1)}_{l+\frac{1}{2}}(ka)}\approx-\frac{i}{2}e^{-(2l+1)(\alpha-\operatorname{th}\alpha)},\quad(19)$$

where

$$\alpha=\operatorname{argch}\left(\frac{l+\frac{1}{2}}{ka}\right).\quad(20)$$

Substituting (20) into (19), we obtain

$$\frac{J_{l+\frac{1}{2}}(ka)}{H^{(1)}_{l+\frac{1}{2}}(ka)}\approx-\frac{i}{2}\exp\left\{-(2l+1)\left[\operatorname{argch}\left(\frac{l+\frac{1}{2}}{ka}\right)-\sqrt{1-\left(\frac{ka}{l+\frac{1}{2}}\right)^2}\right]\right\}\quad(l>ka)\quad(21)$$

(of course, we can set $l+\frac{1}{2}\approx l$ everywhere in this formula).

According to (21), in the region $l > ka$, the ratio $\frac{J_{l+\frac{1}{2}}(ka)}{H^{(1)}_{l+\frac{1}{2}}(ka)}$ is less than unity and decreases very rapidly with increasing l.*

Let us now consider the region of values of l, for which $l+\frac{1}{2} < ka$. In this case, the asymptotic expansions of the cylindrical functions have the form ([13], p. 356)

$$J_p\left(\frac{p}{\cos\beta}\right) \approx \frac{\cos\left(p \operatorname{tg}\beta - p\beta - \frac{\pi}{4}\right)}{\sqrt{\frac{\pi}{2} p \operatorname{tg}\beta}}, \tag{22}$$

$$H_p^{(1)}\left(\frac{p}{\cos\beta}\right) \approx \frac{e^{i\left[p \operatorname{tg}\beta - p\beta - \frac{\pi}{4}\right]}}{\sqrt{\frac{\pi}{2} p \operatorname{tg}\beta}}. \tag{23}$$

In the given case, p is equal to $l+\frac{1}{2}$, as formerly, while $\cos\beta = \frac{l+\frac{1}{2}}{ka}$. For the ratio with which we are concerned, we obtain

$$\frac{J_{l+\frac{1}{2}}(ka)}{H^{(1)}_{l+\frac{1}{2}}(ka)} \approx \frac{1}{2}\left\{1 + e^{2i\left[\left(l+\frac{1}{2}\right)\arccos\frac{l+\frac{1}{2}}{ka} - \sqrt{k^2a^2 - \left(l+\frac{1}{2}\right)^2} + \frac{\pi}{4}\right]}\right\}. \tag{24}$$

By comparing this with the general formulas of the phase theory of scattering (see below, note to Problem 11), we conclude that

---

*In particular, in the limiting case $l \gg ka$, we have $\operatorname{argch}\frac{l+\frac{1}{2}}{ka} \approx \ln\frac{2l+1}{ka}$, etc. Thus, the modulus of ratio (21) basically becomes

$$\left|\frac{J_{l+\frac{1}{2}}(ka)}{H^{(1)}_{l+\frac{1}{2}}(ka)}\right| \sim \left(e\frac{ka}{2l+1}\right)^{2l+1} \sim \frac{(ka)^{2l+1}}{(2l+1)!} \text{ (cf. the case } ka \ll 1\text{)},$$

where we have used Stirling's formula $\left(\frac{2l+1}{e}\right)^{2l+1} \sim (2l+1)!$

the scattering phases δ_l are equal to*

$$\delta_l = \left(l + \frac{1}{2}\right) \arccos \frac{l + \frac{1}{2}}{ka} - \sqrt{k^2a^2 - \left(l + \frac{1}{2}\right)^2} - \frac{\pi}{4}. \tag{25}$$

From (25) and (21), it is apparent that the phases for $l + \frac{1}{2} < ka$ are not small, while for $l + \frac{1}{2} > ka$ they rapidly tend toward zero $\left(\frac{J_{l+\frac{1}{2}}}{H^{(1)}_{l+\frac{1}{2}}} \rightarrow 0\right)$. Therefore, in sums (8), (9), and (10), only the terms with $\left(l + \frac{1}{2}\right) < ka$ play an important role. For approximate computation of these sums, we can consequently restrict ourselves to summing over l up to $l_0 = ka - \frac{1}{2}$, substituting expression (24) for the ratio $J_{l+\frac{1}{2}} / H^{(1)}_{l+\frac{1}{2}}$:

$$f(\theta) = \frac{i}{2k} \left\{ \sum_{l=0}^{l_0} (2l+1) P_l(\cos\theta) + \right.$$

$$\left. + \sum_{l=0}^{l_0} (2l+1) P_l(\cos\theta) e^{2i\left[\left(l+\frac{1}{2}\right) \arccos \frac{l+\frac{1}{2}}{ka} - \sqrt{k^2a^2 - \left(l+\frac{1}{2}\right)^2} + \frac{\pi}{4}\right]} \right\} \tag{26}$$

$$\sigma = \frac{2\pi}{k^2} \left\{ \sum_{l=0}^{l_0} (2l+1) + \sum_{l=0}^{l_0} (2l+1) \cos 2 \left[\left(l + \frac{1}{2}\right) \times \right.\right.$$

$$\left.\left. \times \arccos \frac{l + \frac{1}{2}}{ka} - \sqrt{k^2a^2 - \left(l + \frac{1}{2}\right)^2} + \frac{\pi}{4} \right] \right\}. \tag{27}$$

The scattering amplitude (26) consists of two components. As we shall show below, the second of these describes the classical isotropic scattering, while the first gives the diffraction scattering through small angles. In the total cross section (27), the first

---

*Since, in the given case of fast particles, the wavelength $\lambda\!\!\!^{-}$ is much smaller than the dimensions of the scattering potential δ_l. it would have been possible to use the quasi-classical approximation to compute the phases ([1], p. 470). As we would expect, this yields the same result.

sum represents the sum of the total cross sections of classical scattering and diffraction scattering, while the second sum gives the part of the cross section connected with the interference of these two types of scattering. Since the classical scattering and the diffraction scattering take place in essentially different angles, the interference between these two types of scattering should be small. This fact is confirmed by the alternation of the signs of the terms of the second sum in (27). As a result of this alternation of the signs, the different components of the sum cancel one another, and the entire sum is small. If we neglect it, we obtain the following value for the total cross section:

$$\sigma \approx \frac{2\pi}{k^2} \sum_{l=0}^{l_0} (2l+1) = \frac{2\pi}{k^2} \frac{(2l_0+1)+1}{2} (l_0+1) \approx \frac{2\pi l_0^2}{k^2} \approx 2\pi a^2 \qquad (28)$$

(where we have used the fact that $l_0 \approx ka \gg 1$). Thus, the total scattering cross section is equal to twice the classical cross section. The reason for this lies in the intensity of the diffraction scattering through small angles $\theta \lesssim \frac{1}{ka}$, this diffraction scattering accounting for the value πa^2 of the total cross section (see below, Equation 50).

We shall now show that the second sum in the scattering amplitude (26) does indeed describe classical scattering. First of all, we note that, since this sum contains many terms with $l \gg 1$, we can use the asymptotic expression for large l for the Legendre polynomials ([1], p. 199)

$$P_l(\cos\theta) \approx \sqrt{\frac{2}{\pi\left(l+\frac{1}{2}\right)}} \frac{\sin\left[\left(l+\frac{1}{2}\right)\theta+\frac{\pi}{4}\right]}{\sqrt{\sin\theta}}. \qquad (29)$$

This expression is correct for $\theta \gg \frac{1}{l}$. Since l is large and classical scattering is isotropic, approximation (29) makes it possible for us to obtain the amplitude of classical scattering for by far the greater part of the region of angles with which we are concerned. Thus, the amplitude of the classical scattering assumes the form

$$f_{cl} = \frac{1}{k\sqrt{2\pi\sin\theta}} \sum_{l=0}^{l_0} \sqrt{l+\frac{1}{2}} \times$$

$$\times \left\{ e^{2i\left[\left(l+\frac{1}{2}\right)\arccos\frac{l+\frac{1}{2}}{ka} - \sqrt{k^2a^2-\left(l+\frac{1}{2}\right)^2} + \frac{\pi}{4}\right] + i\left(l+\frac{1}{2}\right)\theta + i\frac{\pi}{4}} - \right.$$

$$-e^{2i\left[\left(l+\frac{1}{2}\right)\arccos\frac{l+\frac{1}{2}}{ka}-\sqrt{k^2a^2-\left(l+\frac{1}{2}\right)^2}+\frac{\pi}{4}\right]-i\left(l+\frac{1}{2}\right)\theta-i\frac{\pi}{4}}\Bigg\}. \tag{30}$$

The exponential factors, regarded as functions of l, are rapidly oscillating functions (since their phases are large). In connection with this, the majority of the terms in the sum (30) cancel one another. The sum will be determined basically by the region of values of l which are close to the value at which one of the exponents has an extremum. To find this extremum, we set the derivative of the exponent equal to zero. After performing the necessary differentiation, we see that the first exponent does not have an extremum for any value of l. Therefore, the first sum in (30) is small and can be neglected. The condition for the extremum of the second exponent has the form

$$2\arccos\frac{l_e+\frac{1}{2}}{ka}-\theta=0. \tag{31}$$

Hence, the extreme value of $l_e+\frac{1}{2}$ is equal to

$$l_e+\frac{1}{2}=ka\cos\frac{\theta}{2}. \tag{32}$$

This equation expresses exactly the classical relationship between the impact parameter $\rho=\lambda\!\!\!^{-}\left(l+\frac{1}{2}\right)$ and the scattering angle θ:

$$\rho=a\cos\frac{\theta}{2}. \tag{32'}$$

Thus, for scattering through an angle θ, the important values of l are those equal to $l_e=k\rho-\frac{1}{2}$, where ρ is the impact parameter, i.e., the distance at which a particle must pass from the center to be scattered through an angle θ.

The change of the exponential near the extremum will be determined by the second derivative of the exponent with respect to l taken at the point of the extremum. For this quantity, we obtain the following expression:

$$-2i\frac{1}{\sqrt{k^2a^2-\left(l_e+\frac{1}{2}\right)^2}}=-\frac{2i}{ka\sin\frac{\theta}{2}}. \tag{33}$$

If we compute the value of the actual exponent for $l=l_e$, we obtain the following approximate expression for the exponential near the extremum:

$$\exp\left\{2i\left[\left(l+\frac{1}{2}\right)\arccos\frac{l+\frac{1}{2}}{ka}-\sqrt{k^2a^2-\left(l+\frac{1}{2}\right)^2}+\frac{\pi}{4}\right]-\right.$$
$$\left.-i\left(l+\frac{1}{2}\right)\theta-i\frac{\pi}{4}\right\}\approx\exp\left[-2ika\sin\frac{\theta}{2}+i\frac{\pi}{4}-i\frac{(l-l_э)^2}{ka\sin\frac{\theta}{2}}\right]. \quad (34)$$

Substituting this expression into (30), we obtain the following expression for the classical part of the scattering amplitude:

$$f_{cl}\approx-\sqrt{\frac{a}{4\pi k\sin\frac{\theta}{2}}}\,e^{-2ika\sin\frac{\theta}{2}+i\frac{\pi}{4}}\sum_{l=0}^{l_0}e^{-i\frac{(l-l_э)^2}{ka\sin\frac{\theta}{2}}} \quad (35)$$

(we have placed the coefficient $\sqrt{l+\frac{1}{2}}$ outside the summation sign at the point $l=l_э$).

In regard to this expression, it is necessary to make two remarks: 1) the summation in (35) is taken within finite limits $\left(l\leqslant l_0=ka-\frac{1}{2}\right)$. For the sum to be great, it is necessary that the extremum of the exponent of the exponential ($l_э$) lie within the region of summation: $l_э<l_0$. Using the value (32) for $l_э$, we see that this condition implies $\cos\frac{\theta}{2}<1$, and thus it is always satisfied. 2) In obtaining expression (34), we expanded the exponent into a series. For this to be correct, it is necessary that the succeeding terms of the expansion be small relative to unity for values of $(l-l_э)$ which are important in sum (35). The values of $\Delta l\equiv l-l_э$ which are important in sum (35) are of the order of $\sqrt{ka\sin\frac{\theta}{2}}$, since for large values of Δl the exponent is large and consequently the exponential oscillates rapidly. Let us now evaluate the magnitude of the next term of the expansion of the exponent for these values of Δl. If we differentiate (33) once again with respect to $l_э$, and proceed as usual, we have

$$\frac{1}{3}\frac{l_э+\frac{1}{2}}{\left[k^2a^2-\left(l_э+\frac{1}{2}\right)^2\right]^{3/2}}(\Delta l)^3\sim\frac{\operatorname{ctg}\frac{\theta}{2}}{\sqrt{ka\sin\frac{\theta}{2}}}. \quad (36)$$

For angles $\theta\sim1$, this expression is of the order $\frac{1}{\sqrt{ka}}\ll1$, and therefore the expansion (34) is correct. As $\theta\to0$, expression (36) tends toward infinity, and thus the condition for the validity of the expansion is violated. Let us evaluate the values of the angles at which this occurs. Because of the smallness of these angles, (36) assumes the form $\frac{1}{\sqrt{ka\theta^{3/2}}}$. Consequently, the range of validity of expansion (34) is given by the inequality

$$\theta \gg \theta_{min} \sim \frac{1}{(ka)^{1/3}}. \tag{37}$$

This condition is more rigorous than the condition for the validity of the approximate expression for Legendre polynomials $\theta \gg \frac{1}{l}$, which, from (32), reduces to the form $\theta \gg \frac{1}{ka}$. Nonetheless, because of the large value of ka, inequality (37) is correct for the greater part of the region of angles with which we are concerned.

Let us now compute the sum (35). We note that because of inequality (37) the region of values of Δl which is significant in this region is much greater than unity. Indeed,

$$\Delta l \sim \sqrt{ka \sin\frac{\theta}{2}} \gg (ka)^{1/3} \gg 1.$$

Thus, a large number of terms play a significant role in sum (35), and it is possible to replace the summation by integration. On the other hand, this region of values $\Delta l \lesssim \sqrt{ka}$ is much smaller than the region $0 < l < ka$ over which the summation or integration is taken. Therefore, the integration can be extended to infinity. Thus,

$$f_{cl} = -\sqrt{\frac{a}{4\pi k \sin\frac{\theta}{2}}}\, e^{-2ika \sin\frac{\theta}{2} + i\frac{\pi}{4}} \int_{-\infty}^{\infty} dl\, e^{-i\frac{(l-l_e)^2}{ka \sin\frac{\theta}{2}}}. \tag{38}$$

If we compute the integral in (38), we obtain the following final expression for the amplitude of the classical scattering:

$$f_{cl} = -\frac{1}{2}\, a e^{-2ika \sin\frac{\theta}{2}}. \tag{39}$$

Hence, we obtain for the differential cross section and the total cross section the expressions

$$\frac{d\sigma_{\text{cl}}}{d\Omega} = |f_{\text{cl}}|^2 = \frac{1}{4} a^2, \qquad \sigma_{\text{cl}} = \pi a^2. \tag{40}$$

Let us now consider the diffraction scattering. The amplitude describing this scattering is expressed by the first sum in (26)

$$f_{\text{diff}}\ (\theta) = \frac{i}{2k} \sum_{l=0}^{l_0} (2l+1) P_l(\cos\theta). \tag{41}$$

Let us compute first the scattering amplitude "exactly forward." According to (41), this amplitude is

$$f(0) = \frac{i}{2k} \sum_{l=0}^{l_0} (2l+1) \approx \frac{i}{2k} l_0^2 \approx \frac{i}{2} ka^2. \tag{42}$$

As we would expect (see Problem No. 8), the quantities (28) and (42) are connected by the relation

$$\sigma = \frac{4\pi}{k} \operatorname{Im} f(0).$$

According to (42), we have, moreover,

$$\left.\frac{d\sigma}{d\Omega}\right|_{\theta=0} = |f(0)|^2 = \frac{1}{4} k^2 a^4 = (ka)^2 \frac{a^2}{4}; \tag{43}$$

i.e., the intensity of scattering through the smallest angles is smaller than the intensity of the classical (isotropic) scattering by a factor of $(ka)^2 \gg 1$.

At the same time, since the order of magnitude of the total cross section (28) is no greater than that of the classical cross section, it is clear that the intensive diffraction scattering (43) can occur only in a narrow cone about $\theta = 0$, while for $\theta \sim 1$, $\frac{d\sigma}{d\Omega}$ should be equal (at least on the average) to its classical value. It is easy to evaluate the order of magnitude $\Delta\theta$ of the angle of the cone of diffraction scattering. On the basis of our discussion, the share of the diffraction scattering in the total scattering $2\pi a^2$ is πa^2. Considering (43), we obtain the condition

$$\pi a^2 \approx 2\pi \int_0^{\Delta\theta} |f(\theta)|^2 \sin\theta \, d\theta \sim$$

$$\sim 2\pi |f(0)|^2 \int_0^{\Delta\theta} \theta \, d\theta = \pi |f(0)|^2 (\Delta\theta)^2 = \frac{\pi a^2}{4}(ka)^2(\Delta\theta)^2.$$

Hence,

$$\Delta\theta \sim \frac{2}{ka}. \tag{44}$$

It is also possible to obtain this estimate of $\Delta\theta$ in another way. For angles which are not small, sum (41) is much smaller than its particular value (42) as a result of the mutual cancellation of the many oscillating terms — the Legendre polynomials. In the interval θ from zero to π, the polynomial $P_l(\cos\theta)$ has l roots. Therefore, the interval between two of its adjacent roots is $\sim \frac{\pi}{l}$. On the other hand, as $\theta \to 0$, all the $P_l \to 1$. It is clear that all the P_l will definitely have one sign (and accordingly will not cancel one another) in the interval of angles θ from zero to the first root of the most rapidly oscillating polynomial $\left(\sim \frac{\pi}{l_{\max}} = \frac{\pi}{l_0}\right)$.

Consequently, the interval of angles which is free from "interference" of the Legendre polynomials is equal to

$$\Delta\theta \sim \frac{\pi}{l_0} \approx \frac{\pi}{ka} \tag{44'}$$

as an order of magnitude, in agreement with (44).

Let us now examine in somewhat more detail the behavior of the scattering amplitude (and of the differential cross section) for angles $\theta \ll 1$. Since $l_0 \gg 1$, and because of the factor $(2l+1)$ in sum (41), the most important values are $l \gg 1$. But for $l \gg 1$ and $\theta \ll 1$ the approximate equation

$$P_l(\cos\theta) \approx J_0\left[\left(l + \frac{1}{2}\right)\theta\right] \qquad (l \gg 1, \quad \theta \ll 1) \tag{45}$$

([1], p. 198) is correct, where J_0 is the zeroth-order Bessel function. By substituting (45) into (41) and replacing the summation by integration (which is obviously legitimate), we obtain

$$f(\theta) \approx \frac{i}{2k} \int_0^{l_0} (2l+1) J_0\left[\left(l + \frac{1}{2}\right)\theta\right] dl = i\frac{a}{\theta} J_1(ka\theta) \quad (\theta \ll 1). \tag{46}$$

where we have used the well-known equation $\int xJ_0(x)\,dx = xJ_1(x)$. The differential cross section for scattering per unit solid angle is

$$\frac{d\sigma}{d\Omega} = |f(\theta)|^2 \approx \frac{a^2}{\theta^2}[J_1(ka\theta)]^2 \qquad (\theta \ll 1). \tag{47}$$

For the smallest angles $\theta \ll \frac{1}{ka}$, the Bessel function $J_1(ka\theta)$ can be replaced by $\frac{1}{2}ka\theta$. Therefore, in agreement with (43), the intensity of the scattering tends toward a constant limit

$$\frac{d\sigma}{d\Omega} \approx \frac{k^2a^4}{4} \qquad \left(\theta \ll \frac{1}{ka}\right). \tag{48}$$

On the contrary, for angles $\theta \gg \frac{1}{ka}$ (but, of course, $\theta \ll 1$), it is possible to use the asymptotic expression $J_1(x) \approx \sqrt{\frac{2}{\pi x}}\sin\left(x - \frac{\pi}{4}\right)$. This yields

$$\frac{d\sigma}{d\Omega} \approx \frac{2a}{\pi k}\,\frac{\sin^2\left(ka\theta - \frac{\pi}{4}\right)}{\theta^3} \qquad \left(\frac{1}{ka} \ll \theta \ll 1\right). \tag{49}$$

In this region of angles, the cross section, which oscillates rapidly, decreases rapidly as the scattering angle increases.

By comparing expressions (48) and (49), we arrive at the former conclusion that the angular distribution of the scattered particles has a sharp diffraction maximum about $\theta = 0$ with a width $\Delta\theta \sim \frac{1}{ka}$. It is apparent from (49) that the angular distribution has secondary maximums, but their intensity is much smaller than the intensity (48) of the main maximum.

In conclusion, it will be useful to verify the assertion we made above that the contribution of the diffraction scattering to the total cross section is πa^2. If we integrate (47) over the angles, extending the integration to ∞ (because of the rapid decrease of the function under the integral) and using the formula $\int_0^\infty \frac{J_1^2(x)}{x}\,dx = \frac{1}{2}$, we find

$$\sigma_{\text{diff}} = \int_{(\theta \ll 1)} |f(\theta)|^2\,d\Omega \approx a^2 2\pi \int_0^\infty \frac{J_1^2(ka\theta)}{\theta^2}\,\theta\,d\theta = \pi a^2 \quad (ka \gg 1). \tag{50}$$

We emphasize that no matter how narrow the diffraction angle becomes with increasing ka, the total cross section for scattering is constant and equal to (50).

We plot here an example of the angular-distribution curve $\frac{d\sigma}{d\Omega}$ for $ka \gg 1$. The horizontal line represents the classical intensity of scattering $\frac{d\sigma_{cl}}{d\Omega} = \frac{a^2}{4}$.

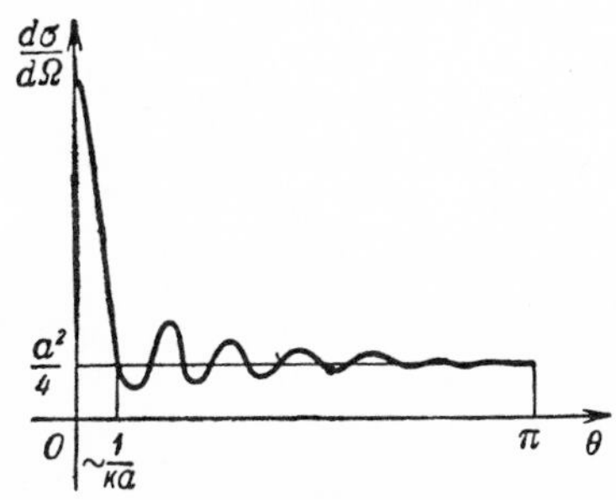

11. We are required to obtain a simple but nonrigorous solution of the preceding problem for two limiting cases. The general formula for the total cross section for scattering has the form

$$\sigma = \frac{4\pi}{k^2} \sum_{l=0}^{\infty} (2l+1) \sin^2 \delta_l. \tag{1}$$

1) $ka \ll 1$ (slow particles).

In this case, s-scattering predominates (scattering with $l=0$). The radial function corresponding to the value $l=0$ has the form $\frac{\sin(kr+\delta_0)}{r}$ in the region $r \geqslant a$. The requirement that this function becomes zero at the edge of the scattering sphere, i.e., at $r=a$, defines δ_0 directly:

$$\delta_0 = -ka. \tag{2}$$

The non-single-valuedness of δ_0, which arises formally because of the periodicity of the sine, is removed here as a result of the requirement that $\delta_0 = 0$ in the limit of free motion ($a=0$). Since $ka \ll 1$, we have $|\delta_0| \ll 1$, Therefore,

$$\sigma \approx \frac{4\pi}{k^2} \sin^2 \delta_0 \approx \frac{4\pi}{k^2} \delta_0^2 = 4\pi a^2.$$

2) $ka \gg 1$ (rapid particles).

First, let us evaluate the maximum value of l which is important in scattering. Since $\lambda\!\!\!^{-} \ll a$ in the given limiting case, we can use approximately the classical concept of the "distance of the greatest approach" r_0 of the particle to the scattering center.* Since the potential is equal to zero outside the sphere, r_0 is determined by equating the energy to the centrifugal potential energy

$$\frac{\hbar^2 k^2}{2\mu} = \frac{\hbar^2 l(l+1)}{2\mu r_0^2},$$

Hence,

$$r_0 = \frac{\sqrt{l(l+1)}}{k} \approx \frac{l}{k}.$$

It is obvious that only particles for which $r_0 \leqslant a$ will be significantly affected by the scattering field. Hence, we obtain the interval of values of l which are significant in scattering**:

$$l \leqslant l_0 \approx ka. \tag{4}$$

For these values of l, the phases δ_l are large, while for $l > l_0$ they are small.*** Therefore, the summation in (1) can be taken only up to $l_0 = ka$ as an approximation. Moreover, since $\sin\delta_l$ oscillates rapidly for $l < l_0$ as a function of l, it is possible to replace $\sin^2\delta_l$ by its average value $\frac{1}{2}$. If we consider in addition the fact that $l_0 = ka \gg 1$, we obtain

$$\sigma \approx \frac{4\pi}{k^2} \sum_{l=0}^{l_0} (2l+1)\sin^2\delta_l \approx \frac{2\pi}{k^2} l_0^2 = 2\pi a^2.$$

---

*In the given case, r_0 is identical with the impact parameter $\rho = \frac{M}{\mu v} = \frac{\hbar\sqrt{l(l+1)}}{\hbar k} \approx \frac{l}{k}$.

**It is interesting to note that criterion (4) leads to the correct result ($l_{\text{эфф}} = 0$) even in the case $ka \ll 1$, for which the quasi-classical approach (the use of r_0, etc.) is not legitimate.

***The explicit formulas for the phases are obtained without difficulty by comparing the exact formula (8) obtained in the preceding problem with the general formula of phase theory for $f(\theta)$: $\frac{J_{l+\frac{1}{2}}(ka)}{H^{(1)}_{l+\frac{1}{2}}(ka)} = -\frac{1}{2}(e^{2i\delta_l}-1)$, etc. (see above, Problem 10, Equation 25).

12. The potential energy of the particle is equal to $-U_0$ for $r \leqslant a$, and to zero for $r \geqslant a$. Thus, the Schrödinger equation in the two regions of r has the form (E is the energy of the particle)

$$\Delta\psi + \varkappa^2\psi = 0, \text{ where } \varkappa^2 = \frac{2\mu}{\hbar^2}(E + U_0) \qquad (r \leqslant a), \tag{1}$$

$$\Delta\psi + k^2\psi = 0, \text{ where } k^2 = \frac{2\mu E}{\hbar^2} \qquad (r \geqslant a). \tag{2}$$

The general axially symmetric solution of equations (1) and (2) has the form $\psi = \sum_{l=0}^{\infty} R_{kl}(r) P_l(\cos\theta)$. However, since $\lambda \gg a$, only the partial wave with $l = 0$ undergoes appreciable scattering (i.e., the scattering is isotropic). Therefore, the part of the ψ-function which describes the scattering reduces to just one radial function R_{k0}. This function satisfies the equations

$$\frac{1}{r}\frac{d^2}{dr^2}(rR) + \varkappa^2 R = 0 \qquad (r \leqslant a), \tag{3}$$

$$\frac{1}{r}\frac{d^2}{dr^2}(rR) + k^2 R = 0 \qquad (r \geqslant a). \tag{4}$$

The solution of equation (3) which satisfies the necessary condition of finiteness at $r = 0$ has the form

$$R \equiv R_I = c\frac{\sin \varkappa r}{r} \qquad (r \leqslant a), \tag{5}$$

where c is a constant.

The solution of equation (4) must be a superposition of the spherically symmetric part of the incident plane wave e^{ikr} and of the spherically symmetric divergent wave

$$R \equiv R_{II} = \frac{\sin kr}{kr} + f\frac{e^{ikr}}{r} \qquad (r \geqslant a) \tag{6}$$

where f is a constant. We note that because the well has a sharp boundary, solution (6) is correct everywhere outside the well, and not just asymptotically as $r \to \infty$.

For the normalization of solution (6) which we have selected (the coefficient of the spherical component of the plane wave equal to unity), the differential cross section for scattering per unit solid angle is

$$\frac{d\sigma}{do} = |f|^2. \tag{7}$$

Of the two constants c and f, only the second interests us. To determine it, it is simplest to use the condition of the continuity of the logarithmic derivatives of the functions (rR_I) and (rR_{II}) at the boundary of the well $r=a$:

$$\left.\frac{(rR_I)'}{rR_I}\right|_{r=a}=\left.\frac{(rR_{II})'}{rR_{II}}\right|_{r=a},$$

where the primes indicate differentiation with respect to r. If we substitute into this (5) and (6), we obtain

$$\varkappa \operatorname{ctg} \varkappa a=\frac{\cos ka+ikfe^{ika}}{\frac{1}{k}\sin ka+fe^{ika}}.$$

Hence,

$$f=\frac{\cos ka-\frac{\varkappa}{k}\operatorname{ctg}\varkappa a\sin ka}{\varkappa\operatorname{ctg}\varkappa a-ik}e^{-ika}.$$

Since $ka\ll 1$ from the given conditions, we can set $\cos ka\approx 1$, $\sin ka\approx ka$. Finally, according to (7), we find

$$\frac{d\sigma}{do}=\frac{(1-\varkappa a\operatorname{ctg}\varkappa a)^2}{\varkappa^2\operatorname{ctg}^2\varkappa a+k^2}=\frac{(\operatorname{tg}\varkappa a-\varkappa a)^2}{\varkappa^2+k^2\operatorname{tg}^2\varkappa a} \tag{8}$$

The total cross section is equal to

$$\sigma=4\pi\frac{d\sigma}{do}=4\pi\frac{(\operatorname{tg}\varkappa a-\varkappa a)^2}{\varkappa^2+k^2\operatorname{tg}^2\varkappa a}=4\pi\frac{(1-\varkappa a\operatorname{ctg}\varkappa a)^2}{\varkappa^2\operatorname{ctg}^2\varkappa a+k^2}. \tag{9}$$

These formulas are correct for any relation between E and U_0. In the special case where $E\ll U_0$ [i.e., according to (1) and (2), $k\ll\varkappa$] and where, moreover, $\varkappa a$ is not too close to $(2n+1)\frac{\pi}{2}$, we obtain in complete agreement with 1 :

$$\sigma\approx 4\pi\left(\frac{\operatorname{tg}\varkappa a-\varkappa a}{\varkappa}\right)^2,\text{ where } \varkappa\approx\frac{1}{\hbar}\sqrt{2\mu U_0}. \tag{10}$$

Equation (9) also makes it possible to consider the case of resonance scattering, where (for $E\ll U_0$) $\varkappa a$, is close to $(2n+1)\times\frac{\pi}{2}$ $(n=0, 1, 2, \ldots)$, which implies that the energy levels of the well include a level close to zero (and consequently close to the energy E of the particle in question).

The solution of the problem of finding the energy levels with $l=0$ in a spherical rectangular well is given in [1], p. 140. In the notation (1) and (2) of the given problem, the equation for determining the levels $-\varepsilon (\varepsilon > 0)$ has the following form:

$$\frac{2\mu (U_0 - \varepsilon)}{\hbar^2} \operatorname{ctg}^2 \left[\sqrt{\frac{2\mu (U_0 - \varepsilon) a^2}{\hbar^2}} \right] = \frac{2\mu\varepsilon}{\hbar^2}. \quad (11)$$

In the case with which we are concerned, namely that of a level close to zero, we have $\varepsilon \ll U_0$. Therefore,

$$\frac{2\mu U_0}{\hbar^2} \operatorname{ctg}^2 \sqrt{\frac{2\mu U_0 a^2}{\hbar^2}} \approx \frac{2\mu\varepsilon}{\hbar^2}. \quad (12)$$

However, according to (1), for $E \ll U_0$, this last equation can be written in the form

$$\varkappa^2 \operatorname{ctg}^2 \varkappa a \approx \frac{2\mu\varepsilon}{\hbar^2}. \quad (13)$$

From (12) and (13), it follows that, since $\varepsilon \ll U_0$, the cotangent must be $\ll 1$; i.e., the argument of the cotangent is close to $(2n+1)\frac{\pi}{2}$:

$$\varkappa a \approx \sqrt{\frac{2\mu U_0 a^2}{\hbar^2}} \approx (2n+1)\frac{\pi}{2} \qquad (n = 0, 1, 2, \ldots). \quad (14)$$

If we confine ourselves to the case of a not very deep well, in which there is a small number of levels, we have $n = 0$ or $n \sim 1$, and therefore $\varkappa a \sim 1$ and $\varkappa a \operatorname{ctg} \varkappa a \ll 1$. From this fact and equations (13) and (2), we can write (9) in the approximate form

$$\sigma \approx 4\pi \frac{1}{\frac{2\mu\varepsilon}{\hbar^2} + \frac{2\mu E}{\hbar^2}} = \frac{2\pi\hbar^2}{\mu} \frac{1}{E + \varepsilon}. \quad (15)$$

Thus, we have obtained the Wigner formula for resonance scattering by the given specific type of potential well.*

As is apparent from (15), for $E \gg \varepsilon$, the total cross section is approximately equal to

$$\sigma \approx 4\pi\lambda\!\!\!^{-2} \gg 4\pi a^2, \quad (16)$$

where $\lambda\!\!\!^- = \frac{1}{k} = \frac{\hbar}{\sqrt{2\mu E}}$ is the de Broglie wavelength of the scattered particle.

---

*In [1], § 109, there is a derivation of this formula without any assumption as to the explicit form of the scattering potential.

In the opposite limiting case where $E \ll \varepsilon$, the cross section (15) is approximately constant

$$\sigma \approx \frac{2\pi\hbar^2}{\mu\varepsilon} = \text{const} \; (\gg 4\pi a^2). \tag{17}$$

13. The potential energy is equal to $U_0 > 0$ for $r \leqslant a$, and to zero for $r \geqslant a$. The problem is solved on the basis of the preceding one. In region II $(r \geqslant a)$, the radial function R_{k0} (which describes the s-scattering, which predominates in this case) naturally has the same form as in the case of an attractive field (with, however, another value of f):

$$R = R_{\text{II}} = \frac{\sin kr}{kr} + f\frac{e^{ikr}}{r}, \text{ where } k^2 = \frac{2\mu E}{\hbar^2}. \tag{1}$$

The form of the function in region I $(r \leqslant a)$ depends on the relation between the energy E and the height of the hill U_0. Thus, for $E > U_0$, the radial equation in region I has the form

$$\frac{1}{r}\frac{d^2}{dr^2}(rR_{\text{I}}) + \varkappa_1^2 R_{\text{I}} = 0,$$

where

$$\varkappa_1^2 = \frac{2\mu}{\hbar^2}(E - U_0) > 0, \tag{2}$$

while for $E < U_0$, it has the form

$$\frac{1}{r}\frac{d^2}{dr^2}(rR_{\text{I}}) - \varkappa_2^2 R_{\text{I}} = 0, \quad \text{where } \varkappa_2^2 = \frac{2\mu}{\hbar^2}(U_0 - E). \tag{3}$$

In the first case, it is obvious that all the derivations are identical with those of the preceding problem, except for the replacement of $\varkappa$ by $\varkappa_1$. This gives immediately the following exact expression for the amplitude of the s-scattering:

$$f = \frac{\cos ka - \frac{\varkappa_1}{k}\operatorname{ctg}\varkappa_1 a \sin ka}{(\varkappa_1 \operatorname{ctg}\varkappa_1 a - ik)\, e^{ika}} = \frac{k\cos ka \operatorname{tg}\varkappa_1 a - \varkappa_1 \sin ka}{k(\varkappa_1 - ik\operatorname{tg}\varkappa_1 a)\, e^{ika}}. \tag{4}$$

Since $\varkappa_1 a < ka \ll 1$ in the given case, the expansion of f into powers of the small quantities $\varkappa_1 a$ and ka should be made by replacing the trigonometric functions by two terms of the corresponding series. This yields

$$f \approx \frac{1}{3}a^3(\varkappa_1^2 - k^2) = -\frac{2}{3}\frac{\mu U_0 a^3}{\hbar^2}. \tag{5}$$

Hence,

$$\sigma \approx 4\pi f^2 \approx \frac{16\pi}{9} \frac{\mu^2 U_0^2 a^6}{\hbar^4}. \tag{6}$$

This result is also obtained from Born's approximation* for the scattering of slow particles

$$\sigma \approx \frac{\mu^2}{\pi \hbar^4} \left(\int U \, dV \right)^2.$$

We would expect this, since $ka \ll 1$ is equivalent to $E \ll \frac{\hbar^2}{\mu a^2}$, and therefore the condition for the validity of Born's approximation in the case $ka \ll 1$, namely $U_0 \ll \frac{\hbar^2}{\mu a^2}$, is automatically satisfied for $U_0 < E$.

In the second case $(E < U_0)$, a solution in the region $r \leqslant a$ which is finite at zero has the form

$$R_l = \text{const} \frac{\operatorname{sh} \varkappa_2 r}{r}. \tag{7}$$

If we compare this equation with equation (5) of the preceding problem and if we take equation (1) into consideration, we easily see that the difference between the succeeding equations of the two problems (or, what is the same, the difference from the case $E > U_0$) reduces to the replacement of the trigonemetric functions of $\varkappa a$ by hyperbolic functions of $\varkappa_2 a$. Therefore, instead of (4), we obtain

$$f = \frac{k \cos ka \operatorname{th} \varkappa_2 a - \varkappa_2 \sin ka}{k(\varkappa_2 - ik \operatorname{th} \varkappa_2 a) e^{ika}}. \tag{8}$$

In the given approximation $ka \ll 1$, this expression can be expanded into a series of powers of ka. This yields (in view of the fact that $\operatorname{th} \varkappa_2 a < \varkappa_2 a$):

$$f \approx -a\left(1 - \frac{\operatorname{th} \varkappa_2 a}{\varkappa_2 a}\right) + a(ka)^2 \left(\frac{1}{6} - \frac{1}{2} \frac{\operatorname{th} \varkappa_2 a}{\varkappa_2 a}\right). \tag{9}$$

For $U_0 \gtrsim \frac{\hbar^2}{\mu a^2}$ (i.e., for $\varkappa_2 a \gtrsim 1$), we can neglect the second term in this formula. Thus,

$$f \approx -a\left(1 - \frac{\operatorname{th} \varkappa_2 a}{\varkappa_2 a}\right), \quad \sigma \approx 4\pi f^2 \approx 4\pi a^2 \left(1 - \frac{\operatorname{th} \varkappa_2 a}{\varkappa_2 a}\right)^2. \tag{10}$$

---

*Cf. Problem No. 3. The sign of the potential of course plays no role in the Born approximation.

In particular, for $U_0 \gg \frac{\hbar^2}{\mu a^2}$ (i.e., for $\varkappa_2 a \gg 1$, $\operatorname{th} \varkappa_2 a \approx 1$), we arrive at the well-known result $\sigma = 4\pi a^2$.

We note that, in the region where formula (10) is valid, $U_0 \gg E$, i.e., $\varkappa_2 = \frac{1}{\hbar}\sqrt{2\mu U_0}$.

For $U_0 \ll \frac{\hbar^2}{\mu a^2}$, when $\varkappa_2 a \ll 1$, we have $\operatorname{th} \varkappa_2 a \approx \varkappa_2 a \quad \frac{1}{3}(\varkappa_2 a)^3$. Accordingly, both terms are of a comparable order of magnitude, and we obtain

$$f = -\frac{1}{3} a^3 (\varkappa_2^2 + k^2) = -\frac{2}{3}\frac{\mu U_0 a^3}{\hbar^2}, \qquad \sigma = \frac{16\pi}{9}\frac{\mu^2 U_0^2 a^6}{\hbar^4}.$$

As was to be expected, we have again arrived at Born's result (5),(6).*

14. From the problem, the potential energy of the scattered particle has the form

$$U(r) = U_0 e^{-\frac{r}{a}}, \tag{1}$$

where U_0 and a are positive constants.

The condition that the particles be slow is expressed by the inequality $ka \ll 1$ $\left(k = \frac{1}{\hbar}\sqrt{2\mu E}\right.$, where E is the energy of the particle). As we know, when this condition holds, s-scattering ($l = 0$) predominates. For the function $\varphi(r) = rR(r)$ (R is the radial function describing the scattering), we have the equation

$$\frac{d^2\varphi}{dr^2} + \frac{2\mu}{\hbar^2}\left(E - U_0 e^{-\frac{r}{a}}\right)\varphi = 0. \tag{2}$$

For R to be finite, it is necessary that at $r = 0$ the solution of this equation satisfy the boundary condition

$$\varphi(0) = 0. \tag{3}$$

On the other hand, as $r \to \infty$, the solution must have an asymptotic form, corresponding (after division by r) to the sum of the s-components of the incident plane wave e^{ikr} and of the divergent spherical wave:

---

*Since Born's result does not contain E for $U_0 \ll \frac{\hbar^2}{\mu a^2}$, it can also be obtained from formula (10) (by expanding into powers of $\varkappa_2 a = \frac{a}{\hbar}\sqrt{2\mu U_0} \ll 1\Big)$.

$$\varphi \approx \frac{1}{k}\sin kr + fe^{ikr} = \left(\frac{1}{2ik} + f\right)e^{ikr} - \frac{1}{2ik}e^{-ikr}\,(r \to \infty), \tag{4}$$

where f is the amplitude of the s-scattering. For this normalization of the asymptotic form of the wave function of the scattered particles, the intensity of the scattering $\frac{d\sigma}{do}$ is equal to $|f|^2$, while the total cross section σ is equal to $4\pi|f|^2$ because of the isotropy of the scattering.

Let us find the required solution to equation (2). The substitution $y = e^{-\frac{r}{2a}}$ reduces this equation to the form

$$\frac{d^2\varphi}{dy^2} + \frac{1}{y}\frac{d\varphi}{dy} + \left(\frac{p^2}{y^2} - \lambda^2\right)\varphi = 0, \tag{5}$$

where

$$p^2 = (2ka)^2 = \frac{8\mu E a^2}{\hbar^2}, \qquad \lambda^2 = \frac{8\mu U_0 a^2}{\hbar^2}. \tag{6}$$

A solution of equation (5) is a linear combination of Bessel functions with imaginary indices $\pm ip$ and an imaginary variable $i\lambda y$:

$$\varphi = AJ_{ip}(i\lambda y) + BJ_{-ip}(i\lambda y). \tag{7}$$

From the boundary solution at $r=0$, i.e., at $y=1$, we obtain the relationship betwen the constants A and B:

$$AJ_{ip}(i\lambda) + BJ_{-ip}(i\lambda) = 0. \tag{8}$$

Let us impose the asymptotic condition (4) on solution (7). Since we have $r \to \infty$ as $y \to 0$, we shall use the expansion of the Bessel functions into power series

$$J_{\pm ip}(i\lambda y) \approx \left(\frac{1}{2}i\lambda y\right)^{\pm ip}\frac{1}{\Gamma(1 \pm ip)}. \tag{9}$$

Transforming to the variable r, we obtain

$$\varphi \approx A\frac{\left(\frac{1}{2}i\lambda\right)^{ip}}{\Gamma(1+ip)}e^{-\frac{ipr}{2a}} + B\frac{\left(\frac{1}{2}i\lambda\right)^{-ip}}{\Gamma(1-ip)}e^{\frac{ipr}{2a}} \qquad (r \to \infty). \tag{10}$$

By considering (6), equating the respective coefficients of e^{ikr} and e^{-ikr} in (4) and (10), and using (8), we find

$$f = \frac{1}{2ik}\left[\frac{\Gamma(1+ip)\left(\frac{1}{2}i\lambda\right)^{-ip} J_{ip}(i\lambda)}{\Gamma(1-ip)\left(\frac{1}{2}i\lambda\right)^{ip} J_{-ip}(i\lambda)} - 1\right]. \tag{11}$$

It is convenient to transform this expression somewhat by using the modified Bessel functions $I_{\pm ip}(\lambda) = i^{\mp ip} J_{\pm ip}(i\lambda)$. As a result we obtain

$$f = \frac{1}{2ik}\left[\frac{\Gamma(1+ip)\left(\frac{1}{2}\lambda\right)^{-ip} I_{ip}(\lambda)}{\Gamma(1-ip)\left(\frac{1}{2}\lambda\right)^{ip} I_{-ip}(\lambda)} - 1\right]. \qquad (11')$$

The expression (11) or (11′) for the amplitude of the s-scattering is free of any approximations so far. In the case with which we are concerned, $p = 2ka \ll 1$. Consequently, it is appropriate to simplify (11′) by means of the limiting transition $p \to 0$. We have

$$\Gamma(1 \pm ip) \approx \Gamma(1) \pm ip\Gamma'(1) = 1 \mp ipC, \qquad (12)$$

where $C = -\Gamma'(1) = 0.5772$ is Euler's constant. In addition,

$$\left(\frac{1}{2}\lambda\right)^{\pm ip} \approx 1 \pm ip \ln \frac{\lambda}{2}, \qquad (13)$$

$$I_{\pm ip}(\lambda) \approx I_0(\lambda) \pm ip \lim_{\nu \to 0} \frac{\partial I_\nu(\lambda)}{\partial \nu}. \qquad (14)$$

On the other hand, if we take the limit $\nu \to 0$ in the equation connecting the modified Hankel functions with the modified Bessel functions ([13], p. 361)

$$K_\nu(z) = \frac{\pi}{2}\,\frac{I_{-\nu}(z) - I_\nu(z)}{\sin \nu\pi},$$

we obtain

$$\lim_{\nu \to 0} \frac{\partial I_\nu(z)}{\partial \nu} = -K_0(z) \equiv -\frac{i\pi}{2} H_0^{(1)}(iz).$$

Therefore, (14) assumes the form

$$I_{\pm ip}(\lambda) \approx I_0(\lambda) \mp ipK_0(\lambda). \qquad (14')$$

If we substitute (12), (13), and (14′) into (11′), we obtain after simple computation

$$f = -2a\left[C + \ln \frac{\lambda}{2} + \frac{K_0(\lambda)}{I_0(\lambda)}\right]. \qquad (15)$$

Hence,

$$\sigma = 4\pi f^2 = 16\pi a^2 \left[C + \ln \frac{\lambda}{2} + \frac{K_0(\lambda)}{I_0(\lambda)}\right]^2. \qquad (16)$$

In the limiting case of zero velocity of the particles, relations (15) and (16) are exact; i.e., they completely describe the scattering.

If the height U_0 of the potential hill (1) is great, when, according to (6), $\lambda \gg 1$, we have $K_0(\lambda) \approx \sqrt{\frac{\pi}{2\lambda}}\, e^{-\lambda}$, $I_0(\lambda) \approx \frac{1}{\sqrt{2\pi\lambda}}\, e^{\lambda}$. Accordingly

$$\sigma \approx 16\pi a^2 \left(\ln \frac{\lambda}{2} + C\right)^2. \tag{17}$$

Thus, the cross section for scattering increases logarithmically as the height of the scattering potential hill increases.

For small U_0, when $\lambda \ll 1$, we have

$$K_0(\lambda) \approx -I_0(\lambda) \ln \frac{\lambda}{2} - C\left(1 + \frac{\lambda^2}{4}\right) + \frac{\lambda^2}{4}, \qquad I_0(\lambda) \approx 1 + \frac{\lambda^2}{4}.$$

Therefore $\frac{K_0(\lambda)}{I_0(\lambda)} \approx -\ln \frac{\lambda}{2} - C + \frac{\lambda^2}{4}$, and consequently

$$\sigma \approx \pi \lambda^4 a^2 = 64\pi \frac{\mu^2 U_0^2 a^6}{\hbar^4}. \tag{18}$$

As we would expect, this result is identical with the result obtained by computing from Born's approximation* in the limit $v \to 0$:

$$\sigma = \frac{\mu^2}{\pi \hbar^4} \left(\int U \, dV\right)^2 \tag{19}$$

It differs only by a numerical factor from the corresponding equations of Problems No. 1 and No. 3 for the scattering by fields which are different functions of the radius than that given in (1) (we could have predicted this on the basis of dimensional analysis).

15. The potential energy has the form

$$U(r) = -U_0 e^{-\frac{r}{a}} \qquad (U_0 > 0). \tag{1}$$

We can write the general expression for the amplitude of the s-scattering directly on the basis of the results of the preceding problem (retaining the same notation). Instead of equation (5), we have the equation

$$\frac{d^2\varphi}{dy^2} + \frac{1}{y}\frac{d\varphi}{dy} + \left(\frac{p^2}{y^2} + \lambda^2\right)\varphi = 0, \tag{2}$$

---

*This relation is applicable to the scattering of slow particles when the condition $U_{\text{eff}} \ll \frac{\hbar^2}{\mu a^2}$ [1, § 45], is satisfied, which is equivalent to $\lambda \ll 1$.

whose solution is a superposition of the functions $J_{\pm ip}(\lambda y)$. Hence, it is clear that the only difference between the computations of the two problems consists in replacing $i\lambda$ by λ. Thus, instead of (11), we obtain

$$f = \frac{1}{2ik}\left[\frac{\Gamma(1+ip)\left(\frac{1}{2}\lambda\right)^{-ip} J_{ip}(\lambda)}{\Gamma(1-ip)\left(\frac{1}{2}\lambda\right)^{ip} J_{-ip}(\lambda)} - 1\right]. \tag{3}$$

This expression for the amplitude of the s-scattering is exact. For the case of slow particles ($p \ll 1$), with which we are concerned, let us expand this expression into powers of p, using formulas (12) - (14′) (transformed in the obvious way) of the preceding problem. However, by comparison with the preceding problem there will be a complication in that the function $J_0(\lambda)$, will have roots for real values of λ, as distinguished from the function $I_0(\lambda) = J_0(i\lambda)$. Therefore, in the formula corresponding to (14) or (14),

$$J_{\pm ip}(\lambda) \approx J_0(\lambda) \pm ip \lim_{\nu \to 0} \frac{\partial J_\nu(\lambda)}{\partial \nu} = J_0(\lambda) \pm ip \frac{\pi}{2} N_0(\lambda),* \tag{4}$$

it will in general be impossible to neglect the first term of the right member relative to the second term.

In consideration of what we have said, we find

$$f \approx -2a \frac{\left(C + \ln\frac{\lambda}{2}\right) J_0(\lambda) - \frac{\pi}{2} N_0(\lambda)}{J_0(\lambda) - ip\frac{\pi}{2} N_0(\lambda)}. \tag{5}$$

Depending on the value of the characteristic quantity λ, we must distinguish two special cases in which formula (5) can be simplified.

1. λ is not close to one of the roots x_n of the function $J_0(x)$, and consequently the first term in (4) is much larger than the second

---

*The equation which we have used here $\lim_{\nu \to 0} \frac{\partial J_\nu(z)}{\partial \nu} = \frac{\pi}{2} N_0(z)$ is obtained by taking the limit $\nu \to 0$ of the well-known equation connecting the Neumann functions with the Bessel functions:

$$N_\nu(z) = \frac{J_\nu(z)\cos\nu\pi - J_{-\nu}(z)}{\sin\nu\pi}.$$

term.* In this case, we obtain

$$f \approx -2a\left[C + \ln\frac{\lambda}{2} - \frac{\pi}{2}\frac{N_0(\lambda)}{J_0(\lambda)}\right], \tag{6}$$

$$\sigma = 4\pi f^2 \approx 16\pi a^2\left[C + \ln\frac{\lambda}{2} - \frac{\pi}{2}\frac{N_0(\lambda)}{J_0(\lambda)}\right]^2. \tag{7}$$

Of course, the same result is obtained simply by replacing λ by $\frac{\lambda}{i}$ in formulas (15) and (16) of the preceding problem. In particular, for $\lambda \ll 1$, the same Born result is obtained (18) as for a repelling field, as we would expect.

2. λ is close to one of the roots of the function J_0, and consequently $|J_0(\lambda)| \ll 1$, (the case of resonance). In this case, we find

$$f_{\text{res}} \approx 2a\frac{1}{\frac{2}{\pi}\frac{J_0(\lambda)}{N_0(\lambda)} - ip}, \tag{8}$$

$$\sigma_{\text{res}} = 4\pi|f_{\text{res}}|^2 \approx 16\pi a^2\frac{1}{\left[\frac{2}{\pi}\frac{J_0(\lambda)}{N_0(\lambda)}\right]^2 + p^2} \gg 16\pi a^2. \tag{9}$$

The significance of this result can be found by referring to problem No. 8, Chapter II. The exact equation for the energy levels with $l = 0$ obtained there for the type of potential well we are considering has the form $J_{p_1}(\lambda) = 0$, where $p_1^2 = 8\mu\varepsilon a^2\hbar^{-2}$ ($-\varepsilon < 0$ are the energy levels). Therefore, the equation for the small energy levels ($p_1 \ll 1$) has the form

$$J_0(\lambda) + p_1 \lim_{\nu\to 0}\frac{\partial J_\nu(\lambda)}{\partial\nu} + \ldots = J_0(\lambda) + p_1\frac{\pi}{2}N_0(\lambda) + \ldots = 0.$$

Hence,

$$\varepsilon = \frac{\hbar^2}{8\mu a^2}p_1^2 \approx \frac{\hbar^2}{8\mu a^2}\left[\frac{2J_0(\lambda)}{\pi N_0(\lambda)}\right]^2. \tag{10}$$

---

*From this condition, we also obtain the criterion for the distance of λ from the roots of J_0:

$$|\lambda - x_n| \gg p\,\frac{\pi}{2}\left|\frac{N_0(x_n)}{J_0'(x_n)}\right| = p\,\frac{\pi}{2}\left|\frac{N_0(x_n)}{J_1(x_n)}\right|.$$

Using this relationship and the first of formulas (6) of the preceding problem, we can write the section for resonance scattering (9) in the form

$$\sigma_{\text{res}} = \frac{2\pi\hbar^2}{\mu(E+\varepsilon)}.$$

As we could have expected, we have obtained Wigner's formula.

By comparing (9) and (7), we can conclude that the cross section for resonance scattering is large relative to the cross section for scattering which is far removed from resonance scattering.

For $E \gg \varepsilon$, we have ($\lambdabar$ is the de Broglie wavelength)

$$\sigma_{\text{res}} \approx \frac{2\pi\hbar^2}{\mu E} = 4\pi\lambdabar^2. \tag{12}$$

For $E \ll \varepsilon$, we have

$$\sigma_{\text{res}} \approx \frac{2\pi\hbar^2}{\mu\varepsilon} = \text{const.} \tag{13}$$

Let us write explicitly the condition for resonance $\lambda \approx x_n$. The roots x_n of the zeroth-order Bessel function which have large indices can be obtained from the asymptotic expression $J_0(x) \approx \sqrt{\frac{2}{\pi x}} \cos\left(x - \frac{\pi}{4}\right)$, that is, from the equation $x_n - \frac{\pi}{4} = (2n+1)\frac{\pi}{2}$. Hence

$$x_n \approx \left(n + \frac{3}{4}\right)\pi \qquad (n = 0, 1, 2, \ldots).$$

In conclusion, we note that this formula gives all of the zeros of the function J_0 with good accuracy. Consequently, it gives all the resonance values of λ, and thus the "volume" of the well $U_0 a^2$.

16. For the required equation to be satisfied, it is necessary first of all that the waves scattered by individual centers not be scattered again by other centers.

The squared modulus of a wave $\frac{f(\theta)}{r} e^{ikr}$ which is scattered at one center is $\frac{\sigma}{r^2}$ (in the case where the ψ-function is normalized to unity for a plane wave at infinity). If the waves do not interfere with one another (see below), the intensity of the sum of the waves scattered by all the centers will be

$$\sum_i \frac{\sigma}{r^2} \to \int n \frac{\sigma}{r^2}\, dV \sim n\sigma L,$$

where n is the density of the centers, and L represents the dimensions of the system.

For the secondary scattering to be small, this intensity must be small relative to the intensity of the incident wave, i.e., relative to unity (see above, the note on the normalization).

Thus, the first condition is

$$n\sigma L \ll 1, \quad \text{or} \quad L \ll \frac{1}{n\sigma} = l,$$

where l is the mean free path in the medium.

For the requirement given in the problem, it is necessary, in the second place, that the waves scattered by individual centers not interfere with one another. At large distances, a wave scattered by all the centers can be written in the form

$$\sum_i \frac{f(\theta)}{r} e^{ik|\mathbf{r}-\mathbf{r}_i|} \approx \sum_i \frac{f(\theta)}{r} e^{ikr - ik\mathbf{n}\mathbf{r}_i} = f(\theta) \sum_i e^{-ik\mathbf{n}\mathbf{r}_i} \frac{e^{ikr}}{r} \qquad \left(\mathbf{n} \equiv \frac{\mathbf{r}}{r}\right).$$

Here $\mathbf{r}_i$ represents the coordinates of the i-th center. Thus, the total cross section is equal to

$$\sigma_{\text{tot}} = \left| f(\theta) \sum_i e^{-ik\mathbf{n}\mathbf{r}_i} \right|^2 = |f(\theta)|^2 \sum_{ij} e^{ik\mathbf{n}(\mathbf{r}_i - \mathbf{r}_j)} = N|f(\theta)|^2 + |f(\theta)|^2 \sum_{i \neq j} e^{ik\mathbf{n}\mathbf{r}_{ij}}.$$

Here, $\mathbf{r}_{ij} = \mathbf{r}_i - \mathbf{r}_j$ is the distance between the corresponding centers, and N is the total number of centers.

The lack of interference implies that the second term must be small. This term will be small if the function under the summation sign oscillates, i.e., if $kr_{ij} \gg 1$. Hence, we obtain the second condition $\left(\lambda\!\!\!^{-} = \frac{1}{k}\right)$:

$$r_{ij} \gg \lambda\!\!\!^{-};$$

i.e., the wavelength of the particle must be much smaller than the distances between the centers of scattering.

For this condition to be satisfied, it is sufficient that $\lambda\!\!\!^{-} \ll n^{-1/3}$ ($n^{-1/3}$ is the order of magnitude of the average distance between the centers).

We note that the expression for a wave scattered by one center $\left(f\frac{e^{ikr}}{r}\right)$ which we have used from the start has a meaning only under the condition that neighboring centers do not "overlap":

$$\sqrt{\sigma} \ll n^{-1/3}.$$

It is easily seen that this equation is automatically satisfied when the inequality $n\sigma L \ll 1$ holds in a sufficiently "macroscopic" scattering system, i.e., in a system in which $L \gg n^{-1/3}$.

17. 1. For the given type of interaction, the mutual scattering of different atoms (He^3 and He^4) can be computed (in the center-of-mass system) directly from the formulas of Problem No. 10 or from the equivalent formulas of the phase theory of scattering:

$$f(\theta) = \frac{1}{2ik}\sum_{l=0}^{\infty}(2l+1)(e^{2i\delta_l}-1)P_l(\cos\theta) \quad \text{, etc.,} \tag{1}$$

where θ is the scattering angle in the center-of-mass system, and $k = \frac{\mu v}{\hbar}$ (v is the relative velocity, and μ the reduced mass of the colliding atoms). The cross section for scattering per unit solid angle is $\frac{d\sigma}{do} = |f(\theta)|^2$ in the center-of-mass system. The cross section for scattering per unit solid angle in the coordinate system in which the He^4 atom (for example) is at rest before the collision can be obtained from the obvious equation (which serves to define the function F)

$$d\sigma = |f(\theta)|^2\, do = |F(\vartheta_1)|^2\, d\Omega_1, \tag{2}$$

where ϑ_1 is the scattering angle of the He^3 atom, and $d\Omega_1$, is the corresponding solid-angle element. These angles are connected with the angles in the center-of-mass system by the equations ([1], p. 451)

$$\operatorname{tg}\vartheta_1 = \frac{m_2\sin\theta}{m_1 + m_2\cos\theta} = \frac{\sin\theta}{\frac{m_1}{m_2} + \cos\theta}, \quad d\Omega_1 = 2\pi\sin\vartheta_1\, d\vartheta_1 \tag{3}$$

(in the given case, $\frac{m_1}{m_2} = \frac{3}{4}$).

Let us denote the atomic radius (practically the same for both isotopes) by a. This obviously means that the radius a' of the "sphere of interaction" of the two isotopes is equal to $2a$.

In the limiting case $\lambda\!\!\!^{-} \gg a' \left(\lambda\!\!\!^{-} = \frac{\hbar}{\mu v} = \frac{1}{k}\right)$ we have (see Problem No. 10)

$$f(\theta) \approx -a' = -2a. \tag{4}$$

Hence, we find $\frac{d\sigma}{do}$, and then $\cdot\frac{\overline{\sigma}p}{\sigma p}$ Similarly (also on the basis of the results of Problem No. 10), we can obtain the cross section for the case $\lambda\!\!\!^{-} \ll a'$.

2. In the atomic collisions ($He^4 + He^4$) and ($He^3 + He^3$), we are dealing with the scattering of identical particles. To describe this scattering (in the center-of-mass system to start with), we shall use the equations ([1], Section 114)

$$\psi = e^{ikz} \pm e^{-ikz} + \frac{1}{r} e^{ikr} [f(\theta) \pm f(\pi - \theta)]. \tag{5}$$

First, let us consider the scattering of He^4 by He^4. Since the He^4 atom consists of an even number (six) of Fermi particles, it is a Bose particle. At the same time, its spin is equal to zero since both the spin of the nucleus (an α-particle) and the total spin of the electrons is equal to zero.* This, the spin function of the two He^4 atoms** is symmetric, from which it follows (because of the requirement that for Bose particles the complete wave function must be symmetric) that the position function as well is symmetric with respect to interchange of the two atoms. Therefore, in the given case, we must select the upper sign in the general equation (5):

$$\psi = e^{ikz} + e^{-ikz} + \frac{1}{r} e^{ikr} [f(\theta) + f(\pi - \theta)]. \tag{5'}$$

From (1), if we consider that $P_l[\cos(\pi - \theta)] = P_l(-\cos\theta) = (-1)^l P_l(\cos\theta)$, we obtain the following expression for the scattering amplitude (after setting $l \equiv 2l'$ since all the odd harmonics drop out):

$$f(\theta) + f(\pi - \theta) = \frac{1}{ik} \sum_{l'=0}^{\infty} (4l' + 1)(e^{2i\delta_{2l'}} - 1) P_{2l'}(\cos\theta). \tag{6}$$

The effective cross section for scattering in the center-of-mass system is

$$\frac{d\sigma}{do} = |f(\theta) + f(\pi - \theta)|^2 = \frac{1}{k^2} \left| \sum_{l'=0}^{\infty} (4l' + 1)(e^{2i\delta_{2l'}} - 1) \times \right. \\ \left. \times P_{2l'}(\cos\theta) \right|^2. \tag{7}$$

---

*We recall that the normal term of a helium atom is a paraterm ([6], p. 488).

**This spin function is simply identically equal to 1.

The corresponding quantity for the mutual scattering of two non-identical particles has, according to (1), the form

$$\frac{d\sigma}{do}=|f(\theta)|^2=\frac{1}{4k^2}\left|\sum_{l=0}^{\infty}(2l+1)(e^{2i\delta_l}-1)P_l(\cos\theta)\right|^2. \quad (8)$$

By integrating (7) over the angles, we obtain the total cross section

$$\sigma=\frac{16\pi}{k^2}\sum_{l'=0}^{\infty}(4l'+1)\sin^2\delta_{2l'}. \quad (9)$$

By comparing (7) with (8), we can conclude, in particular, that for $ka'\gg1$ the angular distribution of scattered identical particles in the region $\theta\sim1$ differs more from the classical angular distribution than in the case of non identical particles.*

We also note that the angular distribution (7), which is symmetric about $\theta=\frac{\pi}{2}$, has a maximum at this value of θ (i.e., at $\vartheta_1=\frac{\pi}{4}$ in the local coordinate system).

Let us consider the limiting cases $ka'\ll1$ and $ka'\gg1$. In the first case, we have, according to (4):

$$f(\theta)+f(\pi-\theta)\approx-2a'. \quad (10)$$

Hence,

$$\left.\begin{aligned}\frac{d\sigma}{do}&=|f(\theta)+f(\pi-\theta)|^2\cong4a'^2,\\ \sigma&\approx4\pi\frac{d\sigma}{do}=16\pi a'^2=64\pi a^2.\end{aligned}\right\} \quad (11)$$

Thus, for $ka'\ll1$, the identical nature of the colliding particles results in a fourfold increase* of the cross section for scattering, as compared with the case of nonidentical particles ($\sigma=4\pi a'^2$). (This means that the cross section is 16 times as great as its

---

*This is connected with the fact that, for a given value of ka', the number of "effective" terms in sums (6) and (7) is approximately one half that in the corresponding sums for the case of non-identical particles (since the terms with odd l drop out). This results in an increase in the oscillations of the angular distribution.

**The cause for this is obviously the doubled amplitude of the scattering [see (10)], which in turn is caused by the symmetrization of the ψ-function.

classical value $\sigma = \pi a'^2$.)

In the case where $ka' \gg 1$, the important role in sums (1) and (8) is played by terms with $l \leqslant l_0 \approx ka'$ (see Problems No. 10 and No. 11), and consequently, in sums (6), (7), and (9), by terms with $l' \leqslant \frac{1}{2} l_0 \approx \frac{1}{2} ka'$. If we repeat exactly the same arguments as in problem No. 11, we can reduce (9) to the form

$$\sigma \approx \frac{16\pi}{k^2} \sum_{l'=0}^{\frac{1}{2} l_0} (4l' + 1) \sin^2 \delta_{2l'} \approx \frac{16\pi}{k^2} \cdot \frac{1}{2} \int_0^{\frac{1}{2} ka'} 4l' dl' = 4\pi a'^2. \tag{12}$$

With problem No. 10 as a model, it is also possible to obtain an explicit expression for the angular distribution (7). However, we shall not dwell on this.

This total cross section (12) is twice the cross section for the case of nonidentical particles ($\sigma = 2\pi a'^2$). This doubling of the cross section reflects the trivial (or, as we could say, "classical") indistinguishable nature of the colliding particles. This indistinguishability is not connected with the structure of the probability amplitude of the type of (10), and it can be introduced in classical mechanics (2 , § 22). We recall that the condition $ka' \gg 1$ is indeed the condition for quasi-classical scattering (at least, on the average and apart from the smallest angles).

The transformation to a coordinate system in which one of the atoms is at rest before the collision is carried out, according to (3) (into which we subsititute $m_1 = m_2$), by the substitution $\theta \to 2\vartheta$.

Thus, in the case $ka' \ll 1$, we find from (11)

$$d\sigma = 4a'^2 \cdot 2\pi \sin\theta \, d\theta = 4a'^2 \cdot 8\pi \cos\vartheta \sin\vartheta \, d\vartheta = \\ = 16a'^2 \cos\vartheta \, d\Omega. \tag{13}$$

Therefore, the angular distribution of the scattered particles extends in the forward direction in the local system of coordinates (we recall also that $0 \leqslant \vartheta \leqslant \frac{\pi}{2}$).

3. Let us now consider the scattering of He^3 by He^3. A He^3 atom consists of an odd number (five) of Fermi particles, and therefore the atom itself is a Fermi particle. Its spin in the normal state is equal to the spin of the He^3 nucleus, i.e., to $\frac{1}{2}$. The $He^3 + He^3$ scattering with antiparallel spins is necessarily described by a symmetric position function [the upper sign in (5)], while scattering with parallel spins is described by an antisymmetric position function [the lower sign in (5)].

In the first of these cases, the same formulas as in part 2 are correct.

In the second case, according to (5) and (1), the scattering amplitude is

$$f(\theta)-f(\pi-\theta)=$$
$$=\frac{1}{ik}\sum_{l'=0}^{\infty}(4l'+3)(e^{2i\delta_{2l'+1}}-1)P_{2l'+1}(\cos\theta) \qquad (14)$$

(where we have set $l=2l'+1$, since all the even harmonics drop out). In the limiting case $ka'\gg 1$, where $l'_{\mathrm{eff}}\gg 1$, this expression is approximately the same as (6), and thus the total cross section is equal to (12).

In the opposite limiting case, $ka'\ll 1$, the term with $l'=0$ is most important in sum (14). If we confine ourselves to the zeroth approximation (in terms of ka'), we obtain directly on the basis of (4)

$$f(\theta)-f(\pi-\theta)\approx 0. \qquad (15)$$

Therefore, the scattering cross section is approximately equal to zero.* We could have predicted this result. Indeed, the state with parallel spins is forbidden by Pauli's principle for $k=0$ (i.e., for $p_1=p_2$). On the other hand, for $k\neq 0$, but $ka'\ll 1$, the unperturbed ψ-function of the relative motion ($e^{ikz}-e^{-ikz}$) is appreciably different from zero only for $z\gg a'$, and at these large relative distances the interaction of the atoms is negligibly small and cannot produce any appreciable scattering.

We must note that there is practical interest in the case where the colliding He^3 atoms are not in definite spin states. Here, to determine the effective cross section, it is necessary to take the average of all the spin states, regarding them all as equally probable. In the case of parallel spins, the total spin of the atoms is equal to unity, and there are three corresponding spin states. For the case of antiparallel spins, the total spin is equal to zero, which means that there is one spin state. Consequently, the average cross section for scattering includes the cross section $|f(\theta)-f(\pi-\theta)|^2$ with a weight of $\frac{3}{4}$, and the cross section $|f(\theta)+f(\pi-\theta)|^2$ with a weight of $\frac{1}{4}$.

In consideration of all that we have said above, we can conclude that, in the case where $ka'\ll 1$, the total cross section σ averaged

---

*The computation of the scattering amplitude in the first approximation from the formulas of Problem No. 10 yields $f(\theta)-f(\pi-\theta)\approx 2(ka')^2a'\cos\theta$, so that $\sigma=\frac{16\pi}{3}(ka')^4a'^2$.

over the spins is [see (11) and (15)]

$$\bar{\sigma} \approx \frac{1}{4} \cdot 16\pi a'^2 + \frac{3}{4} \cdot 0 = 4\pi a'^2, \tag{16}$$

which is identical with the cross section for mutual scattering of nonidentical particles.

In the case where $ka' \gg 1$, we obtain [cf. (12)]

$$\bar{\sigma} = \frac{1}{4} \cdot 4\pi a'^2 + \frac{3}{4} \cdot 4\pi a'^2 = 4\pi a'^2, \tag{17}$$

which is twice as great as the corresponding quantity for distinguishable particles. We should have expected this on the basis of the above-mentioned "classical" indistinguishability. In the given case, this indistinguishability is the one factor responsible for the difference from the case of distinguishable particles, whereas the exchange interaction, which is connected with the different mutual orientations of the spins, naturally does not play a noticeable role in this quasi-classical limiting case.*

18. If we select the origin of coordinates at the center of rotation, we can write the potential energy of the interaction of the incident particle with the rotator in the following form (setting the charges of both particles equal to e):

$$U = \frac{e^2}{|\boldsymbol{r} - \boldsymbol{n}a|}, \tag{1}$$

where a is the distance of the rotating particle from the center of rotation, $\boldsymbol{n}$ is the unit vector of the "axis" of the rotator, and $\boldsymbol{r}$ is the radius vector of the scattered particle.

In first-order approximation theory [6], the probability of the given transition per unit time is

$$dw_{0l} = \frac{2\pi}{\hbar} |U_{0l}|^2 \rho_E \, d\Omega, \tag{2}$$

where U_{0l} is the matrix element of pertubation (1) for the given transition, taken between the normalized ψ-functions of the system; and $\rho_E \, d\Omega$ is the number of finite states of the system in a unit interval of energy ($d\Omega$ is a solid-angle element in the direction of the scattering).

---

*This corresponds to the in effect negligible value of the "interference" terms in the general formulas ([1], p. 483) in the quasi-classical case.

The initial and final ψ-functions of the system have the form

$$\psi_{\text{in.}}=\frac{1}{\sqrt{V}}e^{i\boldsymbol{k}_0\boldsymbol{r}}Y_{00}(\boldsymbol{n}),\qquad \psi_{\text{fin.}}=\frac{1}{\sqrt{V}}e^{i\boldsymbol{k}_l\boldsymbol{r}}Y_{lm}(\boldsymbol{n}),\tag{3}$$

where the Y_{lm} are normalized spherical functions describing stationary states of the rotator, $\boldsymbol{k}_0$ and $\boldsymbol{k}_l$ are the propagation vectors of the particle before and after scattering, and V is the normalization volume. According to (1) and (3),

$$\begin{aligned}U_{l0}=U^*_{0l}&=\int\int\psi^*_{\text{fin.}}U\psi_{\text{in.}}\,d\boldsymbol{r}\,do=\\&=\frac{e^2}{V}\int\int Y^*_{lm}(\boldsymbol{n})\,Y_{00}(\boldsymbol{n})\,e^{i(\boldsymbol{k}_0-\boldsymbol{k}_l)\boldsymbol{r}}\frac{d\boldsymbol{r}\,do}{|\boldsymbol{r}-\boldsymbol{n}a|},\end{aligned}\tag{4}$$

where do is a solid-angle element about $\boldsymbol{n}$.

As we shall see from the computations, for any given l, the rotator can be excited to only one state (with $m=0$). Therefore, the density of the final states $\rho_E\,d\Omega$ is given simply by the number of states of the scattered particle. Consequently, the number of final states is equal to

$$\rho_E d\Omega=\frac{Vp_l^2\frac{dp_l}{dE}d\Omega}{(2\pi\hbar)^3},\tag{5}$$

where $p_l=\hbar k_l$ is the momentum of the scattered particle, related to the initial momentum p_0 by the law of conservation of energy

$$E=\frac{p_0^2}{2\mu}=\frac{p_l^2}{2\mu}+\frac{\hbar^2 l(l+1)}{2I},\tag{6}$$

where μ is the mass of the scattered particle, and I is the moment of inertia of the rotator.

If we define $\boldsymbol{k}_0-\boldsymbol{k}_l=\boldsymbol{q}$ and substitute $Y_{00}=\frac{1}{\sqrt{4\pi}}$, and then make the transformation of variables $\boldsymbol{r}-\boldsymbol{n}a=\boldsymbol{r}'$, we can reduce (4) to the form

$$U_{l0}=\frac{e^2}{\sqrt{4\pi}V}\int do\,Y^*_{lm}(\boldsymbol{n})\,e^{ia\boldsymbol{q}\boldsymbol{n}}\int e^{i\boldsymbol{q}\boldsymbol{r}'}\frac{d\boldsymbol{r}'}{r'}.\tag{7}$$

The Fourier component of the Coulomb potential, $\int e^{i\boldsymbol{q}\boldsymbol{r}'}\frac{d\boldsymbol{r}'}{r'}$, which appears here is equal to $\frac{4\pi}{q^2}$.* If we select $\boldsymbol{q}$ as the axis of quantization of the rotator and expand $e^{ia\boldsymbol{q}\boldsymbol{n}}$ into a series of Legendre polynomials, we have

---

*This is easily shown, for instance by means of the equations of problem No. 27, Chapter III.

$$U_{l0}=\frac{\sqrt{4\pi}e^2}{Vq^2}\sum_{l'=0}^{\infty}(2l'+1)\,i^{l'}\sqrt{\frac{\pi}{2qa}}\,J_{l'+\frac{1}{2}}(qa)\times$$

$$\times\int_0^{2\pi}\int_0^{\pi}Y^*_{lm}(\vartheta,\ \varphi)\,P_{l'}(\cos\vartheta)\sin\vartheta\,d\vartheta\,d\varphi.$$

By substituting $Y^*_{lm}=\sqrt{\frac{2l+1}{4\pi}\cdot\frac{(l-m)!}{(l+m)!}}\,P_l^m(\cos\vartheta)\,e^{-im\varphi}$, we can convince ourselves that the only nonzero matrix elements are those for transitions into states with $m=0$. If we use the identity $\int_0^{\pi}P_lP_{l'}\sin\vartheta\,d\vartheta=\frac{2}{2l+1}\delta_{ll'}$ and take the sum over l', we obtain for these matrix elements the expression

$$U^*_{0l}=U_{l0}=4\pi i^l\,\frac{e^2}{Vq^2}\sqrt{(2l+1)\,\frac{\pi}{2qa}}\,J_{l+\frac{1}{2}}(qa). \tag{8}$$

The differential effective cross section for scattering $d\sigma_l(\theta)$ is equal to the probability (2) divided by the density of the flux of incident particles. According to (3), the density of this flux is equal to $\frac{v_0}{V}$. Moreover, according to (6), the quantity $p_l^2\frac{dp_l}{dE}=\frac{1}{2}p_l\frac{d(p_l^2)}{dE}$ appearing in (5) is equal to $\mu p_l=\mu^2v_l$ (where v_0 and v_l are the velocities of the particle before and after scattering). In consideration of what we have said, by combining equations (2), (5), and (8), we finally find

$$d\sigma_l(\theta)=\frac{V}{v_0}\,dw_{0l}=2\pi(2l+1)\frac{v_l}{v_0}\frac{\mu^2e^4}{\hbar^4q^4}\frac{J^2_{l+1/2}(qa)}{qa}\,d\Omega. \tag{9}$$

(As we would expect, the effective cross section does not contain the normalization volume V, a quantity without immediate physical significance.)

Thus, equation (9) gives the required differential effective cross section for scattering of the particle in the solid-angle element $d\Omega$ when the rotator is excited to the l-th level. The quantity q, which appears in (9), depends both on the scattering angle θ, and on l. (Since $\boldsymbol{p}_0=\boldsymbol{p}_l+\hbar\boldsymbol{q}$, the vector $\hbar\boldsymbol{q}$ represents the momentum imparted to the rotator by the particle in the collision.) From the definition of $\boldsymbol{q}$ and equation (6), we have

$$\begin{aligned}q^2&=k_0^2+k_l^2-2k_0k_l\cos\theta=\\&=2k_0^2-\frac{\mu}{I}l(l+1)-2k_0\sqrt{k_0^2-\frac{\mu}{I}l(l+1)}\cos\theta.\end{aligned} \tag{10}$$

To find the angular distribution of the scattered particles irrespectively of their energy, it is necessary to sum (9) over all l for fixed θ. On the other hand, to find the total cross section for scattering with a given transfer of energy, it is necessary to integrate (9) over the angles for a fixed l. Because the function relating the cross section (9) to l and θ is fairly complicated, in the general case both of these operations can be carried out only numerically. However, in the most important special cases, it is possible to use analytic methods as an approximation. These analytic methods we consider below.

Beginning consideration of equation (9), we note first of all that it is also correct for the case $l=0$, i.e., for elastic scattering. In this case $q=2k_0\sin\frac{\theta}{2}$, and therefore the cross section for elastic scattering is

$$d\sigma_{\text{elas}}(\theta)=d\sigma_0(\theta)=2\pi\frac{\mu^2e^4}{\hbar^4q^4}\frac{J^2_{1/2}(qa)}{qa}d\Omega=$$

$$=\frac{4\mu^2e^4a^4}{\hbar^4}\frac{\sin^2\left(2k_0a\sin\frac{\theta}{2}\right)}{\left(2k_0a\sin\frac{\theta}{2}\right)^6}d\Omega, \tag{11}$$

where we have substituted $J_{1/2}(qa)=\sqrt{\frac{2}{\pi qa}}\sin qa$. The total cross section for elastic scattering obviously diverges for small angles θ.

In the limiting case where $2k_0a\ll 1$, expression (11) reduces to the form

$$d\sigma_{\text{elas}}(\theta)\approx\frac{\mu^2e^4}{4\hbar^4k_0^4\sin^4\frac{\theta}{2}}d\Omega=\left(\frac{e^2}{2\mu v_0^2}\right)^2\frac{d\Omega}{\sin^4\frac{\theta}{2}}, \tag{12}$$

i.e., to Rutherford's relation. We could have expected this, since the condition $2k_0a\ll 1$ implies that the dimensions of the region of motion of the scattering Coulomb center of force (the rotator) $2a$ are small relative to the de Broglie wavelength of the particle $\lambda=\frac{1}{k_0}$, and, in turn, this is practically equivalent to the immobility of the scattering center, which is a necessary condition for Rutherford's relation (12) to be correct.

For our subsequent discussion, it is convenient to transform (9) somewhat, by transforming from $d\Omega$ to dq. For a given l, we have, according to (10),

$$q\,dq=k_0k_l\sin\theta\,d\theta=\frac{k_0k_l}{2\pi}d\Omega. \tag{13}$$

Therefore, (9) is transformed to

$$d\sigma_l = \left(\frac{2\pi e^2}{\hbar v_0}\right)^2 (2l+1) \frac{J^2_{l+1/2}(qa)}{qa} \frac{dq}{q^3}. \tag{14}$$

Let us confine ourselves to the consideration of the excitation of the rotator by a rapid particle whose initial energy $E = \frac{\mu v_0^2}{2}$ is large relative to the "rotational quantum" $\frac{\hbar^2}{2I}$.* From (6), this condition implies that $0 \leqslant l \leqslant l_{max}$ with $l_{max} \gg 1$. Moreover, let us make the assumption (confirmed by results) that the chief role is played by collisions in which the particle is scattered through small angles ($\theta \ll 1$) and in which the energy transferred is small relative to the energy of the incident particle ($\Delta E \ll E$). In this case obviously $k_0 - k_l \ll k_0$. Therefore cf. (6) and (10) ,

$$\Delta E \equiv \frac{\hbar^2 l(l+1)}{2I} = \frac{\hbar^2}{2\mu}(k_0^2 - k_l^2) \approx \frac{\hbar^2 k_0}{\mu}(k_0 - k_l), \tag{15}$$

$$q^2 = (k_0 - k_l)^2 + 2k_0 k_l (1 - \cos\theta) \approx (k_0 - k_l)^2 + k_0^2 \theta^2. \tag{16}$$

Combining (15) and (16), we find

$$q \approx \sqrt{\left[\frac{\mu l(l+1)}{2Ik_0}\right]^2 + (k_0\theta)^2} = \sqrt{\left(\frac{\Delta E}{\hbar v_0}\right)^2 + (k_0\theta)^2}. \tag{17}$$

For $\theta = 0$, we have $q \approx \frac{\Delta E}{\hbar v_0}$, while for $\Delta E = 0$, we have $q \approx k_0\theta = \frac{p_0\theta}{\hbar}$. Thus the quantities $\frac{\Delta E}{v_0}$ and $p_0\theta$ have, roughly speaking, the meaning of the longitudinal and transverse components respectively of the momentum $\hbar q$ imparted in scattering.

It is apparent from (17) that, for scattering angles which are not too small, for which $k_0\theta \gg \frac{\Delta E}{\hbar v_0}$, q depends only on θ, but not on l.

---

*It is easily seen that for values of μ and I, which are of an order of magnitude corresponding to the case of collisions of electrons (or, better still, mesons or protons) with molecules, this condition is automatically satisfied when the necessary condition that the perturbation theory we have used be applicable to scattering by a Coulomb field (1 , § 45)

$$\frac{e^2}{\hbar v} \ll 1$$

is satisfied.

In this case, we can sum expression (14) in general form over l, and thus obtain the angular distribution of the scattered (both elastically and inelastically) particles. For this, we shall use the identity*

$$\sum_{l=0}^{\infty}(2l+1)J^2_{l+\frac{1}{2}}(x)=\frac{2x}{\pi}. \qquad (18)$$

According to (14) and (18), we have

$$d\sigma(q)=\sum_{l=0}^{\infty}d\sigma_l(q)=\left(\frac{2\pi e^2}{\hbar v_0}\right)^2\frac{dq}{q^3}\frac{1}{qa}\frac{2qa}{\pi}=8\pi\left(\frac{e^2}{\hbar v_0}\right)^2\frac{dq}{q^3}. \qquad (19)$$

Since $q\approx k_0\theta$ in the region of angles with which we are concerned, we can rewrite formula (19) in the form

$$d\sigma(\theta)=8\pi\left(\frac{e^2}{\mu v_0^2}\right)^2\frac{d\theta}{\theta^3}\approx\left(\frac{2e^2}{\mu v_0^2}\right)^2\frac{d\Omega}{\theta^4}, \qquad (19')$$

which is identical with Rutherford's formula (12) (we recall that $\theta\ll 1$). This result is connected with the fact that $p_0\theta\gg\frac{\Delta E}{v_0}$ in the given region of angles; that is, the scattering is accompanied predominantly by the transfer of "transverse" momentum and is practically elastic.

We can write the range of angles in which the angular distribution (19) or (19) is approximately correct:

$$\frac{\Delta E}{2E}\ll\theta\ll 1 \qquad (20)$$

---

*This identity is obtained by integrating the squared modulus of the expansion

$$e^{ix\cos\theta}=\sum_{l=0}^{\infty}(2l+1)\,i^l\sqrt{\frac{\pi}{2x}}\,J_{l+\frac{1}{2}}(x)\,P_l(\cos\theta)$$

over $\sin\theta\, d\theta$, and by using the orthonormal condition

$$\int_0^{\pi}P_lP_{l'}\sin\theta\, d\theta=\frac{2}{2l+1}\delta_{ll'}.$$

(we have set $p_0v_0 = 2E$). Since by assumption $(\Delta E)_{eff} \ll E$, the range of angles (20) may be fairly large. The nature of the angular distribution function (19) (rapid increase as θ decreases) corroborates the previous assumption that $\theta_{eff} \ll 1$.

It is necessary to make the following comment. We obtained result (19) by summing over all the values of l. At the same time, according to (17), inequality (20) places on l the restriction $\frac{\mu l^2}{I k_0} \ll k_0\theta$, or $l \ll l_1 \equiv k_0\sqrt{\frac{I\theta}{\mu}}$. At first glance, this invalidates formula (16).

However, in reality it turns out that the condition $l \ll l_1$, places practically no restriction on the validity of this formula. Indeed, if we repeat the arguments developed in detail in problem No. 10, we easily see that for a fixed x only the terms with $l \leqslant x$ play an important role in sum (18). Consequently, for the condition that formula (19) be valid, $l_{eff} \ll l_1$, to hold, it is sufficient that the inequality $qa \ll l_1$ be satisfied, or, which is the same, the inequality $\theta \ll \frac{I}{\mu a^2} = \frac{\mu_{rot}}{\mu}$ (where $\mu_{rot} = \frac{I}{a^2}$ is the mass of the rotating particle). In all cases of practical interest, $\mu_{rot} \gtrsim \mu$. Therefore, for $\theta \ll 1$ [cf. (20)], this inequality is automatically satisfied.

Let us now compute σ_l — the total cross section for scattering with excitation of the rotator to the l-th level. For this, we integrate (14) with respect to q within the limits corresponding to $\theta = 0$ and $\theta = \pi$. Since the basic contribution to this cross section comes from the small scattering angles, it is sufficient to use formula (17) to find these limits, substituting into it $\theta = 0$ and $\theta \sim 1$. Thus,

$$\sigma_l = \int_{q_{min}}^{q_{max}} d\sigma_l(q) = \left(\frac{2\pi e^2}{\hbar v_0}\right)^2 (2l+1)a^2 \int_{aq_{min}}^{aq_{max}} J^2_{l+\frac{1}{2}}(x)\frac{dx}{x^4}, \tag{21}$$

where

$$q_{min} = \frac{\Delta E}{\hbar v_0}, \quad q_{max} \sim k_0 \tag{22}$$

(in evaluating q_{max} it is permissible to neglect the first term under the radical, since $\Delta E \ll E$).

Whereas for large x the expression under the integral in (21) decreases rapidly as x increases for any l, the behavior for small x depends to a considerable extent on the value of l. Since we have $J_{l+\frac{1}{2}}(x) \sim x^{l+\frac{1}{2}}$ as $x \to 0$, the above-mentioned expression is proportional to x^{2l-3} as $x \to 0$, and consequently it tends toward zero for $l \gg 2$, and toward infinity for $l = 0,\ 1$. Let us consider these two cases separately.

1) $l = 2,\ 3,\ 4, \ldots$

In this case, we have

$$\int_{aq_{\min}}^{aq_{\max}} J^2_{l+\frac{1}{2}}(x)\frac{dx}{x^4} \approx \int_0^\infty J^2_{l+\frac{1}{2}}(x)\frac{dx}{x^4} = \frac{2}{3\pi}\frac{(l-2)!}{(l+2)!}.* \tag{23}$$

Let us examine the legitimacy of replacing the limits of integration by 0 and ∞. The function $J_{l+\frac{1}{2}}(x)$ (with $l \gg 1$) has its first (and greatest) maximum, as well as its first root, near $x = l$. For $x \ll l$, it is basically proportional to $x^{l+\frac{1}{2}}$, while for $x > l$, it performs rapid oscillations of decreasing amplitude. Consequently, it is clear that the change of the limits of integration is permissible when the conditions

$$aq_{\min} \ll l, \qquad aq_{\max} \gg l \tag{24}$$

are satisfied. If we substitute into this (22), eliminate l by means of (15), and use again $\mu_{\text{rot}} = \frac{I}{a^2}$, we can reduce these conditions to

$$\frac{\Delta E}{E} \ll \frac{\mu_{\text{rot}}}{\mu}, \qquad \frac{\Delta E}{E} \ll \frac{\mu}{\mu_{\text{rot}}}. \tag{24$'$}$$

Since usually $\mu_{\text{rot}} \gtrsim \mu$, as we pointed out above, the first of these inequalities is automatically satisfied for $\Delta E \ll E$, while the second inequality imposes a more rigorous restriction on the ratio $\frac{\Delta E}{E}$. Thus, the legitimacy of extending the limits of integration in (23) has been probed, at least for the case $\mu \sim \mu_{\text{rot}}$

According to (21) and (23), we finally have

$$\sigma_l = \frac{8}{3}\left(\frac{e^2}{\hbar v_0}\right)^2 (2l+1)\frac{(l-2)!}{(l+2)!}\pi a^2 \qquad (l = 2,\ 3, \ldots). \tag{25}$$

This total cross section decreases rapidly with increasing l (as $\frac{1}{l^3}$ or $l \gg 2$, for $\frac{1}{(\Delta E)^{3/2}}$). This corroborates the earlier assumption that $(\Delta E)_{\text{eff}} \ll E$.

---

*The last equation is obtained as a special case of one of the equations given in [13], p. 260.

2) $l=0,\ 1$.

The case $l=0$ corresponds to elastic scattering and was examined earlier.

In the case $l=1$, the integral in (21) diverges logarithmically as $x\to 0$. Thus, only values $x\ll 1$ are significant in the integral. Accordingly, if we replace $J_{3/2}(x)$ by $\left(\frac{x}{2}\right)^{3/2}\times\frac{1}{\Gamma\left(\frac{5}{2}\right)}=\frac{2x^{3/2}}{3\sqrt{2\pi}}$ and integrate from $aq_{\min}=\frac{a\Delta E}{\hbar v_0}=\frac{a\hbar}{Iv_0}\ll 1$ to some value $aq\sim 1$, we obtain

$$\sigma_1=\frac{8}{3}\left(\frac{e^2}{\hbar v_0}\right)^2\ln\left(c\frac{Iv_0}{\hbar a}\right)\pi a^2 \qquad (l=1), \tag{26}$$

where c is a dimensionless constant of the order of unity (its exact value is not very important, since the argument of the logarithm is much larger than unity).

Finally, according to (25) and (26), the total effective cross section for inelastic scattering through all angles and with all excitations of the rotator is

$$\sigma_{\text{inel}}=\sigma_1+\sum_{l=2}^{\infty}\sigma_l=$$

$$=\frac{8}{3}\left(\frac{e^2}{\hbar v_0}\right)^2\pi a^2\left[\ln\left(c\frac{Iv_0}{\hbar a}\right)+\sum_{l=2}^{\infty}(2l+1)\frac{(l-2)!}{(l+2)!}\right].$$

By using the formula ([13], p 24)

$$\sum_{k=1}^{\infty}\frac{k!}{(k+n-1)!}=\frac{1}{(n-2)\,(n-1)!}$$

in summing, we obtain, after some simple transformations,

$$\sum_{l=2}^{\infty}(2l+1)\frac{(l-2)!}{(l+2)!}=\frac{1}{3}.$$

Therefore, finally,

$$\sigma_{\text{inel}}=\frac{8}{3}\left(\frac{e^2}{\hbar v_0}\right)^2\ln\left(c_1\frac{Iv_0}{\hbar a}\right)\pi a^2, \tag{27}$$

where $c_1=ce^{1/3}$ $(e=2.718\ldots)$. Since $\frac{e^2}{\hbar v_0}\ll 1$, the value of σ_{inel} is small relative to πa^2 — the geometric cross section of the region of motion of the rotator. At the same time, the cross section for excitation to the level $l=1$ is larger than the total cross section for excitation to all the higher levels.

19. The nuclear reactions given in the problem are mutually reversible. This can be represented by the scheme

$$\underset{(A)}{n+p} \rightleftarrows \underset{(B)}{d+\gamma}. \quad (1)$$

The principle of the detailed equilibrium [1, 23] for scheme (1) can be represented in the form

$$\frac{\bar{\sigma}_{A\to B}}{\bar{\sigma}_{B\to A}} = \frac{g_B p_B^2}{g_A p_A^2}. \quad (2)$$

Here $\bar{\sigma}_{A\to B}$ and $\bar{\sigma}_{B\to A}$ are the effective cross sections for the corresponding transitions (obtained by integrating over the directions of the velocities and summing over the directions of the spins in the final states, and by then taking the average over these directions in the initial states); p_A and p_B are the momenta of the relative motion of the particles in the states A and B; and g_A and g_B are the statistical weights of the spins (polarization) of these states.

In the given case, we have $\bar{\sigma}_{A\to B} = \sigma_{\text{cap}}$ (the cross section for capture), and $\bar{\sigma}_{B\to A} = \sigma_{\text{ph.}}$ (the cross section for photo-disintegration). Since the spins of the neutron and the proton are equal to $\frac{1}{2}$, the spin of the deuteron is equal to 1, and the photon has two states of polarization, we have

$$g_A = \left(2\cdot\frac{1}{2}+1\right)^2 = 4, \qquad g_B = (2\cdot 1+1)\cdot 2 = 6.$$

For the inertial frame of reference in which the momenta of the relative motion are taken, let us take a system associated with the deuteron. Then, we have $p_B = p_\gamma = \frac{\hbar\omega}{c}$ (where ω is the frequency of the photon). We can easily see that this frame of reference is practically the same as the center-of-mass system in the states A and B. Indeed, in the exact center-of-mass system, we have by definition $\mathbf{p}_d + \mathbf{p}_\gamma = 0$, from which $p_d = p_\gamma = \frac{\hbar\omega}{c}$. Thus, the velocity of the deuteron in this system (and conversely the velocity of the center of mass relative to the deuteron) is equal to $v_d = \frac{p_d}{2M} = \frac{\hbar\omega}{2Mc}$. On the other hand, for a photon energy which is small relative to $\hbar\omega$, but not too close to the binding energy of the deuteron ε (which conditions we shall regard as satisfied), the velocities of the scattered nucleons are of the order of magnitude of $v_n \approx v_p \sim \sqrt{\frac{\hbar\omega-\varepsilon}{M}} \sim \sqrt{\frac{\hbar\omega}{M}}$. Consequently, $\frac{v_d}{v_n} \sim \sqrt{\frac{\hbar\omega}{Mc^2}} \ll 1$. Thus, the relative velocity of the two inertial frames of reference is indeed small relative to the characteristic velocities of the products of the reaction, and both frames of reference can be regarded as approximately identical.

Accordingly, we have $p_A^2 \approx 2\mu E_A$, where $\mu = \frac{M}{2}$ is the reduced mass of the system $(n+p)$ (M is the mass of a nucleon), and E_A is the energy of the relative motion of the system (or, what is the same, the energy in the system of the center of mass). From the law of conservation of energy, we have $E_A = E_B$. The second of these quantities is obviously equal to $\hbar\omega + (-\varepsilon) = \hbar\omega - \varepsilon$. Consequently, $p_A^2 = M(\hbar\omega - \varepsilon)$.

If we substitute all of the quantities we have found into (2), we finally obtain

$$\frac{\sigma_{\text{cap}}}{\sigma_{\text{ph.}}} = \frac{3}{2}\frac{\hbar\omega}{Mc^2}\frac{\hbar\omega}{\hbar\omega - \varepsilon}. \tag{3}$$

We emphasize that this result is not connected with any specific assumption on the mechanism of the reaction and that it is based only on the reversibility of quantum mechanics (i.e., the symmetry of its equations with respect to change of the sign of time).*

*For the application of equation (3) to the two different mechanisms of the transitions $n + p \rightleftarrows d + \gamma$ (namely, to the so-called electric-dipole and magnetic-dipole capture and photo-disintegration), see [22, 23].

CHAPTER XII

Parity. Isotopic Spin

1. First of all, let us note that, since the rest-mass energy of a charged π-meson exceeds the rest-mass energy of a neutral π-meson by approximately 5 Mev, while the maximum possible binding energy of the system $(\pi^+ + \pi^-)$ is only about 2 kev*), the given process is energetically possible irrespective of the value of l.

The selection rule which we must determine arises as a consequence of the identity of the two π^0-mesons which appear in the final state of the given process. Indeed, because of the integral spin of a π-meson (spin = 0), the system $(\pi^0 + \pi^0)$ must be described by a wave function which is symmetric with respect to interchange of the two mesons. Since there is obviously no spin function),** the wave function obviously reduces to a position wave function, which accordingly is symmetric in the coordinates of the two π^0-mesons. Since, as we can easily see, the position symmetry of the wave function of the two particles 1 and 2 is the same as its parity (with respect to the points dividing the segment 1-2 into two), the ψ-function of the system $(\pi^0 + \pi^0)$ can only be even $(I = +1)$. Consequently, in view of the relationship between the orbital angular momentum and the parity $I = (-1)^l$, the orbital angular momentum of the relative motion of the two π^0-mesons can likewise only be even.

Finally, if we apply to the given process the law of conservation of the total angular momentum (which in the given case is simply the orbital angular momentum), we can conclude that this transition is possible from a state with even l, but impossible from a state with odd l.

We note also that our argument is in no way affected by the fact that the π-mesons have negative internal parity, since both in the initial state and the final state there are two mesons, and thus the total internal parity has a trivial value (+ 1).

---

* $E = -\frac{\mu e^4}{2\hbar^2} = -\frac{\mu}{m} \cdot \frac{me^4}{2\hbar^2} \approx -\frac{1}{2} \cdot 270 \cdot (13.5\,\text{ev}) \approx -1800$ ev. (Here we do not consider the possible bound states caused by the non-Coulomb interaction of the π-mesons.

**To be more precise, the spin function ≡ 1.

2. Let us apply to the given process the laws of the conservation of the angular momentum and the parity, as well as Pauli's principle. The total angular momentum of the deuteron J is equal to unity. Consequently, in view of the assumptions regarding the spin and the orbital angular momentum of the π^--meson, the total angular momentum J of the initial system ($\pi^- + d$) is equal to unity, and likewise for the final system ($n + n$). For the system of two neutrons, if we denote the orbital angular momentum by L and the spin angular momentum by S, we see that states with the required total angular momentum $J = 1$ ($\boldsymbol{J} = \boldsymbol{L} + \boldsymbol{S}$) can be achieved in the following four ways:

$$1)\ L=0,\quad S=1;\qquad 2)\ L=1,\quad S=0;$$
$$3)\ L=1,\quad S=1;\qquad 4)\ L=2,\quad S=1.$$

The spin functions corresponding to $S = 1$ and $S = 0$ are symmetric and antisymmetric (respectively) with respect to interchange of the spins of the two neutrons (see for instance Problem No. 9, Ch. VIII). The symmetry of the position functions with a given L is the same as the parity of these functions $(-1)^L$ (since the operation of inversion of the coordinates, $\boldsymbol{r}_1 \to -\boldsymbol{r}_1, \boldsymbol{r}_2 \to -\boldsymbol{r}_2$, is the same as the operation of interchange of the coordinates of both particles in the coordinate system whose origin is at the point $\frac{\boldsymbol{r}_1 + \boldsymbol{r}_2}{2}$): even L correspond to neutron functions which are symmetric in the coordinates, while odd L correspond to antisymmetric functions.

Hence, it follows immediately that modes 1, 2 and 4 are forbidden by Pauli's principle (since in these states the position function and the spin function have the same symmetry, with the result that the complete wave function is symmetric with respect to interchange of the neutrons).

Thus, the only states permitted by Pauli's principle are those corresponding to mode 3, whose complete wave functions are antisymmetric (since $J = 1$, three such states are possible). However, the transition to these states is forbidden by the law of conservation of parity, since these states are odd $[(-1)^L = (-1)^1 = -1]$, while the state of the initial system ($\pi^- + d$) is even, as follows directly from the assumptions and the rules for the addition of parities.

The fact that the given process does actually occur with an appreciable probability is one of the proofs of the pseudoscalar nature of the π^--meson (i.e., its negative internal parity).

3. The smallest difference between the rest-mass energies of the π^--meson and the π^0-meson for which the given process* is

*If we consider that the π^--meson is captured from a bound state, and thus not only contributes no kinetic energy to the reaction, but even "takes away" some energy from it (though it is true a very small amount—of the order of a few kev).

energetically possible is obviously equal to the sum of the difference between the rest-mass energies of the neutron and the proton ($\approx$ 1.25 Mev) and the binding energy of the deuteron ($\approx$2.2 Mev), i.e., to about 3.5 Mev. In actuality, the rest-mass energy of the π^--meson exceeds the rest-mass energy of the π^0-meson by approximately 4.5 Mev. Thus, the reaction is possible in terms of energy, but the particles formed in this reaction have a small momentum (this point is important for our discussion).

Let us apply to the given process the laws of the conservation of angular momentum and parity, as well as Pauli's principle (for the neutrons). The total angular momentum J of the final system $(n+n+\pi^0)$ must be equal to the total angular momentum of the initial system $(\pi^- + d)$, i.e., to unity (see the preceding problem). Let us denote by L and S the orbital angular momentum and the spin of the subsystem, and by l the orbital angular momentum of the π^0-meson relative to this subsystem (or better still, the angular momentum of the subsystem relative to its center of mass, which coincides approximately with the center of mass of all three particles).

First of all, we note that there exists, in addition to the rigorous selection rule following from the conservation laws and from Pauli's principle, an additional factor which reduces greatly the probability of transitions permitted by the selection rules: the smallness of the momentum of the neutrons and of the π^0-meson (as follows from the law of conservation of momentum, all three momenta p are quantities of the same order in the center-of-mass system).

Indeed, the matrix element of any possible transition contains, under the integral sign, some operator for the meson-nucleon interaction. This operator is appreciably different from zero only in a small region of the order of the radius of action of the nuclear forces, i.e., a region of the order of the Compton wavelength of the π-meson $\frac{\hbar}{\mu c}$. This operator acts on the wave functions of the meson and one of the nucleons. However, in the small region $a \sim \frac{\hbar}{\mu c}$ near the origin of coordinates which is significant in the integral, these wave functions change as $\left(\frac{pr_\pi}{\hbar}\right)^l$ and $\left(\frac{pr_n}{\hbar}\right)^L$ respectively [1, §§ 32, 33]. Thus, the probability of a permitted transition obviously contains the factor $\left(\frac{pa}{\hbar}\right)^{2(L+l)}$.

It is convenient to evaluate the quantity $\left(\frac{pa}{\hbar}\right)^2$ in the following way. In the most important case,* the π^0-meson (since $\mu \ll M$) carries

*As A.B. Migdal has shown [25], owing to the interaction of the two slow neutrons in the final state, it is most probable that they will fly apart at a small angle to one another with a small relative

off practically all the kinetic energy exceeding the threshold energy $\Delta E \approx 4.5$ Mev — 3.5 Mev = 1 Mev $\sim \frac{\varepsilon}{2}$ (ε is the binding energy of the deuteron). Therefore $p^2 \sim \mu\varepsilon$, and hence

$$\left(\frac{pa}{\hbar}\right)^2 \sim \frac{\mu\varepsilon}{\hbar^2}\left(\frac{\hbar}{\mu c}\right)^2 = \frac{\varepsilon}{\mu c^2} \sim \frac{1}{60} \ll 1.$$

The existence of three particles in the final state increases considerably (relative to the preceding problem) the number of ways in which the total angular momentum $J = 1$ can be achieved without violating Pauli's principle or the law of conservation of parity.* However, since $\left(\frac{pa}{\hbar}\right)^2 \ll 1$, we shall be justified in considering only those permited transitions for which the sum $(L + l)$ is minimum (and for which, consequently, the probability is maximum).

Let us consider the two conceivable cases.

1. The charged π-meson and the neutral π-meson have the same internal parity.

In this case, the law of conservation of parity permits only even values of the sum $L + l$ [since the total orbital parity of the system $n + n + \pi^0$, $(-1)^{L+l}$ must be equal to +1]. If for $(L + l) = 0, 2$ we form all the combinations of L, S and l which yield $J = |\mathbf{L} + \mathbf{S} + \mathbf{l}| = 1$, we obtain the following states:

1) $L = 0, \quad S = 1, \quad l = 0$; 2) $L = 1, \quad S = 0, \quad l = 1$;
3) $L = 1, \quad S = 1, \quad l = 1$; 4) $L = 2, \quad S = 1, \quad l = 0$;
5) $L = 0, \quad S = 1, \quad l = 2$.

Of these five combinations, only one, namely 3, satisfies Pauli's principle (see the preceding problem). Since $L + l = 2$ for this transition, it follows that the probability of the given process is proportional to $\left(\frac{pa}{\hbar}\right)^4$ when the parity of the π^- - and π^0 -mesons is the same.

2. The charged meson and the neutral meson have opposite parity.

In this case, only odd values of $(L + l)$ are permitted, since it is necessary that $(-1)^{L+l} = -1$.

If we restrict ourselves to the most probable transitions, i.e., if we take $L + l = 1$, we obtain the following states for $J = 1$:

---

energy. Consequently, the π^0 -meson flies out in the opposite direction with a momentum approximately equal to twice the momentum of the neutron.

*Thus, in case 1 (see below), the selection rules permit the states with $L = 2$, $S = 0$, $l = 2$; $L = 3$, $S = 1$, $l = 1$, etc.

$$1)\ L=1,\quad S=0,\ l=0;\qquad 2)\ L=1,\quad S=1,\quad l=0;$$
$$3)\ L=0,\quad S=0,\ l=1;\qquad 4)\ L=0,\quad S=1,\quad l=1.$$

According to Pauli's principle, of these states, states 2 and 3 are permitted.

Since $L + l = 1$ for them, the probability of the given reaction is proportional to $\left(\frac{pa}{h}\right)^2$ when the parities of the π^0- and π^--mesons are opposite. In other words, the restriction here is much weaker than in case 1.

Experiments on the capture of π^--mesons by deuterons show that the reaction follows the schemes

$$\pi^- + d \rightarrow n + n$$

and

$$\pi^- + d \rightarrow n + n + \gamma$$

without any large amount of π^0-mesons being produced. This means that there is a strong inhibition of the given reaction $\pi^- + d \rightarrow n + n + \pi^0$.

On the basis of the above discussion, we can conclude that case 1 holds; that is, the charged π-meson and the neutral π-meson have the same parity.*

4. To the given process

$$p + p \rightarrow p + p + \pi^0 \qquad (1)$$

let us apply the laws of conservation of total angular momentum and parity, as well as Pauli's principle for the protons.

By definition, the pseudoscalar nature of the π^0-meson means that its spin is equal to 0, and its internal parity to - 1. From the problem, the final state of the reaction (1) is a state with an orbital angular momentum $L = 1$, and consequently with an orbital parity $(-1)^L = -1$. The total parity of the final state is thus equal to $(-1) \times (-1) = +1$.

Because of the single-valued relationship between the orbital parity and the orbital angular momentum L, the law of conservation of parity selects from the ψ-function of the relative motion of the protons in the initial state only the spherical harmonics with even L [so that a parity $(-1)^L = +1$ is obtained].

As we have pointed out repeatedly, the orbital parity of a system of two identical particles is the same as the symmetry of their ψ-function with respect to the coordinates. In other words, the initial ψ-function of the system $(p + p)$ must be symmetric in the coordinates and, consequently, antisymmetric in the spins of the protons

---

*All the experimental data have shown that π-mesons have an internal parity (- 1).

(according to Pauli's principle). This ψ-function corresponds to a value of the resulting spin $S = 0$. Consequently, the total angular momentum J in the initial state ($\boldsymbol{J} = \boldsymbol{S} + \boldsymbol{L}$) must be even.

On the other hand, because of the symmetry of the position function of the protons, which corresponds to $L = 0$ from the given condition, the Pauli principle permits in the final state only a state of the protons which is antisymmetric in the spins and which has a resulting spin 0. From the rule for the addition of the angular momenta, we obtain for the final state an odd value $J = 1$, which contradicts the law of conservation of total angular momentum.

Thus, we have proved that the given process is forbidden.

5. The isotopic spin of a nucleon is $\tau = \frac{1}{2}$. Consequently, by complete analogy with the rule for the addition of angular momenta, the isotopic spin T of a system of two nucleons can be equal to either unity or zero. The first of these eigenvalues is threefold degenerate, having three possible values of the component T_3: $T_3 = +1$, $T_3 = 0$ and $T_3 = -1$. Each of the three pairs of (T, T_3) corresponds to an isotopic function which is symmetric in the two nucleons. The eigenvalue $T = 0$ corresponds to one isotopic function (which is antisymmetric in the nucleons).

Once we have noted that the entire problem is completely analogous to the problem of the addition of two spins $s = \frac{1}{2}$ (Problem No. 9, Ch. VIII), we can write without further explanation a table of the normalized isotopic functions and of the values of T and T_3 corresponding to them. In this table, we also give the physical significance of each state. The numbers 1 and 2 represent the isotopic variable τ_3 of the two nucleons.

T	T_3	Function of the isotopic spin	Symmetry	Interpretation
1	$+1$	$\Psi_1^1 = \psi_{1/2}^{1/2}(1)\,\psi_{1/2}^{1/2}(2)$	symmetric	2 protons
	0	$\Psi_0^1 = \frac{1}{\sqrt{2}}[\psi_{1/2}^{1/2}(1)\,\psi_{-1/2}^{1/2}(2) + \psi_{1/2}^{1/2}(2)\,\psi_{-1/2}^{1/2}(1)]$	"	proton + neutron
	-1	$\Psi_{-1}^1 = \psi_{-1/2}^{1/2}(1)\,\psi_{-1/2}^{1/2}(2)$	"	2 neutrons
0	0	$\Psi_0^0 = \frac{1}{\sqrt{2}}[\psi_{1/2}^{1/2}(1)\,\psi_{-1/2}^{1/2}(2) - \psi_{1/2}^{1/2}(2)\,\psi_{-1/2}^{1/2}(1)]$	antisymmetric	proton + neutron

From the table, it is evident in particular that a deuteron (whose position and spin state is ${}^3S+{}^3D$) has $T=0$. Indeed, its wave function corresponds to the values $L=0$ and $L=2$. Thus, it is even, and therefore it is symmetric in the coordinates. It corresponds to spin 1, and consequently it is also symmetric in the spins of the two nucleons. The generalized Pauli principle requires, in view of the multiplicative nature of the complete ψ-function, that the wave function be antisymmetric in the isotopic variables of the nucleons. This requirement is satisfied only by the state with $T=0$.

It can be said that, from the point of view of transformation properties, the isotopic function of a deuteron represents an "isotopic scalar" (i.e., simply a number), whereas the isotopic function of a nucleon is a two-component vector (or better still, a spinor of the first rank), while, for instance, the function of a π-meson is an ordinary (three-component) vector.

6. Since there is a deuteron both in the initial and the final state of both reactions, and since for it $T=T_3=0$, it really has no part in the addition of the isotopic angular momenta. Thus, it is simply possible to "cancel" it out from both sides of the reaction. In other words, the deuteron plays the part of a "catalyst" in the process of the "dissociation" of the proton p into a nucleon and a π-meson:

$$p \rightarrow \text{hucleon}\left(T=\frac{1}{2}\right)+\pi\text{-meson}\ (T=1). \tag{1}$$

In the left side of reaction (1), $T=T_3=\frac{1}{2}$. Because of the laws of conservation of the total isotopic spin and its component (i.e., the charge), the right side of the reaction has the same values of T and T_3. If we expand its isotopic ψ-function $\Psi^{1/2}_{1/2}$ into isotopic functions of the "subsystems" — the nucleon and the meson — (following the rules for the transformation of ψ-functions in the addition of angular momenta; see Problem No. 11, Ch. IV), we have

$$\Psi^{1/2}_{1/2}=-\sqrt{\frac{1}{3}}\,\psi^{1/2}_{1/2}\psi^{1}_{0}+\sqrt{\frac{2}{3}}\,\psi^{1/2}_{-1/2}\psi^{1}_{1}.$$

The squares of the coefficients of this superposition ($\frac{1}{3}$ and $\frac{2}{3}$ obviously give the required relative probabilities of the "dissociation" processes

$$p\rightarrow p+\pi^0 \text{ and } p\rightarrow n+\pi^+,$$

and, as a consequence, the ratio of the effective cross sections.

7. Since $T=T_3=0$ for the deuteron, the right side of reaction (1) corresponds to the values $T=1$, $T_3=1$, while the right side of reaction (2) corresponds to the values $T=1$, $T_3=0$.

The law of the conservation of charge ($T_3=\text{const}$) is satisfied identically. The final states of both reactions (1) and (2) are characterized by a definite value of the total isotopic spin T and are described by isotopic functions Ψ_1^1 and Ψ_0^1 respectively. The isotopic functions of the intial states are the products of the isotopic functions of the nucleons (the "subsystems") and can be represented (by means of the formulas for the addition of angular momenta) in the form of a superposition of functions for a two-nucleon system with definite T:

reaction (1),

$$\psi_{1/2}^{1/2}\psi_{1/2}^{1/2} = \Psi_1^1,$$

reaction (2),

$$\psi_{-1/2}^{1/2}\psi_{1/2}^{1/2} = -\sqrt{\frac{1}{2}}\Psi_0^0 + \sqrt{\frac{1}{2}}\Psi_0^1.$$

Thus, the two nucleons in the state $p+p$ represent that very state of the "isotopic triplet" $T = 1$ which is necessary for reaction (1) because of the law of the conservation of T and T_3. On the other hand, in the state $n+p$ required by reaction (2), the state of the isotopic triplet $T = 1$ ($T_3 = 0$) is represented with a probability of only $\frac{1}{2}$. Since, from the condition for the selection of the cross sections $d\sigma$, both reactions have exactly the same number of degrees of freedom for the coordinates and the spin, the ratio of their cross sections is equal to the ratio of the probabilities of the necessary states of the isotopic triplet in the initial states. Accordingly, this ratio is equal to two, which is what we had to prove.

8. The equality of the cross sections which we are required to demonstrate expresses the charge symmetry of the nucleon-nucleon and the nucleon–π-meson interactions. In other words, it expresses the invariance of these interactions and of the transition probabilities corresponding to them, etc., with respect to the simultaneous substitutions $n \to p$, $p \to n$, $\pi^+ \to \pi^-$, $\pi^- \to \pi^+$. This equality of the cross sections follows directly from the rules for the transformation of isotopic functions in the addition of isotopic angular momenta, in conjunction with the generalized Pauli principle.

Indeed, since the ψ-function of the two protons or two neutrons is anti symmetric with respect to interchange of the coordinates and the spin, it must be symmetric in the isotopic variables; i.e., it must correspond to the resultant isotopic spin $T = 1$.* However, in this case the isotopic function of the $(p+p)$ system does not differ in any way from the function of the π^+-meson (both have the form Ψ_1^1), while the isotopic function of the $(n+n)$ system is identical

*This same result is obtained simply from the fact that it is necessary that $T \geqslant |T_3|$, where $T_3 = +1$ for $(p+p)$ and $T_3 = -1$ for $(n+n)$.

to the function of the π^--meson (Ψ_{-1}^{1}). Consequently, the right sides of (1) and (2) are described by the same isotopic function $\Psi_1^1\Psi_{-1}^{1}$. Therefore the matrix elements for transitions (1) and (2) from the initial isotopic state $\psi_{-1/2}^{1/2}\psi_{1/2}^{1/2}$ into the final state, and likewise the effective cross sections (which are proportional to the squared moduli of these matrix elements), are the same.

9. One of the methods of solving problems of this type consists of forming the matrix elements for the transition and of then applying the selection rules for T and T_3 to them. However, we can solve the given problem in a considerably more simple way. For the time being, we shall consider processes (II) and (III) together (since they have the same initial state), and examine the share of the state $T = \frac{3}{2}$ (which is necessary for the reaction) "contained" in the initial states of processes (I) and (II)-(III).

Since it is obvious that $T_3(\pi^+ + p) = 1 + \frac{1}{2} = \frac{3}{2}$, and T cannot be smaller than T_3, it follows that in the initial state of process (I), the meson-nucleon system will have only the required $T = \frac{3}{2}$. On the contrary, since $T_3(\pi^- + p) = -1 + \frac{1}{2} = -\frac{1}{2}$, the initial state of reactions (II) and (III) is a superposition of the states with $T = \frac{3}{2}$ and $T = \frac{1}{2}$.

The probabilities of each of these two values of T can easily be computed by the method given in Problem No. 13, Ch. IV. Indeed,

$$\overline{T^2} = T_\pi(T_\pi + 1) + T_p(T_p + 1) + 2(T_3)_{\pi^-}(T_3)_p =$$

$$= 1 \cdot 2 + \frac{1}{2} \cdot \frac{3}{2} - 2 \cdot 1 \cdot \frac{1}{2} = \frac{7}{4}.$$

On the other hand, if we denote the probabilities of the values $T = \frac{3}{2}$ and $T = \frac{1}{2}$ by $w_{3/2}$ and $w_{1/2}$ respectively, we have the relationship

$$\overline{T^2} = \frac{3}{2}\left(\frac{3}{2} + 1\right)w_{3/2} + \frac{1}{2}\left(\frac{1}{2} + 1\right)w_{1/2} = \frac{7}{4},$$

and the normalization condition $w_{3/2} + w_{1/2} = 1$.

If we solve the last two equations simultaneously, we find: $w_{3/2} = 1/3$, $w_{1/2} = 2/3$.

Thus, only one third of the initial state of reaction (II) - (III) is the required state of the "isotopic quartet" ($T = \frac{3}{2}$, i.e., $2T + 1 = 4$). From this it follows immediately that the total probability of reactions (II) and (III) is equal to one third the probability of reaction (I). The same is true for the corresponding effective cross sections.

It only remains for us to determine the probability of the "branching" of reaction (II)-(III) into (II) and (III). For this, we note that according to the "reciprocal relationship" of wave functions which we considered in Problem No. 24, Ch. III, the "share" of the final state $(\pi^- + p)$ in the intermediate state $T = \frac{3}{2}$, $T_3 = -\frac{1}{2}$, is equal to the share of this same intermediate state in the initial state $(\pi^- + p)$, i.e., to $\frac{1}{3}$. Consequently, $\frac{2}{3}$ of the intermediate state goes to the final state $(\pi^0 + n)$.

If we combine all of the probabilities we have obtained, we have finally: $\sigma(\mathrm{I}) : \sigma(\mathrm{II}) : \sigma(\mathrm{III}) = 9 : 2 : 1$.

Bibliography

1. L. Landau and Ye. Lifshits, Kvantovaya mekhanika [Quantum Mechanics], Gostekhizdat, 1948.
2. L. Landau and L. Pyatigorskiy, Mekhanika [Mechanics], Gostekhizdat, 1940.
3. V. A. Fok, Tablitsy funktsiy Eyri [Tables of Airy Functions], Moscow, Informotdel NII-108, 1946.
4. E. Jahnke and F. Emde, Tablitsy funktsiy [translation of Tables of Functions], Gostekhizdat, 1949.
5. I. Ye. Tamm, Osnovy teorii elektrichestva [Fundamentals of the Theory of Electricity], Gostekhizdat, 1954.
6. D. I. Blokhintsev, Osnovy kvantovoy mekhaniki [Fundamentals of Quantum Mechanics], Gostekhizdat, 1949.
7. L. D. Landau and Ye. M. Lifshits, Mekhanika sploshnykh sred [Mechanics of Continuous Media], Gostekhizdat, 1951.
8. A. N. Tikhonov and A. A. Samarskiy, Uravneniya matematicheskoy fiziki [Equations of Mathematical Physics], Gostekhizdat, 1951.
9. N. Mott and H. Massey, Teoriya atomnykh stolknoveniy [translation of Theory of Atomic Collisions], Izd. Inostr. Lit., 1951.
10. V. I. Smirnov, Kurs vysshey matematiki [Course of Higher Mathematics], Vol. III, Gostekhizdat, 1954.
11. V. A. Fok, Nachala kvantovoy mekhaniki [Fundamentals of Quantum Mechanics], Leningrad, KUBUCh, 1932.
12. D. Ivanenko and A. Sokolov, Klassicheskaya teoriya polya [Classical Field Theory], Gostekhizdat, 1951.
13. I. M. Ryzhik and I. S. Gradshteyn, Tablitsy integralov, summ, ryadov i proizvedeniy [Tables of Integrals, Sums, Series, and Products], Gostekhizdat, 1951.
14. H. Bethe, Kvantovaya mekhnika prosteyshikh sistem [translation of Quantum Mechanics of Simple Systems], ONTI, 1935.
15. E. Condon and G. Shortley, Teoriya atomnykh spektrov [translation of Theory of Atomic Spectra], IL, 1949.
16. E. V. Shpol'skiy, Atomnaya fizika [Atomic Physics], Vol. II Gostekhizdat, 1951.
17. W. Heitler, Kvantovaya teoriya izlucheniya [translation of Quantum Theory of Radiation], Gostekhizdat, 1940.
18. A. Migdal, Zhurnal eksperimental'noy i teoreticheskoy fiziki 9, 1163 (1939).

19. W. Pauli, Obshchiye printsipy volnovoy mekhaniki [translation of General Principles of Wave Mechanics], Gostekhizdat, 1947.
20. L. Schiff, Quantum Mechanics, 1949.
21. R. Becker, Teoriya elektrichestva [translation of Theory of Electricity], Vol. II, Gostekhizdat, 1941.
22. A. Akhiyezer and I. Pomeranchuk, Nekotoryye voprosy teorii yadra [Some Problems in the Theory of the Nucleus], Gostekhizdat, 1950.
23. E. Fermi, Yadernaya fizika [translation of Nuclear Physics], Izd. Inostr. Lit., 1951.
24. Ye. Feynberg, J. Phys., 5, 177 (1941).
25. A. Migdal, Zhurnal eksperimental'noy i teoreticheskoy fiziki, 28, 3 (1955).
26. V. P. Silin and V. Ya. Faynberg, Uspekhi fizicheskikh nauk, 50, 325 (1953).
27. A. Baz' and Ya. Smorodinskiy, Uspekhi fizicheskikh nauk, 55, 215 (1955).
28. Johnson and Lippman, Phys. Rev., 76, 828 (1949).
29. V. Fok, Zeits. f. Phys., 47, 446 (1928).